HIGH FIDELITY *and the Music Lover*

HIGH FIDELITY
and the Music Lover

by
Edward Tatnall Canby
Author of *Home Music Systems*

ILLUSTRATED

Harper & Brothers, Publishers, New York

Contents

HIGH FIDELITY *and the Music Lover*

Introduction

A few years ago I set out blithely to write a book, *Home Music Systems*, about the then new and burgeoning area of home entertainment known as High Fidelity. I intended to persuade—because persuasion was needed to convince music listeners that this new sort of improved sound reproduction might be of serious musical interest to them. High fidelity was then a sort of Restricted Area, as most people thought of it, fine for engineers, gadgeteers, sound-effects fanatics. It was my job to convince the timid musical soul that hi-fi could be tamed for the home, that it was easy to buy, in all its parts, and to install or have installed, that the equipment was usefully flexible, long-lasting and, sound for sound, considerably *less* expensive—not more—than the usual one-piece home phonograph—which was *not* then labeled hi-fi.

That book went through two editions and now I write again, with the same intentions but an utterly different problem. Hi-fi has since exploded into a national interest. The term itself now covers everything from soberly excellent home sound equipment to hi-fi cigarettes, perfume, lampshades and "hi-vi" television! This is the American Way; as success breeds success, so a good term finds new uses. Maybe it indicates simply that our language is still flexible, growing, adaptable to both new meanings and new persuasions. I'm the last person to suggest that English should be tied to the dictionary (ask the editors!), but I do deplore the crushing falseness of current publicity and advertising, especially in this, my own field.

Just as I object to non-jet airliners named "Jetstream" and non-stereo phonographs called "stereosonic," I deprecate the current use of "hi-fi" to cover virtually all reproducing equipment on the market today. On a

1

personal plane I am frustrated because I am thereby left with no words
of my own! My particular brand of persuasion is put at a linguistic disadvantage that, I assure you, has cost me plenty of sweat and tears. This
book hasn't been as easy as the last.

But I am still out to persuade. For beneath the present hoopla there
are better values in hi-fi for the music listener than before. There are,
too, most of the meaningful distinctions that were there before, notably
those between the mass-produced home phonograph, now universally
called "hi-fi," and those more flexible separate-unit "components" that
were the original high fidelity. These are now positively lavish in their
profusion, and more than ever worth while for music.

The title of this book means what it says, then. Plenty of people now
think that hi-fi is so much noisy gadgetry, sound for sound's sake and the
louder the better. Their privilege. But I suggest that, in the long run,
sound *content* is bound to win over the decibels and the transients of
hi-fi gadgetizing. Music, after all, is the most universal, the most versatile
content, and with intelligent and sensible use, hi-fi equipment can do it
nothing but the highest good.

And therefore though I will go quite deeply into the mechanisms of
hi-fi in the following pages, my philosophy will remain exactly as my
title indicates. High fidelity, in this book, *is* for the music lover.

I must add that I could not have gone into any sort of hi-fi without
the continued devotion of Harper's editor, Margaret Delano, who has
piloted this book to completion with even more perseverance (and pa-
tience) than she displayed in the earlier days of my *Home Music Systems*. And the sympathetic suggestions of a professional audio engineer,
Albert Grundy, have helped me get my basic physics straight within the
layman's language, a serious problem in all books of this sort.

A few things—even in hi-fi—are eternal. Basic principles remain basic.
I have therefore recast a certain amount of my own writing in my earlier
volume to fit today's situation, the modifications varying from slight to
extensive. That I've been able to quote just a few paragraphs untouched
is an indication, perhaps, that hi-fi is beginning to settle down to some
sort of permanence!

                                                              E. T. C.

1

What Is High Fidelity?

"HI-FI"

Before I can so much as attempt to define that all-embracing term, high fidelity, I must bring you straight to a matter that is of fundamental interest to us: the still-sharp distinction (so enthusiastically blurred over by big advertising) between two basic types of home equipment, both now called high fidelity. With but the one term for both—each is hi-fi by description—it is the more important to get at this difference, straight from the beginning.

One type of high fidelity, which for linguistic convenience I shall hereinafter refer to as "hi-fi"—invariably with quotes attached—is the sort of home equipment that was once simply the standard mass-produced commercial home phonograph or radio, one-piece, of all sizes and shapes, at all sorts of prices. It is the same today, in essence, though the designation is "hi-fi" and the suggestion is that these "hi-fi" radios and phonographs are utterly new and unprecedented. They are not, though undeniably their sound is a lot better than their forerunners', in pre-hi-fi days.

The "hi-fi" is the same old machine, improved. It is as convenient, simple and good-looking as ever. It still, as ever, sacrifices internal quality to external appeal, it still tends to last a while, then fall apart, or turn sick just in time for a glamorous replacement. It is still sold through the same thousands of retail radio and appliance dealers, music and department stores, by the same amiably ignorant salespeople who understand no more about its workings now than in the past. It is still mass-produced by the same large companies, and a few small ones, and it is

3

still serviced by the same repairmen, who never seem to correct its ills though they charge as much as ever.

And yet, with all of this, it is still a good bargain for many a music lover, this old-time phonograph, improved and renamed the "hi-fi." For music listeners who want no complications and prefer their machinery out of sight and mind, in the buying as well as the playing, the "hi-fi" machine is a reasonable value, up to as high as $150 (no higher). In the lower brackets, from $19.95 to around $100, it is unbeatable. There is no phonograph value that can compete with it anywhere.

Moreover, this type of "hi-fi" machine is what you will find at your neighborhood dealers if you live in average America—in the country or in a small or medium-sized town. Your local man will not relish the intrusion of fancy hi-fi equipment, bought by you from out of town. He will probably refuse to service it. (He doesn't know how, in any case.) Things may be unpleasant. If you are like most people, then you will not want to by-pass your local people—indeed, you may feel a public-spirited duty to patronize them rather than any out-of-towner. They will stand by whatever they sell you, to the best of their ability, and they will value your patronage, as a friend.

Finally, if you are inclined toward the simple "hi-fi," you may put forth the ultimate argument, namely, that a good musical ear does not need fancy hi-fi sound to enjoy the sense of music. This is quite literally the truth. There is no music on earth that will not convey its meaning to a well-trained ear via the lowliest of phonographs. Only the uneducated ear and mind (you can say with conviction) requires *literal* sound reproduction! And as for most high fidelity—it more often ruins than aids fine music or so you have found.

That, alas, is too often the truth. Misguided high fidelity is musically worse than none at all. The hi-fi addict, the tin-ear expert, the well-meaning audio engineer, the sound perfectionist, all these can commit mayhem upon music in the name of hi-fi, and do. And so—if you feel this way—by all means spend your $150, or preferably not over $100, acquire the latest miracle "hi-fi," and be happy. Put this book aside at once, though, for you will need very little more of its contents. Clamp down on your curiosity as to the how and the why of sound reproduction. Above all, do not allow the thought to cross your mind that there might be something better than your convenient little "hi-fi"—and cheaper, too, sound for sound. Don't even think about quick obsolescence and short life, nor about repairs and next year's new model and the one after that, with never so much as a needle saved from the annual discarding. Especially, don't think about flexibility, adaptability, for these are not generally a part of current "hi-fi!" Make no comparisons, if any are offered, between your "hi-fi" and the other types of high fidelity equipment, for you may find your peace of mind seriously disturbed.

NAMED-COMPONENT HIGH FIDELITY

The other type of equipment, then (if you will read on), is that which was the original hi-fi at a time when ordinary phonographs were still just phonographs. It is equipment that is manufactured and sold basically in separate units, called *components* by the trade, though these units are now so well tailored to home use that you may find among them virtually anything you may need, installed in ready-to-play form or on the loose, as you wish. The makers of this equipment are relatively specialized, the construction process is on a semi-individual basis and the products conform to standards of performance and of durability that are substantially higher in the main than standards for most "hi-fi" equipment.

The slang name for this sort of thing in the home is usually a "hi-fi system." The designation is not in Webster but the meaning is clear enough. Your "system," whether housed in a single cabinet or sprawled all over the living room, is assembled from separately functioning parts, known and definitely enumerated, chosen by brand name and model from various manufacturers. These days, the sections plug together with standardized connections that can't be joined wrongly; your "system" may seem to be one and indivisible, so nicely does it hook up and so neatly may it be concealed in furniture or closet. But the entities remain separable and inviolate, section by section, providing you with a flexibility of arrangement in the home space and a flexibility of replacement, piece by piece, that far removes the home "system" from the one-piece, standard "hi-fi."

As you move upward in the price scale, moreover, the named-component type of high fidelity brings you an increasingly greater value in sheer sound quality for your money, in comparison to those splendidly advertised monoliths of "hi-fi" that crown the upper reaches of the popular "hi-fi" lines. Feature by feature, component high fidelity will bring you better sound—if you are able at all to evaluate the separate sound elements in the "hi-fi."

For, to be sure, today's fancier machines of this sort have borrowed a good deal from the high fidelity component approach, and a good thing too, if somewhat confusing. The larger and more expensive "hi-fis" feature component-style descriptions of their insides: Four-speed hi-fi changer (all changers are called "hi-fi"!), twenty-watt push-pull amplifier, three twelve-inch speakers and the like. This is impressive and, no doubt about it, "hi-fi" has improved a lot in such respects. But, in comparison to the more detailed competitive "specs" on true component equipment, of equivalent description, these "hi-fi" accountings are often studiously vague. "Twenty-watt push-pull" may or may not mean high quality in the amplifier. And there are dozens of twelve-inch speakers, selling (as components, on their own) from a few dollars up to sixty or more.

When you buy a well-known twenty-watt amplifier of the component type from such a maker as Bogen, Grommes, or Bell, or from such mail-order firms as Allied Radio (Knight) or Lafayette Radio, you benefit from close and direct competition within the separate amplifier field—there are far fewer debatables. Standards of performance—for this particular element—are as specific as, say, the standards that govern competition between new Fords and new Chevrolets.

The price discrepancy, then, is downright astonishing when you come to compare, section by section, the offerings in the more expensive advertised "hi-fis" and their rough-priced equivalent in separate components assembled into a system. How can such semicustom machinery, produced by relatively small, specialized concerns, outperform and outprice machines mass-produced by giant companies?

The reasons are complex. A fairly obvious one, it would seem, is advertising. Components are advertised, of course, but not to the enormous extent that big-name "hi-fi" is spread across the pages of our magazines and journals and on the air. Yet there are more fundamental reasons why component hi-fi is generally a better value, if less sensationally advertised.

AUDIOPHILE NET. Component hi-fi equipment is sold generally at what is called the *audiophile net* price, and thereby hangs a story. For most such equipment, there is still, officially, a list price. It is a great deal higher than audiophile net, which represents generally a 30 to 40 per cent reduction from list. But almost nobody pays it. Often it isn't even suggested. It doesn't exist—or not quite.

If, for instance, you order a hi-fi amplifier through your local radio repairman, he is very likely to charge you the almost unknown *list* price, much higher. A familiar changer, for example, that sells audiophile net for $58.80 (with a GE phonograph cartridge and diamond needle included) is no less than $80 *list*. The hi-fi mail order catalogue says so—both prices are given. A neighbor of mine chose to buy an entire hi-fi system in this fashion, at list, from a local dealer and good friend whom he did not wish to offend—he needed this man's services in other ways, year in and year out. The *list* price, for his entire system, meant that he paid literally hundreds of dollars extra, for the privilege of his dealer's friendship. He is happy, and so is the dealer. Would you be? In any one of thousands of perfectly legitimate and honest hi-fi outlets you may buy at the standard audiophile net price. Anywhere, perhaps, but in your own immediate neighborhood.

Now this is indeed odd. "List" and "net" are ancient terms of commerce, and in other areas their meaning is clear enough. The list price is the final price, to the consumer. The net price, in other areas, is that which is charged by the large wholesale suppliers who furnish goods in bulk to the thousands of small dealers. The "mark-up" is high—from 30 to 40 per cent, and for good reason: The small, local seller, in our economy, represents a great convenience to us, at an inefficient economic sales level. The thousands of local dealers are a bottleneck to fast, efficient selling—but they are essential for us, the consumers, who still prefer their accessibility, their personal approach, and their friendship, to much of our big-time, centralized buying. The local dealer is far from being on the way out yet, in spite of supermarkets and shopping centers. To keep him operating, a relatively large profit margin is necessary, a heavy mark-up. Small sales, large unit profit. There's nothing wrong with this; these are simply the facts of our life—and we have the privilege of driving straight to the nearest large marketing center for lower prices and greater variety, if we so wish. Or we may use the mails, to acquire the same impersonal selling service in our homes.

In the component high fidelity area, however, the net price has become to all intents and purposes the official price—for the general public. How? You can already see how it must have happened; in some manner, it would seem, the wholesale-level dealer has become the seller direct to the public. That is exactly what did happen—and the fact that the list price still remains as a vestigial leftover merely confirms it. We adapt ourselves, in America, to the exigencies of a fast-moving

economy. If hi-fi equipment is to be sold by wholesalers, then the re-
tailer must adjust to the situation as well as he can. In our economy, it
is sink or swim. As is clear enough, hi-fi component equipment has
been swimming very nicely at net prices these last years, logically or
no. And often enough, regular dealers, local retailers, are now selling it
on the local scene at net (easy to check—see a hi-fi catalogue). There
is room enough in the price structure, decidedly, and profit enough,
whatever the theoretical "discount" system may be, for hi-fi to reach
you at a saving, even at net.

WHOLES VS. PARTS. Now, I can best approach the peculiar situation
in the component hi-fi area by reminding you of a factor already mentioned but perhaps not considered by you in this mercantile sort of
light. The "component" hi-fi system is not a unit, assembled by one
manufacturer, but rather a poly-machine, made up of parts from different sources.

You cannot buy an automobile in parts at net, nor most common
industrial articles used in the home. If you could buy four wheels, an
engine, body and all other components of an automobile and put the
whole together at home, you could have a new car wholesale, as you
buy a separate-unit phonograph.

High fidelity equipment comes in separate units. It is sold on the
parts basis, at the standard 30 per cent off list price. (Unless, of course,
you buy parts through your local dealer, who legitimately may charge
list and keep the 40 per cent to pay his rent.) Moral: buy parts.

This is a basic distinction, this whole versus parts, and it applies in
the most extraordinary way to "parts" in hundreds and hundreds of
commercial areas. And this in spite of the fact that in a great many
cases it isn't easy to distinguish between wholes and parts, as one can
do so easily in automobiles! Particularly in high fidelity, where the
difference has been breaking down, year by year, until nobody really
knows what is a whole and what is a part.

And yet so rigid is the tradition that whole billion-dollar concerns are
divided up accordingly. General Electric, for instance. It has had in
the home field a "wholes" departments, that has produced complete
radios, TV, even phonographs at one time or another. Now, it also has
a home "components" division that makes hi-fi parts—virtually all the
parts you need for a home system. But this division actually cannot

assemble its parts and sell them as *wholes*, in potential competition with its sister division.

The famed Audio Fairs and High Fidelity Shows have often rigidly excluded all *wholes*—complete, ready-to-play "hi-fi" equipment—in favor of *parts*, even though the parts are more and more often assembled into wholes! The basic reason behind all of this: *Parts sell at net, wholes sell at list.* Parts are for professionals and/or dealers, for resale. Wholes are for the public.

"Hi-fi," the standard, complete home machine, has always sold at strictly list prices, by local dealers, as wholes. Discounts—yes, on occasion. Also sales, special bargains, mass purchases, and so on. But in the main the standard machine is a list-price, retail piece of goods. It was and it still is, rigidly, a whole. And this even when it is sold in "parts"— with separate speaker boxes, as is now happening thanks to the new demands of stereo sound! ("Optional extra" is the term for such appendages.) There is no net price—for you—in "hi-fi." Only for your dealer.

The divisions between our two types of high fidelity are, as you can begin to see, deeply imbedded in the very structure of our economy.

BIG AND SMALL MANUFACTURING. And yet we still have not hit the most important of legitimate causes for the low value of commercial "hi-fi" in musical terms, perhaps the most interesting of all because it would seem to be a contradiction of the usual rule that mass industry puts out the better product.

Generally speaking, it does. But not at a time when there are rapid technological developments. When the fireworks begin and improvements rush upon us, the mass-production industry is stuck. It cannot move fast, it cannot change radically without risk of catastrophe. Then it is that enterprising, quick-moving smaller business moves in. This happened with a vengeance in the very rapid development of sound-reproducing technologies after World War II.

The process of mass producing is complex and delicate beyond the conception of an outsider. Hand-made experimental pilot models cost fortunes in themselves. But the translating of handwork into the incredibly complex procedures of mass production is what counts. We are used to seeing "new models" of this and that appear yearly—we are unaware that the preparations often take years, behind the scenes. The slightest alteration in existing procedure involves staggering industrial recalculations. A tiny new element costing perhaps ten cents at the source may add dollars to the final price. Multiplied by thousands and thousands of units, that thin dime can well throw an entire production setup out of gear.

Perhaps we should say things don't happen overnight. Indeed, this particular development—improved phonograph reproduction—would surely never have occurred at all if there had not been some sort of relentless outside pressure in terms of a demand for something better. Mere internal competition among parallel manufacturers is not enough, alas.

Imagine the agony, then, of the manufacturer who is faced with a tremendous upsurge of change in his own industry that cannot be ignored! Beginning during World War II (and to some extent before), the basic means of phonograph reproduction underwent a sudden development, one of those natural climaxes of change, where long-maturing outside factors seem to converge to make possible tremendous strides in a new direction.

Most of this had in a general way to do with a remarkable decrease in size of components—of everything from tubes to needles and grooves. These changes bore a close relation to the sudden increase in tonal range and fidelity that became technically possible after the war. Radically new devices appeared, too, such as magnetic tape recording and miniature magnetic and ceramic pickups (see Chapter 6) offering superior reproduction of records. The old phonograph needle was replaced by a tiny jewel stylus, semipermanent, scarcely big enough to be seen. The old record groove itself gave way to the new microgrooves; the very center of the phonograph system, the record, was revolutionized.

With these breath-taking changes in the air, the mass-production home-phonograph industry six years after the war had scarcely begun to move. It was not until then that a modernized, updated home phonograph first appeared—and upset the whole industry into those changes which led to the present "hi-fi" terminology for the improved models now available.

But, you see, if the large producer of whole machines is caught up in technical inertia, the small, specialized company, making only subsections of the whole, is not, and that is where our components come in. Nor, for that matter, is the relatively specialized (component) subdivision of a huge company—again, take General Electric, which was a pioneer in postwar pickup development.

What has happened since is interesting. In 1946 there were merely a few isolated suggestions that home record collectors might make a fine market for the new postwar developments, embodied in easily designed and flexible separate components whose manufacture would be relatively simple. (See *Saturday Review of Literature*, October 5, 1946, for comments by this writer.)

A trickle of parts for home use came out, embodying the latest advances. Finding quick acceptance, it grew to the present flood, by-passing the unwieldy retail area altogether, avoiding the costly assembly process, the huge "name brand" advertising budget, the vast mass-production complexity that froze the larger manufacturers into immobility. It is only now that the stream is finding its way back to its old banks, the standard home machine area and the small local dealer.

COMPONENT ANCESTRY. Which leads me to a final step in this account. How did the component sort of high fidelity ever get into the *parts* category, with its net prices and supposedly wholesale-only selling? Clearly, there must have been a freakish bit of economical evolution here, along with the technological improvement. There was.

Long before anyone thought of high fidelity a new professional device was introduced, to provide for public amplification, on the spot, of the speaking voice and of various sorts of music. The "P.A." system— Public Address—was basically the same as our present high fidelity home system today in its components. And it was in Public Address, in its speakers, amplifiers, microphones and so on and in P.A.'s manufacturers and sales outlets that component hi-fi originated.

The reasons for this were simple enough. P.A.'s professional uses required an array of separate items of equipment, sold as units or loosely put together into flexible systems quickly hooked up by plugs. It was this very flexibility, the convenient separate units, the variety of available equipment that first attracted those of us who wanted something more versatile in quality in the way of home music-reproducing systems than the usual one-piece phonograph.

Tack a phonograph pickup and motor onto a P.A. system and you have a phonograph. In fact many a P.A. system comes with built-in record-playing attachment (but not of the quality sort that we expect for the home). A P.A. system consists of microphone, amplifier and speaker. The home machine makes use of two out of these three elements, the amplifier and speaker. In all its externals, in its manufacture, in its sales outlets (at a discount), in its flexibility and convenience, it was easily adapted to home use. All that was needed was a change in emphasis—toward better-quality sound and less volume. (You can have more of either, at a price.) Eliminate the microphone, improve the phonograph end. Make adjustments in the controls, for home-use convenience, use a good speaker in a home-style piece of furniture instead of a batch of suitcase speakers or metal horns—and you have home high fidelity.

The very flexibility that allows P.A. to function in dance hall, skating rink, political convention or church made it an ideal commercial base from which to develop the separate-unit home music system. And so it has happened.

When we Americans want something, we go out and get it. A lot of us found we wanted P.A.-type equipment for our homes and we went straight to the P.A. sources, the wholesale radio parts dealers, to buy it, at the usual professional net prices. The makers in turn, agreeably surprised by this influx of nonprofessional and gadget-minded individuals, hastened to make more home-style P.A. and thus, net or no net, wholesale or no, the component type of hi-fi evolved from year to year —and grew into an immense new business—still technically under the wholesale roof. Zany, but inevitable!

That situation, modified in a million ways of course, is still the controlling factor today. The hi-fi stores, the mail-order outlets such as Allied Radio and Lafayette Radio (see Appendix) are still, to this very day, wholesalers at base, dealing with the radio, P.A. and TV trade. Their hi-fi divisions—huge, modern retail-type stores with shiny color-catalogues—still sell parts, at net, still do a large-volume business with both consumer and dealer alike.

There is a great deal of "cushioning" in this system, as you may imagine. There has to be. Many a small dealer can get a lower-than-net price from his distributor, or from the manufacturer, so that you may have the net price as your own. In effect, the new "resale" prices are not so different from the old list type, via prudent adjustment all along the line. Indeed, there would be no reason to discuss them at all—except for the fact that (a) the list price for component hi-fi still exists, still is maintained, and *still occasionally is charged;* you will find it stated in almost all hi-fi catalogues; and (b) there is still a fundamental division between the now giant component distribution and sales system and the older and still enormous retail "hi-fi" system, a separation that extends its split nation-wide into every community and which reaches straight to you, the buyer of home music equipment, in spite of the increasing overlap.

I do not intend to write an economic textbook and sales manual here and will henceforth put these matters aside except for an occasional reference. But paradoxically, the very fact that these two great systems now overlap at the edges in so many ways requires an explanation, if you are to see clearly how separate they still are. With that off my chest, I am sure that the distinctions between "hi-fi" and named-component high fidelity that I'll make everywhere in these pages will seem reasonable as well as intelligible to you.

WHAT IS HIGH FIDELITY?

For a decade and more, writers in the home music area have been gallantly defining hi-fi for the edification of people who no doubt have already sensed a good deal of its purport. I began in 1947, and have tried many a time since; on this occasion I propose to do a bit of analyzing instead. You know what hi-fi means, but perhaps you haven't thought about its various interesting implications.

First, then, high fidelity means what it says (though *how* high is always a question)—a high degree of faithfulness in the reproduction, as applied to sounds issuing from a loudspeaker that are facsimiles of other sounds heard by a microphone. Faithfulness is the key word.

In radio and TV the original and the facsimile are simultaneous (if not recorded); in recording there is time between.

To many people—quite wrongly—high fidelity is merely an extended range of tones in the reproduction, very high and (lately) very low. "All the lows and all the highs." High fidelity does require this and most of the new "hi-fi" sets do produce the highest tones, if not all the lows, where older standard machines were dismally deficient in both highs and lows. But this is merely a facet of hi-fi.

As a generic term, hi-fi does not "mean," but "is." First of all, it is a hobby area. It is also a business, a conglomeration of manufactured equipment, a vast array of custom-designed cabinetry, tubes, dials, tangles of wire and pounds of solder, not to mention miles of tape and shelves full of records. More than all of this, hi-fi is a way of thinking, a means of emotional release and of creative action. Hi-fi is a big-time hobby, backed by a serious art.

Fine—but what else? I propose, first, an interesting concept that may take you aback. Faithful to what? High fidelity is in one sense a high degree of faithfulness *to an imagined original*. I say "imagined" because, for all our talk of "concert-hall realism," we almost never actually hear the original and therefore we have no direct means of comparison. The vaunted faithfulness, then, must necessarily be imagined. If the sound we hear seems "right"—if it is appropriate and realistic according to some inner standard that we set in our imagination, then we can speak of it as a high fidelity sound.

A useful meaning for the term but unfortunately not closely in accord with popular slang, it refers neither to the technical equipment itself nor to the technical quality of the sound, and these are the essence of hi-fi to most people. Moreover, many a musical listener imagines the tone of his miniature table radio as an agreeable medium for the reproduced original. And he is right, too. Musical imagination can do a lot more than supply an original for comparison—it can actually re-create most of the music itself from the merest sound-sketch of its basic sense.

Nevertheless, you can't deny that truly superior reproduction, technical faithfulness to the actual original, is a desirable virtue in the home machine, imagination or no. We had better assume for the sake of completeness that faithfulness to the imagined original includes the actual re-creating of as much of the actual original sound as possible to give our imagination the greatest possible aid.

Another way of looking at high fidelity, from the musical viewpoint, is to consider it as naturalness of reproduction. Same thing, in a way—naturalness or faithfulness to that imagined original music. But if a musical sound seems artificial in the reproduction, out of balance, false, then it is hardly keeping faith with the real thing, which we can assume to be utterly natural at least as we imagine it.

Plenty of so-called high fidelity sound is anything but natural, and as a musician I claim the right to veto any supposed hi-fi which is musically false, however wondrous it may appear from the engineer's viewpoint. With this I am sure every music-minded reader will agree.

DISTORTION AND HI-FI. With that point made clear, we can safely turn to the more technical aspects of high fidelity. A faithful reproduction of any recorded or broadcast sound—musically faithful or otherwise—must clearly be accurate. If what comes out differs from what goes in, we have distortion, as a wobbly mirror distorts the image it reflects. Distortion is a general term that covers a multitude of perplexing troubles.

As you can easily guess, it is in the nature of electronic equipment to be inaccurate rather than accurate. Perfection, such as we manage to accomplish, is an uphill fight against a thousand and one possibilities for error in the transmission.

The purely physical distortions that creep into electronic music en route through our machinery are at least subject to accurate measurement. The performance of a given system or any part of a system, an amplifier, a speaker, a recording head (its "response"), can be rated in terms of distortion of several prominent kinds. Low distortion means high technical fidelity. We can list four types of distortion, all of great importance and all four subject to plenty of learned talk among the *cognoscenti*. *Harmonic, intermodulation, transient* and *nonlinearity* distortion. Terrible-sounding words, but I can give you even now an idea of what is involved.

Harmonic. Much of the unpleasantness in poor reproduction is due to a prolific type of unfaithfulness, the addition of new sounds created by our machinery and added to the original. When these sounds are extra overtones—extra vibrations that, like the tones of a musical chord, are multiples (in vibration speed) of the original sound, twice, three times, four times as fast (the so-called harmonic series)—then we have harmonic distortion. It can occur in a thousand ways, mostly in electrical form but also mechanically; for we find fractious loudspeakers, phonograph needles and other moving parts that insist on "harmonizing" tones into a sort of chord of ugly overtones.

A chord by itself is a fine musical sound. But when every separate tone of a musical piece is made into a separate chord, clashing with a multitude of others, this harmonizing is a most unpleasant thing. Fortunately, harmonic distortion in the electrical end of sound reproduction has been reduced to very low levels in most of the high fidelity equipment you will use. Some old-time phonographs reproduced up to 50 per cent harmonic distortion—one-half of the sound was false! But a good hi-fi amplifier, even a cheap one, goes no higher than perhaps 1 per cent at its working output. A really fine one has harmonic distortion licked within .01 per cent or so, which is entirely inaudible.

Named-component amplifiers, note well, are sold with very clear specifications stated in respect to this and other kinds of distortion. Have you ever seen a "hi-fi" phonograph with the distortion of its amplifier described? A few—but not many. Though they may well cover the entire "hi-fi" range of tones, these machines, most of them produce

distortion that is still well above that of most component hi-fi equipment, though, of course, much improved over the ancient machines
mentioned above. Note that people could and did enjoy music on older
machines, even with 50 per cent distortion. It can be done. The average
portable radio at the beach, blaring its tinny sound, produces perhaps
95 per cent distortion, but people like it, even so.

Intermodulation. Here is an electrical factor that was formerly ignored,
though it accounts for some very nasty noises. Intermodulation is in
effect a matter of beats, third tones, created not as overtones but as the
result of the clashing interaction of other tones. Music is full of such
beat tones, but we do not want to add more of them than are already
present in our "live" music; that is distortion. A poor amplifier can
make hash of a fine musical sound thanks to this peculiar form of distortion by adding a multitude of highly discordant third tones occurring
for every combination of two tones in the original music. The possibilities are immense and the aural agony extreme. Now that the importance
of intermodulation (often shortened to IM) distortion is understood,
most amplifiers and other equipment do a good-to-excellent job in sup-
pressing this form of extra sound as well as the harmonic form.

Transient. In hotel parlance, a transient is a person who is here today
and gone tomorrow; the electrical sense is similar. Transients are those
millions of subtle tones which last only for a fraction of an instant—
the click of a castanet, the clash of a cymbal, the beat of a drum or the
thump of a piano hammer. Transients are hard to reproduce because
they must start and stop almost instantaneously. In numerous parts
of the phonograph mechanism there is a strong tendency for things to
stay as they are, for a sound to keep on sounding, for a silence to remain silent. If the hit of a drumstick keeps on "hitting" for more than
its fraction of an instant, it no longer is a drumbeat sound; instead we
have a soft, flabby plop. Transients must be hard and clean; to make
them so in the reproduction is one of the major problems of technical
high fidelity. And so transient response, in each section of the phonograph system from the microphone right through to your loudspeaker,
is of vital importance.

You may have heard of a term called "square wave." Simple enough.
If you feed a phonograph (or part of it) a sound that starts and stops
cleanly, like a switch going on and off, you have a neatly tailored series
of transients. Graph it in terms of loudness, from zero instantaneously
to loud, and off again, and it would look like this:

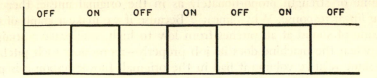

If your amplifier or your loudspeaker, or what have you, is unable to cope with this severe on-off test, it turns out a resulting sound which might graph itself like this—the on-off parts (transients) dismally distorted:

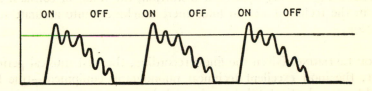

Feed real music into this same machine, or section of a machine (weak link in a chain), and the musical tones suffer the same treatment. The ear can take a lot, but it hears every bit of this transient distortion just as clearly as your eye can visualize it.

An excellent aural test for transients, as I mentioned before, is a sustained drum roll, snare drum or any smaller drum. The sharp, rapid thumps, following each other at tiny intervals, should sound as clear and distinct as they are in "live" music. Poor transient response in your phonograph's innards will blur the drum tones together, sometimes so badly that individual beats disappear and we hear no more than a steady, muffled rumble. You may interpret it as a drum roll—thanks to your imagination—especially if you know the music well; but you cannot honestly say that it sounds like a drum roll.

The ear is astonishingly adaptable and we can supply all sorts of missing musical information that the phonograph is unable to give us properly. But technical high fidelity requires good transient performance and we can get it from the component high fidelity equipment now available.

Nonlinearity. The simplest of all distortions, one which we will come back to, is involved in what the engineer impressively calls nonlinearity. Nothing complex at all. Linearity is just the ability to give tit for tat in terms of sound strength. If all musical tones come forth in the same volume or strength proportionately as in the original music, then we have *linear response*. Why "linear"? Because if we make a graph of the volume of sound at all pitches from low to high, we'll have a straight line when the machine does its job properly—reproduces each pitch at the same relative volume it had in the original. Linear response is proportionately accurate volume over the entire pitch spectrum.

Unfortunately, many home phonographs are anything but linear. Their response is uneven, with abnormally loud spots at some pitches ("peaks," we call them, again referring to a graph) and no response at all in the very lowest musical regions.

Thus—high fidelity equals low distortion, the result of constant striving in the technical area to force mere machinery into accurate reproduction.

Good Listening. Given the finest recording, the best musical performance, the most excellent technical phonograph equipment—true high fidelity reproduction still depends, and depends vitally, on another factor. The listening situation in your own home.

There are, of course, plenty of undeterminable matters here such as your personal mood, your neighbors' likes and dislikes, the state of your own musical education. But aside from these there are plainly objective physical matters that count immensely. A vast amount of agony is occuring every day among those who in their search for hi-fi have acquired the best of everything—only to go dismally off the track at this final stage.

In addition to good equipment, you must have a proper room, a proper speaker location in that room, a proper place from which to listen. (And a good hi-fi recording—but see Chapter 4 for that.)

The physical intricacies of actual sound waves are incredibly complex. Sound can play every sort of trick on us after it has left the actual loudspeaker and is no longer even a part of our high fidelity system. It takes a lot of experiment—unless you are lucky in a beginner's way and hit it right—to find a good setup for your equipment in your own home. With the wrong one, you may own fine equipment but you will not hear high fidelity. Read on, and Chapter 15 will elucidate at a later moment when we've acquired a better background for detailed discussion.

Can high fidelity be as complex as all this? No one, other than a too willing salesman, ever said it was simple. At my own risk—for most "how to do it" books go in for oversimplification—I am making no bones about the elaborate picture that high fidelity involves, if we choose to look beyond the "hi-fi" machines, the standard phonographs now universally graced with the high fidelity designation.

2

Hi-Fi and the Music Lover

SUGGESTIONS FROM ALL SIDES

The toughest problem for any newcomer in high fidelity is to establish a personal sense of values, in the face of the sharply different opinions that are thrown at him from one side and another as soon as he makes known his budding interest in hi-fi music. I am quite aware that plenty of intelligent people don't happen to know even the first principles of hi-fi and, indeed, are in deadly fear of those who do, notably such holy terrors as their own brilliant progeny, who always know or think they do.

There's plenty of agreement on hi-fi matters—within each specialized group. The audio engineers know fairly well what they consider a "good" amplifier and a "good" phonograph system. They'll tell you. It may cost $800 to $1,500. So do the retail radio-store salesmen, who will sell you the new "hi-fi" one-piece machines with a conviction that they are giving you a proper buy. The recommendations are worlds apart. Neither is right for you, and you are left somewhere in between.

Let me look at a few of the points of view which you are likely to run into en route to a satisfactory personal high fidelity.

THE HI-FI BUG AND THE GRADUATE EXPERT. Your first contact with component hi-fi—unless you are lucky—will probably be through one of those high powered hi-fi enthusiasts that we gray-haired sages of home music wearily term (behind their backs) hi-fi bugs, audio fanatics. They aren't necessarily unmusical though many, it seems, are immune to any message that music itself may bring to their ears, aside from the simpler forms of popular music and old-fashioned melody. Indeed, many who in my private book are decidedly hi-fi bugs know their music quite well. They simply don't listen—to music. Some, sad to relate, are actual professional musicians; a few are well-known experts on music and high fidelity! But their advice to you, if you were to ask them about hi-fi, would not to my way of thinking be good. It would involve you in far fancier operations than you will probably envisage.

We must recognize that the reproductive phase of hi-fi, that perfection in the re-creation of electrified sound, has become so much a desired end in itself that even musicians with otherwise sound musical judgment have fallen for its tantalizations. Possibly you may fall for the same, to a greater or lesser degree; if so, you will suffer no great harm from my book—you'll merely want to spend more money, oftener, than I suggest.

But if you are *not* a hi-fi bug and do not intend to be one, if you are primarily interested in intelligent use of hi-fi as a means toward a musical end, you must beware the hi-fi bug's special values.

It is less likely, but you may run into the real hi-fi expert, the graduate student of advanced audio (though often it is his hobby, not a profession), the man who builds amplifiers and speaker enclosures to his own designs, who winds his own coils, glues his own exponential mid-range horns, and as a matter of course deals only with the ultimate in quality hi-fi equipment.

I once visited a hi-fi club of this sort, made up of men in all sorts of professions other than hi-fi itself. It was an experience! These people have developed their ears to an astonishing pitch of audio perfection, though at the same time they are blissfully unaware of music—even as they play it on their equipment. It simply does not exist for them. It is merely so much audio reproduction. I admire and respect these people—they do hear what they say they do, shades of audio perfection that are utterly beyond most unobservant musical listeners. Interesting, and a fabulous skill in its own terms. But musical hearing is something else again.

Now I myself, perforce, have had a good deal of experience (and, thus, training) in this technical listening. I'm not bad at it, relatively speaking. I can spot the poor transients, the peaks and dips in response. But I find that, from this viewpoint, music is constantly getting in my way. It distracts and confuses me. And since I simply cannot ignore music, good or bad, I find my judgment is often less than ideal from this graduate viewpoint! I prefer good musical sound to good audio. And you may well be glad to go along with me, since *musical* hi-fi—so far removed in many a way from this sort of advanced audio, yet so intimately related to it—depends on a composite of many factors. Sheer electrical perfection is merely one of them.

You will find that the same reservations apply, with a different slant in detail, to that much calmer individual, the professional audio engineer who designs and builds hi-fi components for a living. (You may find him at work as a custom hi-fi builder, ready to build a system into your home, at a good price.) Where the hi-fi bug must have perfection at any cost and is emotional about it, the audio engineer will simply lose interest if you suggest a modest system; you are clean out of his area.

SALESMAN. On the one hand you will find the convinced perfectionist—and at the opposite extreme, you will find the local salesman in the standard radio and music store, who has his answer to your problem. He sells the "hi-fi" that was once the ordinary commercial home machine. He, too, is likely to be a reasonably sincere person, always allowing for salesmanship. Why not? He has his own set of values, is convinced of their factualness (with a bit of help from the powers above) and is out to convince you too. But look at his standard of sound values, as compared with the assorted hi-fi men we've talked of already!

It isn't easy to line up these values with exactitude—but take a hypothetical "good" machine, as recommended by this type of salesman in response to your inquiry at his store. "Good" will likely mean, to him, a "hi-fi" that sells for a minimum of perhaps $180, more probably up in the $300 area. Not merely adequate, but really "good."

Now look at one part of it, the loudspeaker. "Miracle tone chamber" and all that—and perhaps three speakers, not one—let's say two twelves and an eight-inch. That is a common sort of arrangement now; "hi-fi" reproduction almost always involves several speakers in one box.

If you were to seek their equivalent in any convenient component hi-fi catalogue (selling at net), you could buy these three speakers separately—you, yourself—for possibly $20 or less. Perhaps as much as $40 for those in fancier "hi-fi" sets. They are good speakers, these, but not very expensive. They are good because of the peculiar values always evident in low-priced equipment as compared to the more perfect sort that sell for higher prices. (See Chapter 10.) They are a bargain, no doubt, at $20 or at $40.

But suppose you had forearmed yourself with recommendations from an engineer friend or a hi-fi-bug neighbor, as to what would be a "good" component-type speaker for your purpose. Now I'll bet a hat that their choice of several possible speakers, for you, would have run between $100 and $300. A ten-to-one difference!

At least the retail "hi-fi" salesman isn't likely to break your bank account. He is quite accustomed to moderate-cost equipment though his sound values are, as I have said, less than the best except at the lowest prices.

In any case, don't expect to get much useful advice from the salesman as to the merits of component-type equipment in comparison with his own "hi-fi." It sells, after all, in competition with him; he may carry a limited selection of amplifiers and the like and may even give you a net price; but his heart isn't in it.

A MIDDLE COURSE. And so it goes, negatively speaking. Perhaps I sound discouraging; possibly, at this point, I am failing in the prime duty of a "hobby book" writer, which is to make the world look rosy, at least in his special field. At this juncture I wish to establish a sort of entente with you, the reader. If we disagree, you need merely slant in one direction or another what I suggest later in this book. The important thing is to know where you stand and where I stand.

I am, therefore, plotting out a deliberately middle-of-the-road course. From one point of view I am a "hi-fi bug" myself, just because I do recommend that you, a sane, sensible, intelligent music lover, seriously consider all this hi-fi rigmarole as an end to better musical enjoyment. That makes me a radical, in thousands of people's view. I'm well aware that the "hi-fis" still make up the bulk of the playing equipment in this country in spite of the continuing rise of the named components. They are (in the bottom price brackets) excellent bargains. Nevertheless —from this radical viewpoint—I recommend component hi-fi for all intelligent music listening (except perhaps on the beach and in your car!) and for everyone with a musical ear.

Yet from the other extreme, in the opinion of my numerous friends who are audio engineers and hi-fi enthusiasts, I am amateurish and conservative. The equipment I recommend is much too unprofessional. The gulf is really immense, and I am well aware of the uncertainty into which you may easily be led, whether in the one direction or the other.

It has cost me much agony and plenty of hair-tearing to arrive at a sensible compromise for music, and I have no better claim than that to advise you on the matter. Except, of course that I love music and listen, always, to music first.

3

The Hi-Fi System

THE THREE-PART PHONOGRAPH

I have spoken of amplifiers, players and loudspeakers, the high fidelity system, these being terms in common use in the field. Let's look at the phonograph system itself, hi-fi or any other kind.

I say "system" advisedly. We refer to "it"—but no matter how one-piece it may look, every electric phonograph is actually a system of three basic devices, working together. In the newer separate-unit equipment, these three sections are physical entities in themselves. Yet whether your machine is an ancient portable or a wall-filling edifice of expensive furniture, the three basic sections are always present. Whatever else it may include, every phonograph has a pickup with its motor and turntable, an amplifier, a speaker: the tripartite phonograph.

THE PICKUP AND MOTOR

The first section of the phonograph "system" is the most familiar to sight and to touch, and is your most immediate contact with it—the pickup arm and its turntable and motor with or without changer mechanism. *The pickup arm is that movable piece* which has at its business end the phonograph needle, set into the *cartridge.* With utter inconsistency we speak of the cartridge-and-needle end of the pickup arm as the "head"—where common sense would envision, I suppose, a hand. Slang terminology, however, is scarcely common sense and "head" it is. In the pickup's head the cartridge is securely fastened but removable; in some arms fitted with plug-in heads it takes an instant to change from one type to another for playing different types of records. Most cartridges are screwed down via two standard half-inch-apart mounting

25

holes, which is useful when it comes to interchangeable replacements or modernizations. Needles are mostly removable. (A number of expensive pickups require factory replacement of their built-in diamond points.) They don't come out as easily as the old steel ones but the job is never more than mildly annoying and certainly nothing to bother an unmechanical soul. The pickup arm itself may be part of a changer mechanism or a "manual" player; in either case the principle is the same.

Need we say much at this point of the motor and its turntable? Its function is merely to turn the record at the right and steady speed or speeds, with as little rumbling and vibration as can be managed at the price. The motor also operates the changer, between sides, when playing is "automatic." Motors, as we shall see, come in numerous forms, as do pickups, cartridges, styli (the proper term for "needle" is "stylus" —they don't look like needles any more), arms and the rest. You can acquire the whole of this first section as a unit or, if you are so minded, you may buy separate parts and assemble your own first section.

The pickup, as its name implies, "picks up" sound from the record. More accurately, it converts the minutely wavy pattern of the standard spiral record groove into side-to-side mechanical vibrations of the needle, which generate a very tiny fluctuating electric voltage in the cartridge, varying exactly in step with the needle's motion. The pickup's output voltage, as the engineer puts it, then carries a "signal," an intelligence: to wit, the vibration pattern of the record grooves, the sound pattern that was received by the recording microphones from the actual music— Beethoven or boogie.

An incredibly feeble current, it is useless by itself. The most potent crystal pickup turns out a maximum of a few volts and a tremendously small current flow, whereas the fancy magnetic pickups never produce more than a few hundredths of a volt. (You need not worry about electric shocks from the pickup circuit!) But this tiny current carries the all-essential intelligence, the music-to-be.

THE AMPLIFIER

A set of earphones can convert the pickup's small output directly into a very tiny sound—so small that only one ear can hear it, at extremely close range. Theoretically, an earphone phonograph can be made with only two sections—pickup and, shall we say, softspeaker. (I've actually used such a system in lecturing, to "cue up" records ahead of time.) To get more sound, however, we need a larger current. For a loudspeaker an enormously larger current is necessary.

An intermediate device, the *amplifier*, is therefore essential for any "out-loud" phonograph. It must, as you can see, build up the power of the signal-carrying voltage while preserving the pattern of fluctuations that is the signal itself—the music.

The amplifier does not actually amplify—i.e., make bigger—the tiny pickup current. One can seldom make something out of almost nothing. Instead, it uses the infinitesimal voltage as a *control*, as a guide, in order to turn out an enormously larger current carrying the same pattern of fluctuations. (Or nearly the same—we have yet to achieve ultimate perfection.) This is an idea that few of us have absorbed and more of us should.

I can compare the process with driving a car. The tiny motion of your right foot on the accelerator controls the enormously greater power of the engine. The engine's performance directly reflects the pressure of your toe. Indeed, if we add also the brakes and the horn, the car's response to your driving movements is so acute that, as we all know, an automobile on the highway is a fine indicator of its driver's personality! Yet not one bit of the driver's actual personal energy is involved in what happens—starting, stopping, horn blasting. It all goes into *control* of large amounts of energy by small ones.

So with an amplifier. The vacuum tube is an ingenious electronic gate. A tiny voltage, in this case from the pickup, directly controls the passing through the tube of enormously greater currents. When the small signal ceases, so does the large; as the pickup voltage increases in its very miniature way, so does the relatively huge current increase in proportion—and thus the signal, the intelligence is passed along, "amplified." "Copied," would be more like it, as the artist's mural is copied in the large from tiny cartoon sketches. The newer transistors operate similarly; they are increasingly used in place of tubes.

The relationship between the infinitesimal incoming signal and the enormously larger outgoing replica is the amplifier's *gain*, as the technical jargon goes. We control what goes out by controlling what goes in, via the *volume control*, often called *gain control* or *level control* by engineers. In practice, the output of an amplifier must be modified in a good many ways. Nevertheless, its basic function is to act as a "transparent" medium for sound in its electrical form, to transmit electrified sound changed in one single respect—made larger.

Perhaps you can understand why all high-quality amplifiers should be about the same in the listening. If they sound unlike, given the same material to work upon, then the difference must be distortion, or much more likely a difference not in the amplifier itself but in the associated elements—the tone controls, the preamplifier, and so on. A large amount of discussion is involved on this score among expert hi-fi *cognoscenti*. "So-and-so amplifier is a piece of junk—it sounds terrible—you ought to hear such-and-such." Impossible, I say, unless there is something very seriously wrong. The amplifiers proper, if both are anywhere near reputable, should sound *exactly alike*.

THE LOUDSPEAKER

Out of the amplifier comes a more potent electric current, enough to give you a small jump of a shock occasionally at the louder places, which in its fluctuations still carries the sound pattern. It may reach to fifty or sixty volts. The *loudspeaker* is the device that converts these more powerful electrical fluctuations back again into mechanical ones, duly transmitted to the surrounding air as air waves—actual sound in the image of the original (more or less). The loudspeaker is actually a form of electric motor which, instead of turning about itself in response to electrical stimulus, moves back and forth like a piston, pushing out waves in the air ahead of it and behind. Its construction is basically simple, though the details of design are enormously complex and the tiniest deviations in shapes and patterns are crucial in their effect on the resulting sound. (See Chapter 11.)

The familiar loudspeaker cone, made of a sort of cardboard-paper, is flexible and springy. Its center is a circular coil of wire, the voice coil, which is the actual motor, set between the poles of a heavy magnet. In this magnetic field, every thrust of current coming from the amplifier becomes a thrust of motion. The coil moves back and forth, reflecting the current's fluctuations, and the cone, attached to it springily, moves with it, pushing air, creating sound. (The "pushing" is of course extremely rapid; sounds of high pitch vibrate thousands of times per second.)

It is sometimes possible actually to see the motion of the loudspeaker cone when very low notes (i.e., slow-speed vibrations) or various extraneous thumps and bumps of electrical static and distortion are fed to the speaker.

Low-pitched sounds involve slower vibrations, relatively speaking. To reproduce a low organ note a speaker must move air back and forth only about thirty times a second in contrast to five or six thousand times for a higher musical tone.

But to make an equally loud noise, a low-pitched, slow-vibrating sound must vibrate a greater *distance* back and forth than a high one. The faster the changes or "cycles" are, the smaller the distance or "excursion," as the engineers have it. A loud high-pitched sound might vibrate thus:

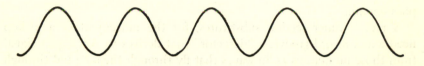

while an equally loud low sound might have to move thus:

You may try a simple arm motion by which you can feel this important relationship for yourself. Pump your fist back and forth from the distance of a foot, at medium speed. Now double the speed—and for the same amount of work you'll only be able to move half as far, back and forth. Move four times as fast and the distance will be half that again. So it is with the speaker cone (and all sound wave motions). Low-pitched, slow vibrations move farther. (See footnote in Chapter 6, p. 55.)

What's more, it is much harder to get hold of the air for these slower-moving low tones. The larger your speaker cone is, the better it can grab the low tones—and the more bass you are able to hear. Little speakers tend to be weak on the lows—though they project the highs easily enough. That's why baby radios and portable phonographs have such tinny voices.

Whether you have followed this last somewhat special information or not, you can easily envision the place of this third major section of the phonograph. It finally reverses the process which began at the microphone, the conversion of actual sound, the physical motion of air, into electric current. The speaker reconverts the facsimile electric current back into original air sound waves, or as nearly the original as we can manage.

RADIO AND TAPE

Three basic sections—pickup, amplifier and speaker; there are alternatives and additions that may also be included in either the separate-unit high fidelity system or in the "hi-fi" standard machine. Commonest is the radio. A radio *tuner* as it is called is another first section, another source of the tiny, signal-carrying current that is fed into the amplifier. What we call a radio, you see, is actually a three-section affair like the phonograph, of which only the first part, the tuner, is different. A radio is already two-thirds of a phonograph, with both a built-in amplifier and a built-in speaker. That is why we can buy a separate phonograph first section, a record player, and thus supply an alternative first section; plug a record player into your radio and you have a complete phonograph.

A radio's tuner section substitutes, for the movement of a pickup needle in a record groove, a "detector" that derives its intelligent signal from those mysterious radio waves that fly through the air (and through almost everything else) with the greatest of ease. Let's skip the complex business of *detecting* a radio signal, removing the impressed message from it and passing that message along in the form of the familiar small current. However complex that process may be, the resulting signal current is not unlike that which the pickup delivers. The amplifier doesn't know the difference, so to speak; it will amplify any signal whatever the source—including such unwanted sources as static from thunderstorms and unpleasant man-made noises from elevators, electric shavers, diathermy machines and what not.

As usual, the tuner of the common radio is not separately visible, being built into the standard one-piece cabinet. But it is there and it may be AM (standard), FM (frequency modulation) or an AM-FM combination, which amounts to two separate radio tuners built together into a single unit. Whatever the arrangement, the principle is the same. The several first sections, radio, phonograph and any other, feed to a switch which allows one or another to supply its signal to the accommodating amplifier and so on into the speaker.

It should be added that the home tape recorder is in this respect not unlike a radio. As a complete unit it can play tapes through its own built-in second and third sections, amplifier and speaker; or you may divert the played sound from its first section directly into your main hi-fi system, using the larger amplifier and speaker for better sound.

Thus tape becomes one more of the possible "inputs" that feed your amplifier, along with phonograph and radio.

THE SEPARATE-UNIT SYSTEM

The separate-unit high fidelity system is no more than an extension of all this. Not that your separate units can't be installed in a single cabinet, at home or by someone else, perhaps the selling store, if you don't want to bother with installations yourself. But the point is that each of the major subsections is manufactured separately, usually by a different concern specializing in that type of equipment. You pay the low "audiophile" price. And because the separate unit manufacturing process, specializing in one thing at a time, is so much simpler and more flexible, you acquire more up-to-date equipment, as already explained, and quality usually unavailable at all in the standard one-piece machine.

Still better—you have licked the problem of obsolescence. The standard one-piece "hi-fi" machine, ready-made, must stand or die as one. After a year, or three or four, it is obsolete—but not all over. Just in one or two departments. For instance, its record changer may no longer change; your serviceman isn't interested in repairing it and can't install a new one. Not worth it; better to buy a whole new machine, he'll insist. That's what he is in business to sell you. So you must get rid of the whole, including cabinet, amplifier and speaker, and buy another cabinet, amplifier and speaker of strikingly similar quality, in order to acquire a changer that changes.

The separate-unit outfit suffers from no such oneness. If you wish to replace your changer, unplug it, lift it out and put a new one in—leaving all else exactly as is. Minimum obsolescence. If the cartridge in your changer arm is obsolete—unscrew it, put in a newer-style cartridge and your changer is sound instantly. Perhaps a new speaker is in order? Pull out the old, insert the new. Flexibility is the word.

Moreover, if you decide later on to take a step upward in hi-fi and buy yourself more expensive equipment, you may do it in stages and budget your improvements, knowing that the best in one section will complement the best in another. All of which adds up to an impressive difference in value between separate-unit and conventional machines.

What Separate Units? There are, admittedly, a bewildering variety of possible "units"—components—now on the market. Amplifiers, like changers, come as separate entities, but many a supplementary gadget is now built into them. Some are built in two pieces, for convenience as well as for good electrical reasons, isolating the whole array of controls and gadgets from the main amplifier itself, which can be thus shoved off into a corner and out of the way. Many of these units are also sold as separate items—an amplifier without controls ("power amplifier" or "basic amplifier"), or a control system minus amplifier.

Loudspeakers are often sold separately, their enclosures or boxes acquired ad lib according to taste and need. But the relationship between the loudspeaker and its cabinet or enclosure is so close and so crucial for good sound that now most companies sell largely complete speaker-enclosure systems, built together as a single unit, the enclosure designed specifically to go with the speaker—or speakers, in the case of models with woofers, tweeters and the like. In numerous cases, the loudspeaker units are unusable in any other enclosure and, in effect, form part of the box.

There are separate units that combine numerous functions: AM-FM radio tuners, the double unit ready to plug into an amplifier; separate tuners for FM only, or for AM only; there are AM-FM tuners combined with a built-in amplifier, all on a single "chassis," so that only a loudspeaker is needed to complete a basic three-part system, plus optional record player or tape if you are interested. These last have been popular simplifications of hi-fi for a good many years with beginners who prefer fewer units. There are tape recorders combined with radio tuners (they can record off the air), pickup and turntable combinations, stereo amplifiers that add an extra channel to your present one for the new two-way sound, assorted control units, preamplifiers, control-and-preamplifier units . . . but I'll leave these for later chapters.

Suffice it to say, in winding up this discussion of units, that their flexibility in home use will in the end probably offer as much appeal as anything else. I know, that, at first, you'll be inclined to disagree—but I assure you that even the touchiest housewife will find this flexibility helpful, as compared to the inflexible oneness of the usual all-in-one "hi-fi" machine with its loudspeaker uncompromisingly built in right next to the controls so that you must choose arbitrarily between operating convenience and listening ease.

Separate-unit high fidelity no longer has to be ugly and "practical" in appearance; if you don't like it that way (madam), it can be as decorative—as flossy, indeed—as you wish and yet it retains all of its flexibility in use. So, with all my heart, I recommend separate units for your hi-fi

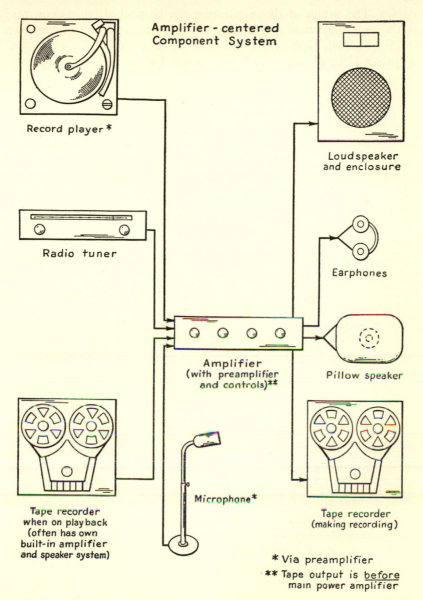

Amplifier - centered
Component System

Record player *

Loudspeaker
and enclosure

Radio tuner

Earphones

Amplifier
(with preamplifier
and controls)**

Pillow speaker

Tape recorder
when on playback
(often has own
built-in amplifier
and speaker system)

Microphone*

Tape recorder
(making recording)

* Via preamplifier
** Tape output is before
main power amplifier

system. The details of that separation can be worked out as you read further and understand better what will turn out to be best in your own special situation. Next, let me leave the home system itself for a look at its principle be-all and end-all, the recorded sound it brings you.

4

The Hi-Fi Recording

The phonograph record is technically out of bounds for me in this volume but since it is the main source of audible sound for every high fidelity system—whether on a home player or relayed by a radio station—I have a few things to say about hi-fi as it relates to records. The hi-fi record complements the hi-fi system.

We've already looked at a number of meanings for high fidelity. I think you will find that all of the legitimate, nonadvertising senses of the term fall into one or another of two fundamental categories. Both of these apply to the hi-fi recording. The first of these is the expected one, that literal faithfulness to the sound originally picked up by the microphones which is the preoccupation of every designer of hi-fi equipment, including that used in the recording process.

But it is the second variety of high fidelity with which I am concerned here. In this sense, hi-fi is not a matter of engineering but of style. And as with all styles, hi-fi style changes, tastes for hi-fi effects change.

What is a high fidelity recording? I suggest that the very first implication of that term today is a type of sound—not a degree of faithfulness. Moreover, the sound we call hi-fi today is becoming *less* faithful to the musical original all the time—if more faithful to the microphone's message; and this is not as paradoxical as it may seem.

Each year, music on records takes on more of its own unique sound quality, in spite of remaining true to the composers' notation. Every year we approach more closely a purely detached interpretation of musical sound, unique to recording itself, only casually related to the sound of "live" music. And this is because we have come to realize, after these many years, that recorded music can never be a literal reproduction but must always be a new interpretation of the musical sound in terms of the recorded medium itself. That is what "hi-fi" means today on records.

As we have understood this more clearly, we have paid more attention to living room realism. We have learned that musical effects which are striking in the concert hall can be uninspiring on records and vice versa. We have found, in fact, that the whole hierarchy of desirability on records is utterly different from that of the concert hall. Recorded music has therefore brought new success to vast amounts of music long lost or out of favor and has, indeed, reshaped the entire field of musical performance, to suit its special needs.

But this, though it is surely a thought to interest the music listener, is not my point in this chapter. What concerns us here is the fact that hi-fi sound today is a special musical sound for a special purpose— effectiveness in the home-listening situation. That's what really matters for the music listener. Sometimes, indeed, the musical intelligence via "home hi-fi sound" is well ahead of anything the concert hall can offer.

One of the basic points of this entire volume, in and around the more technical discussions of equipment and so on, is that good sound reproduction is always a matter of ingenious illusion, the better to provide a seeming naturalness (that is wholly unnatural, in fact) and so to convey a maximum of musical intelligence. In Chapter 15, for instance, you will find practical tips on improving your home acoustic situation. There is not a thing said in that entire chapter about electrical or literal hi-fi; it has to do with sound after it has left the hi-fi system. It doesn't matter how good your equipment is; the illusion of musical naturalness is so utterly dependent on the listening place itself that even the finest equipment can be "thrown for a loss" in an unfavorable situation. Without a good illusion, literal hi-fi is useless.

If you are inclined to be skeptical, consider that reproduced sound is not even two-dimensional, let alone three. In standard reproduced music we are able to make distinctions in space in exactly one *dimension*, no more. (In stereo there is a slight degree of two-dimensionality —see Chapter 16.) The single dimension that we can perceive is the in-and-out one, forward-and-back; we can judge (though far from accurately) whether a sound, a musical instrument, is near to us or far. As to side-to-side spacing, we have absolutely no perception whatsoever. All the reproduced sound comes from all points at once. The solo pianist is spread out impartially across his entire orchestra; each instrument of the orchestra itself comes from everywhere at once.

If this is "natural," then it surely is an illusion! The remarkable thing is that we do enjoy and understand such incredibly unliteral reproduction. We do so because the illusion is pleasing to our ears, literal or no, and because it conveys intelligence, literal or no.

Because we can change our tastes in illusion, learn new styles, appreciate novel and unheard-of effects, hi-fi recording has been changing right along. It has reached an extreme in some forms of popular music, notably in rock and roll music, where strange voices shout hysterically inside huge caverns of space that are often wholly synthetic. But hi-fi sound is active, too, in so-called classical music.

What is hi-fi sound? That depends on the style you have in mind. Back just after the war, the first deliberate hi-fi sounds in classical music came from London Records. The description and trade name were, as usual, strictly on the technical side—"full frequency range recording" or "ffrr." The full frequencies were there and still are; but what was much more important was a "new sound" in the music that at first shocked many people including myself. Essentially, it combined two impossible opposites—distance and nearness. The violins of the orchestra, for example, seemed very close and yet at the same time far away. It couldn't be true, but once we adjusted our home-listening ears to the novel effect, we found that this way of using microphones actually contributed to a new and more lively sense of illusion in the home-listening spot. It worked. (Many another company used the same technique if perhaps not at first with the éclat of the London firr sound.)

What was radical in the early ffrr days is now, as you must realize, strictly middle-of-the-road, which means that the new hi-fi styles of sound have been completely accepted by millions of listeners. But there is nothing static about the situation; styles continue to change to this day, to become even more strange—or convincing, if you wish. The remarkable thing is that we learn to accept these new sounds without so much as a thought that they are unlike the original and a law unto themselves. We do the same, and we always have, with any reproduced music.

Recorded opera, for instance, has gone through a gradual evolution from the early days when the music was taken down very much as it might sound to an opera-goer, toward a special technique that is now

almost taken for granted—where the solo singers are close to the microphone and amplified so that they are usually as loud as the entire orchestra. The same is true for the concerto soloist on records; he, too,
is enormously louder in proportion to the orchestra than upon any real
concert stage. We like these effects; indeed we demand them, as a
matter of course. We are right. The recorded medium requires this
exaggeration for its own proper musical emphasis. The louder, bigger
solo sounds balance the missing sense of sight and the three-dimensional
space that are available to the concert and opera listener.

"Hi-fi sound," then, is simply the conscious carrying-to-an-extreme
of a principle that has been inherent in all reproduced sound from the
beginning. The more recent hi-fi styles carry the principle forward to
new degrees of impact, to a new and more distant departure from the
concept of the original music in the flesh. Granted that a great deal of
it is grossly done, exaggerated, unmusical. That is no criticism of the
basic premise. And we must keep in mind that as in all forms of art,
what may seem a blatant extreme today may well turn out to be a
familiar and cherished effect in the future. Almost all recordings are
made today from very close range, some of the instruments often only
a few feet away as you listen (you can hear breathing sounds, occasionally), others more distant, for a dimensional (one-dimension) contrast. But no matter how close they may be, there is virtually always
that compensating big "liveness," a great space-suggesting "echo" or
reverberation in which the music is immersed, so to speak. This is a
superbly effective device for illusion, in all its many variations. It does
not matter a bit that sometimes the "concert hall" is an echo chamber,
an underground labyrinth or an old disused stairwell—or even an electronic circuit that fakes a convincing electrical "echo" that never existed
as sound at all. If the illusion is good, we are pleased, and (note well)
we may be just as well pleased via a table model radio, strictly non-hi-fi,
as via a super-high-fidelity home system. These matters are even more
fundamental than literal fidelity itself.

It took many years for sound engineers to understand these things.
The famous Studio 8H at NBC, where Toscanini did his earlier broadcasts with the NBC Symphony, was deliberately built "dead," completely sound-absorbing, upon the mistaken theory that removing the
reverberation (liveness) would clarify the sound and so improve the
musical effect! Instead, the Symphony sounded small, puny, swallowed
up in ineffectiveness. It was a miniature, literal, pipsqueak orchestra as

we heard it on the air, and all the press-agentry of NBC could not restore the illusion that was so painfully missing in the quality of the
reproduced sound itself. (Later, Toscanini was moved to Carnegie Hall,
where the acoustics were favorable for good microphone placing.)

There will be more of this, in a new dimension, in the chapter on
stereo sound, which is the first new development to affect the basic
illusion itself since the very beginning of reproduced sound. But next,
we return to a literal world to study the "fi" in the record itself—the
literal kind of fidelity to the sound picked up by the recording microphones.

5

Record Curves and Equalizing

There is not space in this discussion nor perhaps in your mind for a good accounting of the complex of steps, electrical and mechanical, that go into the producing of a phonograph record. If you want to supplement this reading you'll find it treated at considerable length in the present author's portion of another opus.* For the sake of your own interest in music, however, I give herewith a bit of the story. To produce good music your own phonograph must do a special job of direct compensation for certain steps in the recording process—one is the mirror of the other—and you'll be concerned with this yourself in the management of the controls. So it is worth investigating.

SOUND. As you have probably discovered, formally or informally, sound consists of physical vibrations transmitted through air (or on occasion, water and other substances) to your ear in the form of waves. Not hilly waves like those of the ocean but waves of pressure moving outward three-dimensionally from the source: longitudinal waves. They impinge upon the eardrum and cause it to vibrate in and out, in sympathy, and from thence the actual motion moves through liquid into a spiral, the cochlea, and by the most miraculous of living means (evidently electrical) are translated into that sensation we know of as sound.

Sound waves come in many frequencies or vibration speeds, the rate of vibration determining the pitch—within a range which varies roughly from twenty back-and-forth movements (cycles) per second for the very low tones up to fifteen or eighteen thousand cycles for the highest.

* The Saturday Review Home Book of Recorded Music and Sound Reproduction, 2nd Edition, 1956, Prentice-Hall. $4.95.

Sound vibrations are rarely pure and simple. Normally they are vastly complex, made up of dozens or hundreds of different vibration frequencies piled one upon the other into an elaborate composite vibration as, upon the sea, waves of different sizes and directions move simultaneously over the surface. Some selective objects pick up selective sound vibrations and ignore all others—they are *resonant* at a particular frequency, i.e., pitch. China on closet shelves, buzzing pieces of wood, loose bolts, are homely examples of highly selective sound pickup and they are a nuisance at times. To pick up the entire sound without favoritism, as does the ear, has never been simple and still is a problem in microphone design.

Since sound is basically motion, the recording of sound involves motion. Reproducing it ends up with the same motion. In today's high fidelity recording the steps in between are many and involved. For the greater part of its journey from original to reproduced motion, the sound pattern is electrical. Patterns of motion are converted into pulsing electrical currents. We are so used to this electrical form of sound that we often confuse it with real air-sound in our speaking— we talk loosely of "bass" and "highs" and the like, never bothering to explain that the electrical form of sound is in question. I'll probably do it myself, since this is the present linguistic convention and, to tell the truth, I find it a convenience. After all, electrical sound is entirely meaningless; it can be heard only when converted into actual sound waves and so we consider the deed as done.

LATERAL DISC. Two types of recording have dominated the field, both of great importance: lateral disc and magnetic tape. Disc recordings, of course, include "platters" of all sizes and speeds. Stereo disc adds a third type but I'll save it for Chapter 16.

The earliest recording, without benefit of electricity, was done on a cylinder and consisted of vertical or up-and-down "waves" in a groove, indented there by a vibrating needle as the cylinder turned, reproduced as the needle retracked the same grooves and revibrated its own story. Vertical grooves ("hill and dale") still exist in dictating equipment, in some broadcast transcriptions and in stereo disc; but the rest of our disc recording uses the lateral groove system where the motion of the original sound wave is preserved in a side-to-side groove pattern.

As in the ocean waves and in musical sound itself, the motion of the recording needle or stylus is a composite of numberless vibrations. The eye sees only one motion, or in the record groove, one wiggly trace. But the ear, when that single trace is reconverted into corresponding sound waves, can hear each separate sound or tone coloration just as in the original. That is the lucky miracle which allows the enormously complex sound of a symphony, combining tones from half a hundred or more instruments, to be represented exactly in the mere sideward motion of one tiny needle tracing a single wavering groove.

Today's disc recording process is largely electrical as is our reproducing system. The microphone is the original conversion agent that makes electrical pulses out of the sound waves it "hears." The complexities that follow merely prepare that electrical pattern for convenient reconversion into motion—of a recording stylus cutting its wobbly spiral groove into a blank recording disc. Processed and multiplied, these same grooves reach you as the commercial record, ready to be traced by your pickup. A very much abbreviated account, this, but these are the essentials.

The new tape process for recording is an intermediary "must" in the process of making discs. Tape is used universally now to make the original recording and for assorted copying, from tape to tape, and from tape to disc. Tape recording is a growing hobby and a useful tool in many another way as well. Tape records now supplement disc records in the home. But for tape, see Chapters 13 and 18; for stereo tape, Chapter 16.

WHY RECORDS ARE NOT FLAT. But let us get on from this overcondensation to the part which directly concerns your understanding of your own playing equipment. The ideal recording would preserve sound patterns not only with no distortion but exactly as "heard" by the microphone, "flat"—yet even a theoretically distortionless recording can never do that.

In every disc record the bass tones are intentionally weakened in proportion to the higher ones. In every recent disc record and many older ones the highest tones are deliberately "boosted," given extra strength over the normal balance. This is not a distortion in the usual sense, though it surely distorts the sound pattern as originally heard. It is a calculated modification, introduced deliberately, to be canceled out again by reverse "distortion" built into the response of your phonograph playing system. Your amplifier boosts the bass back to normal and similarly the treble is weakened or "rolled-off" to compensate for the strengthening of the record.

But why? Remember that to transmit a given amount of energy (and therefore volume of sound), a slower vibration must move farther back and forth than a fast one, as per the arm-and-fist-demonstration on page 29. Sound, which varies from 30 to 15,000 cycles a second, is subject to this principle. At 15,000 cycles the distance of movement is extremely tiny even for a powerful sound. But at 40 or 50 vibrations per second, the movement must be enormously greater for the same transfer of plain energy. Too great for a record groove.

Think of this in terms of that groove. Higher tones wiggle fast, but their "excursion" is extremely small even for the louder sounds. On the other hand, the lower you go in pitch, the slower are the vibrations— and the *wider must be their swing*. At the lower pitches (frequencies, we should say) the recording process becomes increasingly difficult— the record groove must swing wider, taking more space, moving the needle itself farther against its own natural resistance. The recording of the very lowest tones in this fashion is just plain impossible. Needles won't move far enough sideways. And if they could, the resulting groove would take up a wasteful amount of space on the record.

But in an amplifier we can operate upon sound in a purely electrical form. No width, no stylus. Electronic circuits can be made to do useful things in the way of selectively affecting sound strength (electrical) by pitch. We can progressively "boost" the bass tones the lower they go, or we can progressively weaken them, and the same with the higher tones—the two tone controls on your amplifier do exactly that for you.

EQUALIZATION. This is the ingenious idea behind *equalization*—a term you will often have heard. First, the bass tones are deliberately and progressively weakened in their electrical form from a mid-point downward into the bass, before they even arrive at the groove cutting head, weakened enough so that the sideways needle wobbles remain quite small even for the lowest bass tones—and that means a great deal of weakening. The grooves stay within bounds. Your record itself, then, has a very weak bass in proportion to the treble recorded on it. As it is traced by the phonograph needle, the bass is still weak—weak enough to be accurately traced.

But in your phonograph amplifier is a compensating electrical circuit which exaggerates the bass, and so boosts the recorded sound back again electrically to what it had been in the first place. Thus you have your cake and eat it. The record itself is held within bounds as to sidewise wobble and yet you have (more or less) the full range of bass tones. The readjustment is called equalization, or sometimes record compensation.

Second, the treble end, on most records, is also altered in recording, but differently and for different reasons. It is boosted (pre-emphasized), whereas the bass is weakened. It also must be equalized, in the playing, by a compensating ("roll-off") circuit.

The principal reason for treble boost is to better the ratio between the surface noise, the scratches and pops on a record, and the actual recorded music. The record's higher tones are therefore made abnormally loud in proportion to the rest. (Remember that fast vibrations don't move the needle sideways very far, and so this is quite feasible.) Your amplifier, equalizing similarly in the treble range for the too-strong high tones, cuts them down to size again—and simultaneously cuts the "normal" surface noise that has been picked up from the record to a decided subnormal. The amplifier can't tell the difference. This is such a good idea that all commercial records now have boosted highs even though there is risk of distortion in the equalizing of the very highest tones, the ones that get boosted the most.

Now if all records were made with exactly the same amount of bass weakening and treble strengthening, and always had been, there would be no problem at all as far as you are concerned. Phonographs would automatically equalize for these changes and you would never need know about them. Unfortunately, there has been much disagreement—and so you must know.

The particular plan of weakening and strengthening used in a given record is called its *recording curve*—or just "curve," for short, referring to a hypothetical graph of proportionate response according to pitch. A "flat" recording, one where at all pitches the sound has its original proportionate strength, is as we have seen impossible. The recording curve or graph always drops at the low end, because of the decrease in bass strength, and tips upward at the high end, thanks to the boosted highs. Recording curves look like this:

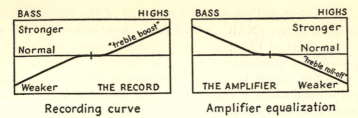

Recording curve   Amplifier equalization

But who determines the recording curve's exact characteristics? There's the rub; until recently there were various opinions among the many manufacturers on seemingly minor but vital points. Where shall we begin the progressive weakening of the bass—how far down? Some records had more bass removed than others. Some had a "twisty tail" at the bottom end of the curve, to help remove rumble in the extremely low recorded tones. More significant—how much shall the highs be boosted? Some felt it should be a lot—16 db (Chapter 7) at 10,000 cycles. Others halved that figure; vast numbers of older records were made, conservatively, with no boost at all. Basic disagreements.

Properly equalized, every one of these types of records can be made to sound the same—like the original sound. But who is to do the adjusting, from one record to the next, during the playing? Who but you!

In the prewar days, phonographs were not so accurate as they are now, and neither the very low tones nor the very high ones were reproduced; hence the most sensitive parts of the recording curve, at the extremes, were largely inoperative and out of the running. Today we hear much more bass, and even the cheapest phonographs bring us the very high highs, virtually to the top of our hearing range. Therefore, with both the extremes of the sound range audible—where the boost is the greatest in the highs and the weakening greatest in the bass— the differences between one recording curve and another have become decidedly noticeable and therefore a real problem in home listening. That is why you hear about recording curves now, though you didn't before the war, and it is why your modern amplifier or control unit must provide facilities for equalizing different types of records.

AGREEMENT AND RIAA. The advent of the LP record actually brought the beginnings of agreement as to this essential matter of the recording curve, at least in this country. The original Columbia LPs made use of

a then convenient and recognized curve, that of the National Association of Broadcasters (NAB), who did much recording in their radio
work. This "original LP" curve (still found on most amplifiers) was
widely used for a number of years; but some record makers felt that its
highs were too sharply boosted for best quality at the extreme upper
end and so used different curves with more moderate boost—requiring
of course, a correspondingly moderate reduction of the highs in the
playing amplifier. London "ffrr" records, for instance, needed quite a
different playback equalization from Columbia's.

As usual, you, the unknowing home listener, had to do the switching and the button-pushing in order to get it—if you knew how. Mostly
you didn't, and blamed the records. Engineers tend to think in terms
of their own interest, to uphold their own special standard regardless
of such mundane considerations as the practical needs of home users.
"Compromise" is a deadly word in such circles—it should be—and the
choice of recording curves for commercial records was one of those
things that, in engineering minds, admitted of no compromise.

This "Original LP" curve did give rise, after the complaints began
to multiply, to a new feeling that a universal standard should somehow
be agreed upon. The Audio Engineering Society tried first, with the
so-called AES curve (it was a reverse "playback" curve, intended for
phonographs, putting the cart before the horse) which gained some
acceptance—but not enough. Still, agreement seemed possible and,
when the psychological moment arrived, no less than three new "standard" curves were almost simultaneously proposed—and turned out to
be similarly inspired. They were almost immediately consolidated. The
New Orthophonic (ORTHO) curve of RCA Victor records, the revised
NAB—now NARTB (Radio and Television Broadcasters) and, issued
by a new association in the record manufacturing industry, the RIAA
(Recording Industries), these three to all intents and purposes are the
same, and even the Audio Engineering Society has joined the bandwagon with a revised AES curve the same as the others.

So, at last and reluctantly, the desired standardization has been
achieved. Now, practically every record made conforms to the RIAA
curve. One single equalization position plays all records made since
about 1955, whatever the label. If you own no others, you don't need
to bother about equalization at all. Just switch to RIAA and play away.

But, unfortunately, most of us do own older records, of numerous
sorts. The confusion of the past is going to stay with us as long as these

old records last. The confusion now is somewhat different from that in the past, however. The trouble is that now you must know which curve various brands of records required *before* they changed over to the standard RIAA. Older London require the "LON" curve (as marked on some amplifiers) but not new Londons, which are RIAA. Older Columbias need the "ORIG LP" or NAB curve, but all recent Columbias are also RIAA. So it goes; old RCA long-play records were a law unto themselves, and so were many others. (Note that many older releases are being recut from the master tapes, the new issue featuring the RIAA curve. Hundreds of Westminster's earlier "5000" series, mostly "Original LP," have now been reissued as RIAA records, for example.)

Amplifier instruction booklets, magazines, books, often contain detailed charts that purport to tell you which records need which curves. They are impressive, these lists, but they seldom agree! At this stage, the thread of recording history is so hopelessly tangled, after only a few years, that nobody will ever get it all straight.

Luckily for you, it doesn't really matter. You can do your equalizing very nicely by ear, if you understand the general picture. I propose the following simple principles, by which you can operate easily enough.

1. All recent U.S.-recorded records, since around 1955, can be assumed to be RIAA. Play them that way as a matter of course, unless they sound very wrong. (Note that most RIAA records are so marked on the record jacket. "*This recording conforms to the RIAA curve.*")
2. Older LP records fall into two opposite classes, which are quite easy to tell apart by ear: Those with *sharper* highs than the present records—a greater boost—and those with *less* strength in the high range—less boost.
   A. The *sharper-highed* older records are those with the old Columbia pattern, and its variants. They will sound somewhat shrill to you at the RIAA setting. For them, try setting marked COL, NAB, NARTB, "ORIG COL," etc. One of these, with perhaps a trace of tone control adjustment, should fix them nicely.
   B. The records with *weaker* highs than is now standard will sound, conversely, somewhat dull and muffled at the RIAA position. They are mostly older London "ffrr" records. Use the position marked LON; or try the AES (OLD AES) position—which is nearer to them than our present RIAA.

Alternatively you can use your tone-control knob to take care of both types—raise the highs a bit, or lower them a bit.

Yes, there is a difference in the bass too. But this is not nearly as noticeable to the casual ear and will not ordinarily bother you. By all means, turn up the bass knob a bit, or lower it, if you are conscious of any pronounced bass imbalance. But fix the treble first. Your tone controls actually can do a very practical job of adjustment on their own without extra help from special settings. Just raise or lower the treble (and the bass if you need to), leaving things at the RIAA setting. These controls have enough flexibility to cope with all major differences in the old records.

OLD 78s. As you no doubt already realize, the old 78 rpm records have another and even more varied set of recording curves. Many of them had no boost in the highs at all; the RIAA curve will make these sound very dull. Many had a heavier bass than is now common—and this, too, must be adjusted for. Most amplifiers have a position designed to take care of the simplified and average old 78—sometimes it is labeled EUR, for the European recordings that were so widely sold here before the war. (The masters were cut in Europe, even when pressed in this country. Today, we usually import tapes, make our own domestic discs from them; foreign-made LP records are now cut RIAA for sale on the American market, with very few exceptions.)

For all 78s, set your controls to EUR or 78, or equivalent; make extra adjustments with your tone controls. You probably will have to, and you should try, before you accept an old record's sound. It's always worth dickering a bit, in view of the known wide difference between records. Don't even allow an old record to sound "tubby" or bass-heavy for an instant—do something about it! You can with your hi-fi equipment.

TAPE EQUALIZATION. It should be added that magnetic tape recording also involves the principle of equalization in the playback, though the details are quite different. There are "curves" for magnetic recording and playback, too. But fortunately, tape came along, brand-new, at a time when the arguments over equalization among disc record makers were becoming a clear public nuisance; the tape people did not wander so far apart and, as of today, they have reached to all intents and purposes a real standardization. Tape, in other words, is more or less automatic. No special equalization "positions," just one playback, for almost all tapes.

So you see, as a music lover you cannot get along without equalization, and as an intelligent inquirer into the art of recorded musical sound you will find some knowledge of it surprisingly useful. Every phonograph must have equalization, in one form or another, to play any record. A "flat" pickup and a "flat" amplifier will give you exactly what's on the record—feeble bass and raucous, exaggerated highs. Equalization fixes that, but many a bewildered experimenter has accidently omitted it and wondered what could be the matter with his fine equipment!

For that matter, there has been much misguided professional music criticism, as you now can understand, complaining of such things as weak bass, strident highs. The British used to complain mightily about our strident and characteristically shrill American records; our own Anglophiles noticed that English discs were unusually "rich" in bass. Actually, with correct equalization for each type, these differences disappear, the supposed virtues or deficiencies turn out to be meaningless.

6

The Record Player

THE PICKUP CARTRIDGE

Two principal types of pickup are now in use for disc records, the *magnetic* and the *ceramic* or *crystal* (piezo-electric). Both, of course, serve to convert movements of the stylus into electric voltage, but beyond that their operation is utterly different, adding a new factor to equalization—for we must count the operation of the pickup itself as a part of the over-all faithfulness or lack of it in sound reproduction. There are other types of pickup, too, some demanding still different operating conditions, the capacitor (condenser) pickup, for example— but these are less important in the large picture.

CRYSTALS AND CERAMICS. The so-called crystal cartridge was used without exception in the older standard home phonographs. There were, and necessarily still are, dozens of types of crystal cartridge in accord with the chaos that has long existed in the purely mechanical aspect of the pickup and record changer—each manufacturer demanding his own pet cartridge with his own kind of mounting, needle, weight, etc. The need for replacements and for "modernization" keeps many of these old crystals on the market in every record store, mixed in with more recent pickup cartridges, even though they are technically out of date, heavyweight, oversized, with high distortion and strictly limited frequency range.

Today, the crystal has been superseded in almost all new domestic equipment of the home "hi-fi" type, by its improved variant, the ceramic. Technically speaking, the ceramic is also a crystal; it is a ceramic crystal instead of a Rochelle salt crystal. Its operation is according to the same principle; it is a piezo-electric device, a term that will be explained in a moment.

It isn't that the performance of the ceramic is inherently better—indeed, until recently, it was generally considered inferior. The essential difference is in durability, and it is here that the ceramic wins out, at least in our many-climated country. The older Rochelle salt crystal is sensitive to both moisture and heat. The ceramic, an altogether different crystal, is as durable as its name implies; moisture doesn't affect it at all, nor does reasonable heat. Barring fracture, it should last forever.

The widespread use of the ceramic had to await development of good sound quality, which for technical reasons was slow. But now, the ceramic can turn out hi-fi sound. Only the magnetic cartridge is better—and there is much argument as to just how much better. That, as you may imagine, depends for you not on engineer's measurements but on the state of the ear—your ear. If you can't hear the difference, there is none. There is not much in any case. Ceramics are now pretty good.

It should be added that the Europeans continue to prefer the crystal and, in fact, have developed it to a fine point of sound perfection. Partly conservatism, perhaps, but also because Europe has less of our weather extremes, a generally more even climate. Crystals do better there than here. Some of the new foreign crystals—top quality and ultra-modern—are now imported and put to work in our "hi-fi" systems, notably the Dutch Ronette crystal, used in the original Columbia 360 phonograph. Don't confuse these tiny new-style elements with the old flat, heavyweight prewar style crystals still widely sold. Except for their greater delicacy in harsh climates, these recent small crystals are equal to the new ceramics. In most situations they will do just as well; don't be scared of them.

Confusing? Yes, and I wish I could apologize—but the fault isn't mine. Instead, I toss you an easy suggestion for your hi-fi shopping: Generally speaking, the modern, high-quality crystals and ceramics are small and very light, mostly the size of a big thumbnail or a sugar lump. The older models are relatively much larger, longer, coarser in looks—and in sound too. Don't let anybody palm off a big cartridge on you, of any type.

PIEZO-ELECTRIC AND CONSTANT AMPLITUDE. Unlike the magnetic, the crystal or ceramic bends to create voltage. Certain materials have the strange power of generating electricity when they are strained or bent.

The crystal and ceramic pickups make use of this to generate electricity out of needle motion. The needle, tracking the record groove, bends the material inside the cartridge, generating a corresponding voltage which is fed off to the amplifier as we've already seen. This bending sort of voltage generation is called the *piezo-electric* effect, and a useful phenomenon it is, too.

More important for our own practical purposes is the peculiar way in which this bending pickup responds to high and low tones of sound. It generates a voltage directly in proportion to the *degree of bending*—whatever the pitch may be, high or low.

Now this may quickly raise a query in your mind concerning that matter of the slower bass tones that must vibrate *farther and wider for a given volume* than the fast high tones. That principle has already shown up in the loudspeaker's action and in the recording of bass on disc records. What does a crystal or ceramic pickup do to the balance between high and low tones?

It treats them with its own kind of impartiality—it responds only to the width or *amplitude* of their vibrations. All tones of a given vibration *width* produce the same amount of current—whether they are high or low. Since we know, however, that bass tones must by nature move much farther from side to side for a given strength than high tones, the crystal's warped point of view can be understood; it grossly favors the bass tones, exaggerating them according to their naturally greater width. It discriminates against the high tones because of their relatively narrower vibrations. The lower the bass, the more it is exaggerated by the crystal and the higher the treble, the more it is weakened. That is *constant amplitude* response, so called.

But this throws the highs and lows all out of proportion! Feed a normally balanced sound into a crystal pickup and it comes out with the bass strengthened, the treble weakened.

How can these pickups be used so widely, then? With such an odd kind of response, how can they give us acceptable sound from the usual disc record—why isn't it out of all balance?

If you will glance back a few pages at the playback graphs for equalizing records you may make a brilliant deduction. *The equalization curve needed to play records and make them come out "flat" is not very different from the constant amplitude curve of these cartridges' response.* Look at page 45. When you play a record with a ceramic pickup, the bass is strengthened, as explained above, and the treble weakened. What could be better? That's what a record requires for equalization.

Of course the curves aren't exactly alike and the older crystals, at least, did only an approximate job of equalizing. The older home machines weren't accurate enough to make the difference very important. But the principle held—the crystal could be used as is, to give a sort of automatic, if accidental, equalization for the average record. It sounded good enough, then, and it was practical and cheap to use, which accounts nicely for the millions of crystal cartridges put to work during some twenty years or so by the phonograph manufacturers.

Today we require more exact equalization, with better records and better-trained ears. Yet the ceramics (and the new European crystals) still base their sound on the old principle. The natural ceramic response is still close to that of the record itself, the RIAA curve already discussed, and all that is now needed is a slight but ingenious internal adjustment to make it match the record with the necessary accuracy. "Internally equalized to the RIAA curve," you may read, and that is the way it is done, for hi-fi response.

When you understand that the crystal and ceramic both give such a relatively healthy output "signal" that the main amplifier can accept it without need for a special preamplifier, you'll realize why these versatile cartridges have continued to spread through the "hi-fi" field into all areas. They are simple, direct, and relatively inexpensive. Soon, they'll be everywhere in stereo form, too.

Indeed, so useful is the ceramic that there are now ceramics with a special modification so that they can be used to feed into a preamplifier intended for magnetic cartridges. That involves changing the response curve radically and cutting down the output to make it weak enough to feed the preamplifier—which again builds it up to where it started! A series of contradictions here, but economics and convenience work in strange ways, and this is one of them.

A word of warning. Most of the big two-needle crystal pickups and the deadly "all-groove" one-needle singles, still often furnished with changers and phonographs and available in stores as replacements, are unsuited for high fidelity use. For convenience in multispeed operation they sacrifice tone quality. Avoid all of them. And steer strictly away from all metal (osmium) tipped needles, unless perhaps, for little-used speeds. They last only a few dozen plays, then begin to ruin your records. Get sapphires as a minimum; but diamonds are cheaper in the long run, play for play.

Crystal-ceramic cartridges fall into three rough categories now. (1) Large, heavy "replacement" types, both single and turnover, for older home phonographs, of no use for quality sound. (2) Large numbers of newer small and light cartridges with improved performance but still well below the hi-fi quality of magnetic and good ceramic units. (3) A handful of really top-quality lightweight ceramics (a few crystals, from Europe) that cost about as much as a magnetic of the GE type, require no preamplifier, offer really fine sound quality.

Low voltage output goes with good quality; the good cartridges are rated at about .5 to .7 volt (as compared to hundredths of a volt for magnetics). Cheap amplifiers require higher voltages, up to 2 or 3 volts; such equipment isn't worth bothering about if you want good sound.

Leading high-quality ceramics. The *Sonotone* line, both single and dual (with turnover needle), sapphires and/or diamonds, includes two models; the 1P and 2T dual is suited to changers, the top-quality 3T model, slightly higher cost, gives top performance at ultra-light weight.

Electro-Voice sells many small medium-performance cartridges; the top-quality *Ultralinear* cartridge is the only one worth considering for hi-fi sound. Among the great many *Astatic* cartridges, the "50" series are good in sound. The *Shure* Musician's cartridge is good—if and when available.

From Europe, the *Ronette* crystal miniature cartridges have excellent quality; as with the Sonotone, there are two lines (plus a high-output model you may ignore); the standard turnover, with two sapphires, is sold at very low prices—under $3. A bargain for medium-hi fi. The top-quality TX-88, preferable, is about $7.50 with two sapphires, $13 with one diamond, one sapphire.

MAGNETIC PICKUPS. The magnetic pickup is a straight generator, not far removed from the electricity-maker in your automobile. Like all dynamos or generators (like all pickups and microphones, too) it makes current out of motion. But unlike the ceramic, it uses the principle of the auto and household electric generator, motion of a conductor in a magnetic field, creating current in proportion to the motion. In the common "variable reluctance" magnetic cartridge, the needle or stylus lies close to the poles of a strong, tiny, horseshoe-type magnet wrapped with coils of fine wire; whenever the stylus moves, cutting through the invisible lines of magnetic force, the coils obligingly emit an electric current. In others (e.g., the moving coil) the stylus and coil move together within the magnetic field; or the magnet moves. Because there is no major mechanical action here except that of the tiny needle, the magnetic pickup is very accurate in its response and rates as the finest type of widely available cartridge for high fidelity work.

But there are two vital things about magnetics that directly affect your use of them and that in a way may be called disadvantages or, better, inconveniences.

FEEBLE AND "FLAT." First, the output of the magnetic pickup is infinitesimally small. Where the crystal gives from a half to three or more volts, the magnetic cartridge playing the same record gives a signal as low as one-hundredth of a volt or less. (The engineers make it sound big by calling it ten millivolts—ten thousandths of a volt.) Now the ordinary power amplifier can't do a thing with this. At top volume you can just barely hear a faint sound from your loudspeaker. Therefore a special preamplifier must be used with magnetics, designed to bring the tiny output up to a voltage where it can compete with that of a crystal or of radio tuners and the like. However, preamplifiers are now universally built into high fidelity amplifiers, as well as into the various separate preamplifier-control units and into "hi-fi" phonographs with magnetic cartridges. There is no problem then, outwardly. But this means more tubes (or transistors), more wires, more chance for distortion, more expense and, most important, a susceptibility to hum pickup. The preamplifier enormously magnifies any trace of unwanted hum or extra noise that gets into it. And so the preamplifier is the weakest point in any equipment and the section most likely to cause trouble or to deteriorate in performance. It would be nice to by-pass it; ceramic cartridges do so. And yet, for top quality, the magnetic-with-preamplifier is de rigueur, or so most of us have been persuaded.

But this is only the first complication involved in the magnetic pickup cartridge. One of its virtues is, oddly, another major headache when it comes to playing records. The magnetic, unlike the ceramic, is literally "flat" in its response, however feeble. It responds, that is, with impartiality to sounds (electrical sounds) both high and low, giving out precisely what it receives. It reacts to the actual power of the vibration of its stylus, not to the mere width or amplitude of the vibrations as with the ceramic or crystal. Constant velocity is the term for this kind of response.*

* If you can cope with a mental puzzle, here's why. A sound wave has several measurable attributes. We've spoken loosely of vibration speed, more correctly called frequency, the number of back-and-forth motions or cycles per second. The width of the vibration swing is its amplitude or size. There is also the actual speed

Now this is a significant difference as compared with the crystal, which favors the bass and weakens the highs because of its special concern with the amplitude of vibration, regardless of pitch. It would appear to be a great advantage to have a pickup that is strictly "flat"—"transparent" to sound, passing it from the groove to the electrical form with a minimum of interference.

But there is a paradox to be considered here. The musical records this pickup must play are not "flat." The crystal pickup and the ceramic happen by accident more or less to compensate for the record's peculiar tonal balance—lacking in bass, too strong in highs. But connect a magnetic cartridge and you'll get most unpleasant music, because it is a literal reflection of exactly what the record has on it—screechy, harsh highs and feeble bass!

I could not count the number of distressed letters I've had from people who complain of exactly these symptoms in their fine new hi-fi equipment! The magnetic cartridge, you see, is too faithful to do any equalizing on its own.

An *equalized preamplifier* for magnetic cartridges is intended to solve these problems. It does two things. It builds up the voltage from the magnetic pickup sufficiently to drive the main amplifier, and it equalizes the cartridge's output to balance the recording curve. A fine idea and it works—with the reservations already mentioned.

At the moment, many brands of magnetic cartridge share the competitive hi-fi limelight, at varying costs. Of them all, the inexpensive GE VR II magnetic cartridge is to my mind the best and most practical bargain if you will be satisfied with, perhaps, 95 per cent of possible perfection. In a higher bracket, giving even better sound (if you can hear the difference) are many excellent magnetics of a similar type. Among the fanciest mag-

---

or *velocity* that the vibrating material has. A needle wiggling down the length of a record groove moves as an automobile does down a winding road. A car's energy—as we know when it hits a tree—is according to its speed. So with sound vibrations. The needle travels faster when it must zip around wider swings and its faster motion transmits more energy to the pickup.

This relates to the fact that a slow vibration, as in a bass tone, needs a wider swing to be equally strong energy-wise. Look at an enlarged hypothetical sound: Take a vibration swinging 12 inches, at two back-and-forth cycles per second. Distance traveled is 48 inches: $4 \times 12'' = 48''$. A vibration of the *same strength* at four cycles a second (a "faster" or higher-frequency vibration) travels only 6 inches from side to side yet covers the *same distance*, in the same time: $8 \times 6'' = 48''$. Distance traveled is thus the same for the same energy so the speed of travel is the same too. Hence a pickup that responds equally to equal *strengths* of sound, high or low, actually responds to equal *velocity* or speed. Constant velocity. A crystal pickup responds to equal width of swing—*amplitude*—and so is constant amplitude.

netics are the moving-coil types, with extremely high quality but extremely low output (sometimes requiring a transformer ahead of the preamplifier, at another eight or ten dollars).

The newer magnetics are improved in many details: (1) in small size and weight; (2) reduced point pressure, now commonly lower than 6 grams; (3) greater convenience in installation and use, as well as stylus change; (4) improved lateral compliance (ease of sidewise motion of the point) and small moving mass, to follow complex record groove shapes; (5) ever-lower distortion in various other respects and (6) extended tonal range response, now up to 25 thousand cycles or so in the supersonic region and down into the subsonic bass region. The net result of all this is to make the best cartridges more than ever "transparent" to sound signals.

The *General Electric* variable reluctance magnetic in its new VR II models remains the semi-universal, all-purpose value leader, available everywhere at remarkably low prices. It will be your inevitable choice unless you are ready to spend a lot more for a slightly nearer approach to perfection. Most ears will not be able to tell the difference between the GE and the expensive top-grade cartridges, though you can spot it by careful comparison if you have had considerable listening experience in hi-fi. The VR II modernizes the basic GE concept in a smaller, lighter unit than the old RPX model, with improved compliance, lighter tracking weight, wider tonal range. In general the sound is much like the older models; the improvement is most noticeable in (a) loud, complex musical passages and (b) in less record wear, point wear. The clip-in stylus feature, somewhat clumsy engineeringwise, is a practical aid to quick stylus interchange and replacement in both single and dual models. (Clip-in stylus tips were used in late versions of the old RPX models; modernizing adapters are available for all the old cartridges—see dealer. The old clip-in points will *not* fit the new cartridge.)

Typical GE prices: Single model, with sapphire point: $7. Dual turnaround ("triple-play") with 78 sapphire, LP-45 diamond $19. GE diamond clip-in points are now less than $10, too good a bargain to miss—don't bother with sapphires for LP-45. (Don't buy unknown "replacement" diamonds.)

GE has one price rival, the *Goldring (Recoton) 500* (dual, sapphire-diamond $18.50).

Above the GE in cost and minutely better (in important ways) as to performance are the following, available in singles and duals:

The *Pickering Fluxvalve* (single, sapphire $18; dual, sapphire-diamond $42) has convenient large plastic-mounted slip-in stylus assemblies, interchangeable and color-coded. (The standard Fluxvalve has little vertical springiness or compliance—do *not* play stereo discs with it.) The German-made *Miratwin*, single and dual, is a reliable and sturdy cartridge. (Single, sapphire $10; dual sapphire-diamond $32). Stereo models of both.

A number of high-quality magnetics are available in single models only, often with non-interchangeable stylus (return to factory for replacement) to give top-quality sound. The *Fairchild 225* cartridges, with low output but extremely high quality, are $37.50 for any model (various point sizes), diamond only; the mechanism is the desirable high-quality moving-coil type. The moving-coil *Electro-Sonic ESL C-60*, replacing the earlier ESL "Concert" series, gives extremely high quality sound, with enough output to avoid the transformer necessary with the older ESL models. (This one responds beyond 30,000 cycles, has very high compliance and extremely low mass, is reasonably rugged, safe in changers.) Diamond stylus only, nonremovable $40. The *Grado*, with an ingenious adjustable damping arrangement that allows exact compliance to be set at the factory, has similar extremely high performance characteristics, with a forward-aimed stylus visible in front of the cartridge, very high flexibility both laterally and vertically (will play stereo discs monaurally without harm). Single, diamond $45. Stereo versions too.

For magnetic cartridges sold integrally with arms, see below.

Special note: The introduction of stereo disc (Chapter 16) has brought a revolution in the cartridge field—since the stereo cartridge will play both stereo and standard records. Virtually all of the above magnetics, as well as the crystal-ceramics, in all price ranges, will be supplemented by or replaced by stereo cartridges by the time this is in print. Some of these, necessarily, will be entirely different in construction—for better or worse as the case may be. But others will be much like the standard version. The chances are excellent, however, that the general quality and sound characteristics of each regular cartridge will be carried over reliably into its equivalent stereo version; thus the above discussion is still a useful guide.

It would be well to note two points right here concerning magnetics. First, many are available in double models, for both types of groove. In most of these there is no major compromise in quality, for there are either two separate cartridges back to back (Pickering, Miratwin, Goldring), separate needles (Fluxvalve, Audak) or the mechanical arrangement is such that the two joined needles do not seriously interact with each other. (Theoretically, a single GE cartridge might be expected to give slightly better quality than the "triple-play" type with two stylus points, turnaround style, in one cartridge; but the difference is extremely slight, if it exists at all in audible terms.) This is in contrast to the older big turnover crystal cartridges—many still used—where two needles are directly attached to a single crystal. (The new hi-fi ceramics, like the magnetics, manage the two needles without appreciable compromise in sound quality. Several use a single turnaround stylus with two points mounted directly back to back.)

Secondly, note that though most magnetics have replaceable stylus assemblies, some do not. For replacement you must send the entire cartridge to the factory. (The Fairchild and Pickering 200 series are examples—not the Pickering Fluxvalve, which has replaceable styli.) The reason is a good one. For very best performance a stylus must be as small as possible, offering the least mass of its own to counter the vibrations of the music itself. The extra bulk of a replaceable-type needle is sometimes bad for the ultra-best in sound; in those pickup designs where such a compromise would reduce the sound quality, the stylus has been built in.

A fixed stylus is fine—if your working point is a diamond. Diamonds last for many months and even years. But a fixed sapphire is a snare and a delusion. Do not buy one *unless* it is for use in an extra speed, such as with old 78s, where it is played only on rare occasions. (In this case, the sapphire may save you money.) Note here, too, that in some cartridges both needles must be replaced together. If one wears out, the other that goes with it will have to be used up before you can replace the whole. But in most new models, the two points are individually replaceable and you may be as free as you wish. Take all this into account!

THE RECORD CHANGER

I suppose the record changer will go merrily on to hi-fi eternity, but today it is not really necessary for most listening purposes, sacrificing quality in the fundamentals at the price of a convenience. Of the entire changer mechanism, only the automatic shut-off remains really useful for most of us, and this facility appears on a number of manual-type tables that cost less than equivalent changers. Even this is not essential, if you want the best sound for your money. The fanciest hi-fi tables have no shut-off.

The changer mechanism itself reached a seemingly high point of perfection shortly after the war. The same clumsy loading process is still necessary, the same troubles still develop—records that don't drop, arms that land on the wrong spot, reject mechanisms that rudely reject in the middle of a record. You have no doubt had experience with such matters. There has been plenty of improvement, of course. Arms are lighter and more free to move, better balanced, better tracking; motors are stronger, tables are steadier, rumble is lower than in the first postwar models. But the changer mechanism in principle is still very much with us. If you can avoid it—do so. But you will probably end up with one if only by the law of favorable economics, which makes the changer a relative bargain thanks to mass production.

Four speeds? The fourth speed, you must realize, was added by most manufacturers in sheer panic. They had no reason to think that the 16 rpm speed would be vital for home use. Yet when a few four-speed models appeared, most of the other makers jumped on the bandwagon simply to protect themselves—and now we have four speeds. Oddly enough, the mere fact that most players can now revolve at 16 rpm is producing unlooked-for 16 rpm material, and, belatedly, the fourth speed may well find a reasonable place for itself, for ultra-long-play and very inexpensive sound at strictly medium fi. The first use of the slow speed was, and is, for the phenomenal 16 rpm Audio Books—phenomenal in respect to the enormous number of spoken words they offer at very low cost. Whole books full. The quality is so-so, though quite intelligible. You will find a certain amount of music, too, on 16 rpm records—not one but several whole symphonies recorded on a single disc. Again, so-so quality and possible wobbles, at a super-bargain rate. Not a very important factor in the hi-fi field.

The best that can be said for the fourth speed is that it hasn't greatly interfered with the record changer's operation, nor has it raised the cost much. Unless you have a special interest in 16 rpm talking books, don't even think one way or the other as to three versus four speeds. Look at the other factors first.

As suggested above, the changer is today's mass-production bargain in its department—good performance at remarkably low cost, even with the semi-inflation of these last few years. You cannot do better price-wise. But, you will also realize, this mechanism shares the usual characteristics of our American-manufactured consumers' items, brilliant performance with relatively short life. Not that a changer can't be kept changing year after year, with good care and repair. But unless you can manage this maintenance yourself, you will run into the usual service problems when something does go wrong.

If you want conservative durability at somewhat higher cost, try an imported changer, from Germany, Switzerland, or England. Generally, in Europe things are made to last a bit longer than here. There is less money around, things cost more, and people buy close to the chest. European changers made to sell here are "designed for the American market," but you may count, I think, on the inherent character of the people to appear in their product. A German changer is brilliant, useful and durable, like a Volkswagen; a British changer is more conservative, perhaps clumsy, but it is well built even when wrongly built (as in the older Garrards with their rubber belt drive, now happily replaced by the simple idler wheel that everybody else has used for years).

RIM-PUSH, CENTER-PUSH AND INTERMIX. What are the features to look for in changers? By now, the outward configuration of the changer mechanism is fairly well standardized. To begin with, there are two types, the center-hole push-off and the rim push-off—my own names. The rim push-off is clearly better as far as record preservation is concerned since it handles records by their edges, where even a chip or a dent will not affect the playing. You can spot this type by the necessary "shelf" or platform that shoves the records sidewise. It costs more, is less convenient to handle, and is gradually disappearing. The larger Garrard tables still use it; Webcor, in this country, has given it up.

The center-push changer lifts the bottom record on the pile and slides it off, doing its work right next to the center hole, at the spindle. No push-off shelf. There is usually an overhead arm to hold records in place and a feeler mechanism that tells the changer what size it is dealing with so that the pickup can drop at the right place. This type, now almost universal, puts a strain on the region next to the center hole and can easily wear it out of shape. Even a microscopic bit of wear at that crucial point can cause unpleasant wavering in your music. If your records aren't played too often, the center-push changer is undeniably simple and convenient, speaking in relative terms. But here is one more reason, nevertheless, why you should consider a manual player for best quality of sound.

Many changers now have an intermix feature that plays (1) records of various sizes at a given speed or (2) plays various sizes at different speeds, adjusting itself for each record. Not so tricky when you come to think of it; the seven-inch records are all 45s now (except Audio Books), the tens and twelves mostly 33. The mechanisms differ; in some cases you must load the records with the 45s last, whether you like it or not. Note that there is a difference in the shut-off mechanism among changers. Some, mostly obsolete types (on sale cheap), repeat the last record again and again, others return the arm to rest and then shut the motor off. Some even retract the rubber idler wheel when they turn off—an excellent idea (Collaro). In others you must do this yourself, setting the speed-change lever at "O" or neutral (Miracord). In still others there is no retraction and the idler wheel stays against the rim, where sooner or later it develops a "flat" and bumps as it plays, like a flat-wheel on a trolley car. It's worth your time to check on all of this.

MANUAL-PLAY AND TUNABILITY. A very important item on the newest changers and a lovely paradox, too, is the manual-play position. Now, you can have a changer that doesn't change! But the need is very real, as you may have found when you have tried to sample a portion of a record or play single records, on a changer that snatches its arm out of your hand or turns itself off at the most exasperating moments. Be sure to ask for a true manual playing position, and try it out, too. Some changers (the Miracord again), have an optional short manual spindle that replaces the regular spindle, for hand changing. Excellent. Most changers now also have an optional thick center post for 45 records, usually at extra cost. Without this, you must fit inserts into the big holes on your 45 records.

If you are ever likely to need to tune a record to match a musical in-strument (as with the "Add-a-Soloist" and "Music Minus One" records) you will find some players with adjustable speeds. (The adjustment is small—less than a half step—but enough for tuning.)

The Garrard Crown II changer (RC-98) has this feature, as does the Lafayette Japanese manual turntable (P-100A; $50) and the Scott 710 turntable ($125). The Bogen manual turntable has continuously variable speeds (see below). Others will soon have it—ask, if interested.

I suggest that you keep away from cheap "bargain" changers offered in many stores and catalogue sales—they are bargains only if you are sure of your ground and can spot obsolete cartridges, inferior motors, etc. Some are good buys at low prices. Keep away, also, from brand-new models until the inevitable bugs are cleared out! The usual yearly face-lifted versions of older models can be considered but not newly intro-duced lines without previous relatives. This principle applies, alas, to everything in hi-fi, as well as to most products in American life.

BASES AND CARTRIDGES. Changers (and manual players too) come either with or without base. The models which sit on their own bases, metal or wood, are very convenient for separate-unit hi-fi systems of the more movable sort. The changer and base can usually be set into a cabinet space of the right size, if you want cover. Unmounted changers won't stand up and must be set into a hole of the right shape (different for every model); template diagrams are included for your edification. The hole is a devil of a job to cut if you aren't a good carpenter; don't fuss with it unless you are competent. Flat changer boards with hole are available to fit various models, by mail or in any store, and you can have one cut to order at your hi-fi dealer. Similarly with cabinets that feature changer boards, uncut. Some cabinetmakers and dealers will cut the hole to size for you as part of the deal.

The cartridge, needless to say, is an important part of your changer. There is plenty of flexibility in present offerings. (1) You may buy a changer, usually the lower-priced models, with a built-in ceramic dual-point cartridge. Better check on its brand; some are not worth having. (2) Your changer may have a GE VR II turnaround "triple-play" cartridge ready-installed or, in some cases, one of the fancier cartridges; you have a choice of sapphire or diamond points, in most. (3) Many better changers come with plug-in heads (one or two), in which you may mount (or have mounted) the cartridge or cartridges of your choice. As already mentioned, separate cartridges for each type of groove provide optimum quality, but the dual cartridges of the better sorts are just about as satisfactory. A few cartridges of top quality, such as Fairchild and ESL, do not come in dual models; you must acquire one for each type of groove.

Changer sizes are semi-standardized in most lines now, but differences up to an inch or two are important to watch—also differences in height and depth. Catalogues give measurements; templates for holes are included, as above. Dimensions are most about 13″ x 14″, the larger changers running up to 16″ the long way.

For years, most U.S. changers came in two series: one was compact, simplified, lower-priced, intended mainly for manufacturing into standard home phonographs but available separately; the other line was slightly larger and more expensive with better features, intended mainly for separate sale. This distinction is now blurred but still exists, mainly in the flexibility of features such as available cartridge arrangements. The more expensive lines offer arms less cartridge or with plug-in heads; the cheaper lines are confined to the GE cartridge or a ceramic, usually Sonotone. (Do not buy an unidentified ceramic.)

Standard older American lines are *Webcor* and *V-M*, now competing with the new *Glaser-Steers GS-77*. European lines widely available are *Garrard*, *Collaro*, *Monarch* (from England), *Miracord* (Germany), *Thorens* (Switzerland)—the Thorens line is radically unlike others, with direct-drive geared motor.

Note that all models except economy types come with or without base. Cheapest models come with base and cartridge, no choice.

Plug-in heads, less cartridge (use any hi-fi model, to choice), were available at press time in Webcor's "Imperial" line ($43), the Collaro "Coronation" ($41), Thorens ($79), Miracord ($68), all Garrard changers ($42-$67) and others. Some changers come less cartridge but with a one-piece arm, which is an advantage in good performance.

Note that some newer changers have a lightweight, thin arm that will *not* take larger standard cartridges (V-M, for example). Consult dealer if in doubt.

All present changers will take virtually any *stereo* cartridge in place of the standard type with the addition of an extra wire. Wiring details will differ; you may have to run a makeshift wire on outside of arm. Within a short time, all new record players will be wired to take either stereo or standard cartridges. Check this.

MANUAL TABLES AND ARMS

It may at first seem strange to you that you will be asked to pay more—often a great deal more—for turntables *without* a changer mechanism than for those with the changing facility! The difference is one of quality, of potential, or, if you wish, of attitude. The changer is by nature a low-priced convenience, for those who love comfort and are unworried by ultimate hi-fi unattainables. There should be, I insist, a changer line at a high price which combines really fine performance— a heavy twelve-inch table, a long (and clumsy) arm—with the basic changing operation; but aside from a few imports (the Swiss Thorens models, for example) there are no such machines yet. Thinking hasn't gone in that direction.

There is, however, a growing area of compromise that is well worth your attention, the manual player-and-arm, sometimes with automatic shut-off and automatic motor-start as the arm is lifted—but no changer. This type of player gives you the basic values of changer-type equipment at a considerably lower price or, alternatively, raises the basic quality, with heavier, more solid and long-lasting components, at about the same cost as a changer. An excellent idea, if you are leery of the really topflight tables in the range above $50 for the table alone, minus arm and cartridge.

The two pioneers, still very much in evidence, were the Garrard and Bogen (Lenco) manual players, from England and Switzerland respectively; a later addition was the excellent Miraphon from Germany. The early Garrard "T" models (Crest) were not very successful but the current product (about $32, less cartridge) has the new idler wheel drive and should be excellent; the motor starts when arm is lifted, turns off at end of disc. A saving of about $20 over the changer equivalent. The Bogen B-50 series ($40, less cartridge) is larger, has a heavier construction, plays at continuously variable speeds with "notches" at the four standard speed positions. (An economy model, at $10 less, isn't too good an idea.) Both come alternatively with cartridges installed or with plug-in heads, less cartridge. The Miraphon ($37) is mounted on a compact base, has idler wheel retraction, self-starting and stopping. The Lafayette PK-160, a turntable-and-arm combination with two plug-in heads, less cartridge, is $26; wood base $4. Three speeds; available with GE cartridge installed (diamond-sapphire) at $38. Note that all of these are imports.

TOP-FI TURNTABLES. But there are higher ranges of perfection for you to consider. Hi-fi sound quality depends to a serious degree upon your turntable and arm. As the tonal range of speakers has been extended downward, an unpleasant type of heavy, low-pitched motor vibration, *rumble*, has become an increasing problem in motor and turntable design; it gets into the pickup and is grossly amplified through the speaker. (Older speakers and most new smaller ones will not reproduce it, fortunately.) Many older changers cannot be used with the new wide-range speakers because of the loud rumble from their drive mechanism.

"Wow" and other irregular and unsteady fluctuations of the pitch can undermine musical reality to an even more distressing degree—indeed, this factor should be the most important of all in your decision to acquire a high-quality table. To be sure, we can accustom ourselves to pitch waver, as we do to electrical distortion. But, especially with instruments like the piano, the reproduced sound can never be truly convincing until pitch is reproduced with extreme steadiness. Remember that tape recorders and disc cutting machines also contribute their complement to the final wobbles you hear in your recorded music; the unsteadiness of your machine is all the worse for it. Even the best low- and medium-priced changers can produce an unwelcome amount of waver. (Actually, some may be excellent, some poor—individual models often perform better than others of the very same make. This is a typical result of lower tolerances in the manufacturing, which cannot be as critical in low-priced machinery as in the more expensive items.)

Finally, over and above these things, there is the inevitably quicker deterioration of the inexpensive equipment to consider, a factor which involves all the others. A top-bracket hi-fi turntable should last indefinitely.

Consider, then, acquiring a really solid, large turntable with a carefully mounted, vibration-free motor system. Consider, to go with it, a good arm—long, often clumsy and inordinately delicate, expensive but beautifully designed to get the most out of a good cartridge. The arm and cartridge, in higher-priced equipment, are often designed as a unit, the one complementing the other.

Since I myself "converted" to this sort of equipment—arms and turntables—I have never been able to use a changer without immediately noticing a slight but annoying increase in waver, in mechanical rumble and all the rest. Very slight, I admit again, but only too evident to the inquiring ear after it is "spoiled" by the better equipment! You may very well enjoy music to the full via a changer—thousands do. But, paradoxically, you will not regret whatever cash you assign to a real hi-fi table and arm of this sort, though you will probably gasp at first at the cost—from $40 to $130 or more for a turntable—minus base, minus arm, minus cartridge—from $15 to $30 more for an arm to match, plus cost of cartridge and perhaps a base for mounting.

As I say, you can be happy with low-priced equipment, but the chances are good that if you are observant and really listen to your music, you will soon learn to appreciate good performance in these respects, even though at the moment (say, in a hi-fi demonstration room) you can't hear any difference at all. The difference is at the same time both microscopic and huge. It can be measured by engineers, but not *evaluated*; you must do the evaluating—or I must, as far as I can.

Never forget the "geometric disguise," which is the key to this volume's philosophy and to your own peace of mind when it comes to buying and listening. (See Chapter 10.) Your best values for the money *always* remain in the lower-priced equipment. To put it in reverse, you *lose* less and less in quality as you proceed down the price scale.

Quality tables (often called "professional," though actual professional equipment is usually bigger and still more expensive) are invariably twelve inches across or larger, stand quite high, occupy a good deal of room. Generally speaking, the best are the simplest; this sort of equipment doesn't go in for excessive gadgetry. Many come in a single speed (you can use an old changer for your few 78s); others have two, three or four speeds; some even require a separate pulley, changed by hand, for each speed. Clumsy, but good for performance. Don't let these somewhat awkward arrangements stand in your way; you are paying for musical sound, not convenience.

For ultra-quiet performance, extreme pitch accuracy and very low rumble, the expensive hysteresis motor is sometimes used. Extra cost, and you will not need to bother with it unless you are all out for the "hi-est in fi."

At the lower end of the quality-motor price scale are the motors in the $40 area, often "junior" editions of more expensive lines. The Components Junior, for instance, uses the long belt around the outside of the rim that was introduced in the larger and more expensive Components table, one of the best. There is a line of Rondine Jr. tables from Rek-O-Kut at $50-$60. (I still am using one of the original "Jr." models [LP-34] after many years; it is on its last legs, but has outlived, I'd guess, at least five changers! My Rek-O-Kut T-12H, the original hysteresis motor model in this line, is as good now as when new.) *Lafayette* offers a bargain (Japanese) hysteresis-motor turntable (see above) with three speeds, the PK-225 at $65; a standard-motor turntable with four speeds, the PK-400, is $50. These are also sold as parts of various "package" combinations with arms and cartridges included. See others similar.

The Presto "Pirouette" table runs you $66 or more, unmounted, the Rondine standard turntables run from $80 to $130 (with hysteresis motor). The recent Scott 710 turntable, mounted, with adjustable tuning at each speed, costs $125. A Gray combination, turntable plus viscous-damped arm, ready-mounted (no cartridge), is also $125. The D & R turntable, with a solid composition table, nonmagnetic, and an outside drive, the free-floating idler wheel running on the outside rim, is bulky, clumsy to change speeds (slip-over pulleys), but is one of the best performing and most reliable tables on the market. It is my favorite, among those I have used continuously. The Components table (above) is also bulky but of ultra-high quality.

The Fairchild Electronic Drive Turntable is a bulky and expensive precision instrument with a unique feature vital for some users—its speed is independent of line frequency (cycles) and voltage irregularities such as occur in many foreign countries. The motor is driven by a power amplifier with fixed frequency output and the speed will not vary. This is the answer to all pitch troubles due to the power line. Four speeds, each adjustable; about $200. A one-speed LP table for $100 can be converted to four-speed electronic drive later; a two-speed standard model is also available. A simpler aid for foreign playing is the one-speed "G.I. Special" version of the Components Jr. table, with quickly interchangeable 50-cycle (European) and 60-cycle (American) drive. Doesn't help with speed irregularities.

Other tables and combinations in this area are, alas, too numerous to list; these will give you an idea of the field.

ARMS. A great deal has been accomplished, since LP arrived, in the design of phonograph arms for best performance. Almost any one of the better arms now sold will provide you with excellent sound, and low record wear. Main difference—for you—is the outward ease and convenience of handling, which varies greatly according to the design. Some arms are better suited to rough or casual treatment than others; some require rather delicate movements, though a person who is habitually careful will have not the slightest trouble.

The longer "sixteen-inch" (rough length) arms are best in all respects; choose from them unless you are seriously cramped for space and must use one of the shorter "twelve-inch" versions. A number of models come in both sizes. The large size, of course, will not fit in the space where you had a record changer; the quality turntables won't either. Check carefully if you are installing your equipment inside cabinets or in small spaces.

By far the best arm bargains I know of are the three imported viscous-damped arms sold by *Lafayette Radio* (and probably other firms) at astonishingly low prices. The *PK-90*, a solid and ingeniously designed 12-inch arm with a "sticky" silicone fluid bearing that damps out resonances and protects the stylus—it "floats" down to the record when you drop the arm—sells for only $12. I have used one for two years with top satisfaction. Must be kept level, or fluid will spill. A longer (16-inch) model with sealed damping fluid at the joint, the *PK-170*, is $18; a still fancier arm, also sealed, the *PK-150*, is $20. These arms will do as well as any of the more expensive models, offer a maximum of home protection from damage to records and stylus.

The domestic Gray arm, at about $40, offers top-quality viscous-damped performance.

Widely available middle-price arms: the *Garrard*, adjustable both in length and tracking angle, $25; the *GE* "*Baton*," long and short sizes, with a vertically movable head, adjustable weight, on the end of dual tubular supports; best for GE cartridges (adapter for the new VR-II model) but the plug-in holders can be made to take other models (32, $35); the *Rek-O-Kut 120*, a single-tube arm with streamline plug-in-head, long and short sizes ($27, $30); the *Clarkstan 212G*, a long-familiar model in which you merely slide in your cartridge and twist a set screw to hold it in place (but some new smaller cartridges won't fit it—check yours) ($22). In the *Pickering 190D*, the gold-colored arm proper moves only sidewise; an inset head pivots up and down. The Pickering is so balanced that it will even play "uphill" with the table tipped halfway over. Tracking is excellent under extreme conditions. But the arrangement is risky—people try to lift the arm itself and so drag the loose cartridge point hideously over the record. OK for careful users. ($32.) The *Audak KT-12* and *KT-16*, a thin lightweight arm (long and short sizes), was designed for the special-shaped Audak cartridge, now comes inexpensively with heads for standard mounting of other models. It is sold assembled ($25, $30) or in simple kit form at a much lower price ($15, $18).

ARM-AND-CARTRIDGE. A new, yet highly logical development has been the arm-and-cartridge combination, designed as a single unit. As with loudspeakers and enclosures, the cartridge and its arm interact so intimately that the best designing involves tailoring the one to the other. "Universal" arms can never quite achieve this intimacy, and so the ultimate challenge of perfection has led to new arm-cartridge combinations, inevitably in the top price brackets. The difference is microscopic, but it can mean a lot to some people.

The new *Shure Dynetic* is a long, thin, dart-shaped arm on an ingeniously mounted base, jewel-pivoted, with a tiny magnetic cartridge pivoted in the forward end, hardly bigger than a fingernail. Tracks at one or two grams; the stylus is lifted by a top pushbutton. Magnetic arm rest. (About $80, with diamond needle; LP-45 only.) Alternative stereo version.

The *Pickering Uni-Poise*, with Fluxvalve cartridge, is suspended from a single needle point, with a scroll-like rear counterbalance. The tiny cartridge element is of a piece with the arm end, tracking at around four grams; the stylus unit is removable. Somewhat delicate, jars easily, the sharp point is a mild hazard when the arm slips off it. Not recommended for movable equipment or for any sort of rough usage. $60. Also in stereo form.

The *Weathers FM* arm and pickup was one of the first high-quality units, operating on a unique principle, frequency modulation of a carrier signal. It tracks at a gram or two, like the newer Shure gives superb quality at its best; in the past, unstable behavior has made it troublesome for a few users, but newer models are much more reliable. Weathers offers a low-priced modernization service for older models—an excellent idea. $75.

The *ESL Professional* arm and cartridge, made in Denmark and slightly modified here, rates at the top in engineering opinion—but it costs a lot. For the hi-fi connoisseur. Long, thin arm, small head.

The *Volpar* (Panama City, Fla.) is a light, tubular aluminum arm with integral cartridge; should be in medium price-range. ($60?)

(The old *Audak Polyphase L-6*, pioneer arm-and-cartridge combination, is now obsolete, not yet replaced by a new model as of this printing. The arm itself is sold in kit form.)

"NEEDLES"

OLD STYLE. A big subject that's getting smaller. There are hundreds of "needles"—stylus is the right word—still on the market, though there is an ultimate need for not more than a dozen or so. The prolific increase in needles of every shape, size and description that began when the old "universal" straight needle went out, has passed its climax. Dealers and public alike are thoroughly tired of the confusion; replacement models, both gyp and legitimate, have further complicated things and—a change is in the air.

Virtually all the recent lower-priced phonographs use ceramic cartridges. These come in only a few models, more or less interchangeable, and so, once we get rid of the millions of older machines requiring replacements, things will begin to settle down and simplify. And compared to the hundreds of older crystal models, the magnetics are few and require only a few stylus models to service them.

METAL, SAPPHIRE AND DIAMOND. What, then of the "permanent" miniature needle now almost universal? The plain answer is that even these are anything but permanent, regardless of selling claims.

You should not think of considering a precious-metal stylus for your high fidelity equipment unless you are ready to change it every *few days* of use. Good practice indicates that a precious-metal point may be safe for about fifteen LP sides at a good maximum. Fewer is safer. In a few months of this operation it will cost you the price of many jewel points. Metal needles are the *most costly, per playing time,* of any type available.

A sapphire point may last, on the average, something like seventy-five sides, often a lot less with heavy weight, worn or gritty records, cracked spots. I've heard them begin to sound fuzzy long before this quota. Sapphire is excellent if you do not play your machine very often, or are ready to make replacements every few months or sooner. (Note an observation of mine, that the playing of brand-new records seems to wear a jewel faster than the use of "broken-in" records in good condition.) Sapphires are far more economical than metal points, for the playing time.

A diamond point may seem horribly expensive to you—from $10 to $20—but in terms of records safely playable it is the cheapest. Moreover, it removes the point from the nerve-wearing category. You can be sure that when you hear fuzziness it is not the needle! If you can possibly afford it then, acquire a diamond stylus for the type of record you will play most, which will probably be the LP—and note that diamonds are getting cheaper. If you play relatively few old-style 78s, you can use a sapphire with good results. Never a metal point.

Diamonds of many brands are available and at many prices. Some are dangerous. It is risky to use diamonds or sapphires other than those provided by the maker of the cartridge, even though the cost may be less.

Why such rapid wear, considering that these substances are among the hardest known to man? The LP needle point has a radius of only a thousandth of an inch. On that tiny area of contact with the groove walls even a half-ounce weight piles up tons of pressure per square inch. The grooves wear too, but along hundreds of yards of length, whereas the entire friction of these endless stretches of fresh groove bear upon two tiny places on the stylus point with tons of pressure. Ordinary hard steel crumbles away in moments. Precious metal, ultra-hard, is good for

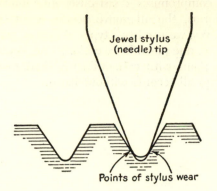

Jewel stylus
(needle) tip

Points of stylus wear

a short time only. Sapphire, the next-to-hardest substance, can stand up for a limited time. Diamond, the hardest of all, is something like ninety times as hard as sapphire, its next rival. Even diamond wears slowly under this withering pressure.

An important added moral must be taken to heart: Do *not* put extra weight on your pickup under any circumstances! A casual nickel placed on top to make the needle stay in the groove can add tons of extra pressure to ruin the record instantly. The pressure increases as the square of the weight!

The reputable cartridges for hi-fi use come with either sapphire or diamond points. (This is as it should be and limits your choice to the desirable jewels alone.) There is no difference between a new sapphire and a new diamond. Be sure you are convinced of that. Wear is the only factor—unless possibility of damage or loss is too great to risk a diamond point. (Children's machines for example, would be rashly provided with diamond styli!) The sapphire is actually more easily chipped than the diamond, I'm told. But it is very unlikely that you will chip a jewel. You'll more likely knock it clear out of its fastening. Even this is a rare occurrence.

ALL-GROOVE POINTS. Numbers of phonographs in the low-priced "hi-fi" field are made with the ultra-convenient "all-groove" point, that plays records of any groove size. So simple, so economical and trouble-free— that you may wonder why you have to bother over triple plays and double cartridges and pairs of plug-ins. The answer is that there's something wrong with the all-groove, of course. It simply fails to fit either groove correctly, compromises disastrously all along the line. In its common home forms, the all-groove needle is an oversimplification. We have two grooves; we need two types of needle point to fit them.

There is, however, one possible exception. The Weathers FM pickup uses an all-groove point with extraordinarily light pressure—a gram or two—and so it plays all records without harm.

7

The Amplifier

If much of this volume seems to involve complication after complication, I am glad to announce that the amplifier, the main central ganglion of any and every hi-fi system, has actually been simplified in the last few years. Simplified, that is, in the externals, in its useful controls and facilities. I would hardly say that the insides are any less complex; the wide use of decorator cases has actually crammed things together and, as observed elsewhere, has led to difficulties with the problem of ventilation. Hum problems, too, have increased and, I suggest, have not been any too well solved in view of other factors of performance. (If you hear no hum in your new amplifier with the volume control at the full-on position, and if a year later you still can hear none—the problem has been entirely solved.)

You may remind yourself of the basic functions of the amplifier via a look at Chapter 3; you'll remember the main points—the amplifier receives a tiny electrical signal voltage, uses it to control the flow of a much larger current in its own image; a good basic amplifier (i.e., not counting controls, equalization and so on) is neutral—flat—delivering the sound signal exactly as it was received (within a tiny percentage) except for the one difference of enlargement. Actually, many home amplifiers are a combination of this basic amplifier—which can be bought however as a separate unit—and a host of assorted modifiers attached to it or built into it, to cope with recording curves, pickups, multiple inputs, room acoustics and so on. It is this compound amplifier that you ordinarily consider first, the type that includes complete controls and all facilities needed to perform its elaborate function as the center of the home hi-fi system.

The amplifier was the first of the present hi-fi components to get
started and its forerunner, the old P.A. amplifier, had already been
around for years before anyone tried to use it as a home phonograph. It
is therefore the most highly developed of all the components and the
most consumer-orientated—the easiest to use, most flexible, best standardized.

It has, to be sure, an electronic superiority too. (This, you'll understand, is an account strictly from the home owner's viewpoint.) Improvements in performance have come along with brilliant regularity,
year by year, and in truth, the tiny remains of electrical unfaithfulness
have been constantly narrowed, the cost of good amplification has
steadily gone down in spite of seemingly higher prices.

I still own a beautifully built amplifier that was originally designed
about 1950 to a circuit outstanding in performance for that time.
Progress in electronics has been such that now this aristocratic old
machine is outperformed in its measured characteristics by the very
lowest-priced component amplifiers of today, which cost less than half
as much as it did, inflation or no.

I hasten to qualify that statement—for I do not intend to junk the
old amplifier for a long time. Performance is one thing and durability
another, and I suggest that durability is of even more interest to some
of us. The old machine was built the way automobiles were built in
the 1930s, solidly and with quality to spare. It was worth its price
in these terms alone. And as for the greater distortion—the chances
are that you would notice no difference between this and the new
models, though it is clearly measurable and perhaps audible to a practiced ear. The old amplifier performance is still far ahead of most "hi-fi"
home machines.

You must keep in mind, too, as part of our sense of musical values,
that even the most extreme distortion in any amplifier is far less than
the relatively huge aberrations accepted as a matter of course in almost
every loudspeaker. This is inherent in the two breeds. (See p. 133.)

The amplifier is all-electric. There is no true sound nor any vibra-
tory movement (as in a needle) involved in its work. It receives electricity and gives forth electricity in the same pattern, in utter sound-
lessness. We speak loosely of "sound" or even "music" within the
amplifier because, after all, we can hear what goes on inside it via
the loudspeaker. But disconnect the speaker and your amplifier is
silent, the only indication of the pulsing "sounds" that race through it

an occasional bluish flash in a power tube. Because, like the radio tuner it is free of the obdurate, unadaptable forces of real sound, the amplifier has come much nearer to perfection than other elements in the home system.

WATTS AND DOUBLING. Amplifier power is measured in watts—and here is a trap for the unknowing. Because of the nature of sound and the ear's hearing of it, the relationship between watts and the ultimate sound power you hear is highly misleading. Amplifiers are sold in several categories of rated wattage—ten watts, twenty watts, sixty watts—and you have undoubtedly been assuming, along with countless others, that a twenty-watt amplifier gives you twice the sound of a ten-watter. Far from it, alas. Twice the power; but not twice the volume.

Sound power as measured in the hearing increases via one of those incredible geometric proportions that are so confusing to most of us (Chapter 10). To help yourself, you may think of the common abbreviation for decibel, "db," as standing for "doubling": for each unit of increased sound volume as we hear it, the total actual power must be doubled. (Actually, for each three decibels.) Thus each successive boost in sound volume involves a far larger increase in power than the last one. A fabulous multiplication when you cover a reasonable range of useful volume.

Luckily for us, sound is an economical kind of power, a very little wattage making a lot of noise. A fifty-watt electric light is not very bright, a thousand-watt stove is slow to boil water; but one watt of audio power, in the form of actual sound, will hit your ears uncomfortably loudly in a small room. We can hear sounds of microscopic fractions of a watt.

Don't confuse amplifier electrical power and actual sound power. Amplifiers at best are perhaps 25 per cent efficient; loudspeakers are worse; don't think that ten electrical watts from the amplifier means ten watts of real sound from the speaker. More likely it's the fraction of a sound-watt that the ears will tolerate. For convenience we use the amplifier's electrical wattage to rate its potency, though sound power at the ear is decidedly another matter. (It depends very much on the loudspeaker's ability, too. See page 131, Chapter 11.)

Because of this "doubling" principle, then, fifty watts of amplifier power is decidedly not twice twenty-five watts in effectiveness—as even the salesmen often suppose. It takes twice as much current and costs twice as much to operate in all probability, but it provides only one small step upward in the volume scale in terms of sound itself— 3 db. A decibel? Approximately the smallest difference in loudness that the ear can detect! Other factors within the amplifier may affect the actual loudness of your music much more drastically than this doubling in watts.

RESERVES AND TRANSIENTS. Why do the experts recommend such high power? Partly because of this very factor; the more you buy, the less you get, and to acquire a really ample reserve of power you will have to jump astronomically into the higher wattages. The argument is not very different from that which now calls for 300 horsepower in your new car. (In fact, the principle is the same in terms of horsepower versus speed and pickup.) Reserve for emergencies is the thing, and the new amplifiers give you the required high power at a proportionately more reasonable price (and at lower distortion) than was possible in the past.

The most important "emergencies" in music are those violent instantaneous transients, the pops, bangs, percussions, that momentarily shove powerful wave-fronts into your high fidelity system, requiring high power-handling capacity for tiny fractions of a second at a time. The less potent amplifiers simply cut them down, blur them into distortion, muddying up the sharpness and clarity of the music itself, and this even though they give you all the volume you can possibly use.

But don't be troubled by this gloomy thought! Again, the difference is not musically severe, though audible if your attention is directly called to it. Poor transient response, easily discernible to the expert ear, is—dare I say it?—relatively unimportant to the good musical imagination and not nearly so much of an impediment to musical understanding as other kinds of distortion. Transient distortion never "hurts." It is an intellectual distortion, a dissatisfaction on ethical grounds, so to speak, rather than an active unpleasantness in the ear. Don't forget that the famous juke box boom bass is a deliberate transient distortion that has been enjoyed by millions over the years.

As usual, these things are important, in a way, and yet not so important, too. You may take transients dead seriously if you will—and buy yourself a whopping big amplifier to insure their purity (also a very expensive loudspeaker system and, of course, a top-quality pickup cartridge)—but it is possible that you will never miss them a bit, in the slight transient distortion that occurs in cheaper equipment.

POWER. We can go one important step further in the matter of wattage. A twenty-watt rating in an amplifier does not mean that twenty watts is its *maximum output.*

Vacuum tubes are capable things; they are almost unlimited in the power they'll pass if you keep pushing them harder and harder. The point at which they'll go into an electrical tailspin or burn up is far beyond where most amplifiers take them. But there's a major qualification that determines the whole character of amplifier performance— the harder they work, the more distortion they produce. Indeed, the "curve" of distortion for light versus heavy work goes upward geometrically in an increasing rush, steeper and steeper. For the lighter working levels (i.e., when the "signal" isn't forcing them to pass very large currents) tube and amplifier distortion is low and can be controlled; but beyond a certain point the increase in distortion becomes extreme.

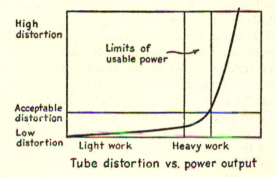

Tube distortion vs. power output

The question is not how much power we can get out of a tube (or an amplifier full of tubes) but how far we can drive it and still get decent amplification. In spite of ingenious corrective circuits to lower distortion, the general principle holds: beyond a certain point tubes or amplifiers go out of control, distortion-wise, and that rather quickly. We must limit them arbitrarily, so that they don't so much as attempt to work at their maximum power.

A very common corrective circuit, as mentioned above, is called *negative feedback.* Not a subject we can go into in detail, but since

you'll be bound to run into the term, you can profitably get an idea as
to what it is, right here.

You may correct a tube's tendency to distort, at the expense of some
gain, by drawing off a part of its output signal and feeding it back
again into the input—but upside down, reversed. This ingenious scheme
makes the tube fight its own nature. Distortion—alteration by the
tube of the "signal" pattern—is fed back in as a reversed distortion and cancels itself; the worse the original distortion, the bigger is
the reversed distortion. This is negative or inverse feedback. Perfect
correction is not possible but a lot can be done to make a tube (or a
whole amplifier section) partially correct itself automatically by this
feeding back of part of the signal, to go through again in reverse. Without feedback, many an amplifier would give much greater gain, but a
greatly distorted sound. A newer and even trickier device is the opposite
—*positive feedback*—which, oddly, does *not* increase but actually lowers
a circuit's ultimate distortion.

Thanks to powerful modern tubes, notably the high-gain pentode
beam-power tubes working in pairs like a team of men on a double
saw (*push-pull output*), a huge amount of amplification is available
and a great deal of corrective wizardry may be applied.

You are likely to see these same terms in present "hi-fi" advertising
that sells the standard home machines. In line with the general bor-
rowing of hi-fi terminology—even the smallest portables now suddenly
have "genuine components" in them (they had them all along, of
course)—many "hi-fis" now boast amplifiers with push-pull output and,
perhaps, feedback too. There is surely nothing wrong with this; in fact,
it represents a part of the undoubted improvement in current home
machines over the earlier ones. But keep in mind, first, that corrective
circuitry of this sort is to be taken for granted in *all* named-component
high fidelity amplifiers and, second, that it can be applied in many
ways, to greater or less effect. Its mere presence, in the ads, proves
very little in respect to true value.

RATINGS. With all of these flexible ifs and buts to account for, the rating
of an amplifier's output must somehow be pinned down to intelligible
factors. The best thing is to state, as above, how much distortion there
is (how little, rather), at a given power output assumed to be its best
safe load. In practice this statement is linguistically turned around—so
many watts, with or "at" such-and-such distortion—thirty watts at 1 per

cent harmonic distortion. For short—and for sales—the whole thing is boiled down simply to "thirty watts." Actually a thirty-watt amplifier may produce double as many watts if you push it hard enough with a strong incoming "signal," but with more distortion (*peak output*).

Still more watts and the distortion increases hugely—the amplifier is overloaded, the sound "blasts." Blasting is extreme distortion. An amplifier with a higher power rating, in these same terms, usually can be assumed to produce that much more power with no increased distortion. Fifty watts at 1 per cent—where the "thirty-watt" amplifier would produce perhaps 20 to 50 per cent distortion if driven to fifty watts of output.

In practice even this comparison must be subject to quality modification. A cheap amplifier is perhaps "cheap" because, among other things, its distortion is not very low—it may rate as twenty watts at 2 per cent distortion (or, more intelligibly, 2 per cent distortion when producing twenty watts); a more powerful amplifier that is also a better one may produce fifty watts at an even lower distortion—say, no more than .05 per cent. The total variance, however, is not very great and should not be of great concern to you, once you have absorbed the general principle. Competition sees to it that virtually any named-component amplifier on the market today (if in working order) produces virtually no audible distortion—the figure is generally less than 1 per cent at the rated output, often a lot less. Other factors count more, as things now stand, and so I suggest, again somewhat negatively, that you spend a minimum of time worrying about distortion ratings.

Note that most small "hi-fi" portable phonographs and tape recorders, even those with three or more speakers, often have built-in amplifiers of no more than two or three watts power, at distortion figures ranging from 3 or 4 per cent up to unmentionable (and unmentioned) levels. And note, too, a distinctly unethical present "hi-fi" advertising use of the term "peak output"—usually about double the rated output—to make inadequate "hi-fi" amplifiers sound adequate. These are reasons for the quotation marks I use around the term "hi-fi"!

DRIVING THE AMPLIFIER. What determines how hard an amplifier will work at a given moment, how much power it will produce? The power output depends on factors we have already looked at, and above all, of course, on the strength of the tiny incoming control "signal." The output, remember, is a replica in the large of this small voltage; the amplifier is its slave and responds to its every fluctuation. The signal current must be large enough to "drive" the amplifier tubes to the power that is their best working level. Not actually large; one volt input will shake the heavens in the output of most amplifiers, turned up to maximum volume! But not too small, either. The magnetic pickup's signal, for instance, (without the aid of a preamplifier) can scarcely stir an amplifier to any output at all. Even with volume control wide-open an amplifier is speechless when its input receives no current. But a big four-volt crystal pickup may drive it into the high-power range of extreme distortion. Overloading. Most portable radios distort this way at even half their volume and you surely know the horrid blasting sound.

You must tailor the input voltage, then, so that the amplifier is "driven" within its proper range, to the maximum safe volume at the loud parts. *And note that the main volume control is no help in cutting down the input*—this control comes later on in the circuit and you can overload the input and cause distortion even with the volume control down to a whisper.

Naturally, manufacturers try to arrange things so that the usual input voltage from the average pickup, radio, etc., is somewhere near right for the amplifier's needs. But things aren't enough standardized so that you can count on this. *Input level controls* (level-sets), individual volume controls at each of the amplifier's inputs, are thus very important in these situations. Radio tuners, for example, often give stronger signals than phonograph pickups; level-sets allow you to adjust so that radio, phono and the rest (if any) are all at the correct incoming strength. A good many amplifiers have this convenience; others dispense with it for economy or because level-sets may add a mild non-linearity distortion. Not an important reason for you. (Some but not all radio tuners and phono players have their own volume or level controls.)

This matter of level-sets is a thing to put on your check list of features when you come face to face with the numerous amplifiers now on sale. You should have at least one input with such a level control on it to accommodate the erratic and unpredictably strong signals from one or another of the components you're likely to have on hand.

SENSITIVITY. There is still one more factor in this picture, that of the amplifier's *sensitivity*.

Given the same rated watt power, the same distortion, the same input level, it is still possible for two amplifiers to differ in how strongly they react to a given signal. An amplifier with *high sensitivity* will jump into action at a very low input signal. *Low sensitivity* means a less positive reaction to the same input signal. A funny idea, but it explains the fact that on occasion a twenty-watt amplifier will give you less volume wide-open than a ten-watt amplifier connected in the same system! The ten-watter is, so to speak, more nervous. It jumps farther. But without a doubt it produces more distortion, too. Most commercial amplifiers are adequately sensitive in the over-all.

VARIABLE DAMPING FACTOR. One of the more confusing of the features now advertised on component-type amplifiers is the *variable damping factor*, provided in some amplifiers at the output to the loudspeaker. My best advice—to you, the nonelectronic music lover—is to ignore it as well as you can! Follow instructions (which at worst means turning around a small control knob until things sound best) and let it go at that. In many cases you will not be able to notice any difference whatsoever, and you can set the control wherever the instructions suggest.

Suffice it to say that damping has very much to do with loudspeaker transient response (page 17). A good speaker system, as we shall see, is supposed to respond as accurately as possible to sudden starts and stops in the sound-signal, avoiding the effect of "hangover"—a vibration that keeps on vibrating instead of ceasing instantaneously as it should. A sound is damped out when its vibration ceases—so, too, with any sort of spurious leftover vibration not envisaged in the original sound. Damping, oddly enough, is possible via electrical means and it is there that the amplifier can exert its damping effect—directly upon the loudspeaker itself. In this case, the speaker is said to be *electrically damped*; the effect is the same, in respect to accuracy of reproduced sound transients, as in the case of an actual physical damping-out of a spurious vibration.

The damping effect of amplifiers in general has been very much improved in the last few years, for improved speaker performance. You can now count on good damping performance from almost any respectable hi-fi amplifier; the shades of difference that excite the experts are, as usual, mostly beyond your ear's immediate comprehension. (If you are a good musician, your ears will be busy elsewhere, absorbing musical sense.)

You will find this variable damping control advertised under special trade names—Fisher's "Z-Matic Control," for instance. Do not distrust those amplifiers that provide no variable control. They'll be all right for almost any use you are likely to put them to. If your dealer is of the communicative sort, you may sound him out on this and, possibly, find a real use for a variable damping control in your particular situation.

OUTPUT TRANSFORMER. A brief word here about an important factor in good reproduction, the amplifier output transformer. Coming electrically after the amplifier has done its job (it is built into the amplifier frame), it is on the main line of communication onward to the loudspeaker and can be a bottleneck to the entire good performance of the preceding equipment. A poor transformer here may drastically limit the tonal range of the sound and introduce serious distortion into it as well.

For modestly priced amplifiers the output transformer should be about three inches or so square, or more; a really good transformer, in the higher-performance amplifiers, is a lot bigger and very heavy; the best are enclosed (*potted*) in sealed outer metal cases, and the top brands are often boasted about in the specifications as important selling points. (There is also a power transformer in every amplifier, usually a bit bigger than the output transformer; its business is not directly with the "signal" current and so its quality is of much less importance.)

TRANSISTORS AND PRINTED CIRCUITS. As everyone knows, the new, tiny transistors are destined to take over most of electronics from the old vacuum tubes. They have already conquered the portable radio and the hearing aid, not to mention the guided missile, with dramatic results in terms of decreased power consumption and miniature size. The professional fields of electronic computation and instrumentation couldn't get along without millions of them. But in hi-fi they have not arrived in any great hurry. Their advantages are not so clear and their circuits are so radically unlike those of the tubes that progress in adapting them to hi-fi use has been relatively slow.

The first advantage, from the hi-fi viewpoint, is that the transistor circuit is inherently humless, like the portable radio. Bonanza! (But hum that is already present in the circuit, picked up on the way, is amplified in the same old manner and so the usual precautions as to shielding of low-level cables are still necessary.) Transistors appeared first, therefore, in the low-level circuits of the preamplifier where hum is most troublesome; they are used along with tubes ("transistorized") or on their own. (But transistors sometimes produce an annoying rustling sound.)

Scarcely less important advantages are those of size and current drain. As to size, transistor circuits will do for hi-fi amplification what they have done for portable radios. We can hope that eventually our hi-fi equipment will be purse-size, though even a less drastic miniaturization would be welcome enough! As to current drain, the same extraordinary economy (efficiency) is applicable to transistor hi-fi though it is less important in view of the limitless power we have available in our house current. Transistor circuits need neither the heater (filament) current nor the high "B" voltage supply necessary for most tube circuits. They use practically no electricity except what actually goes into sound power. That means that there is little of the continuous heat dissipation that makes all tube circuits into small electric stoves—and turns power output tubes nearly red-hot. The transistor amplifier runs cool and a happy by-product of this is that it has no "warm-up" period—it starts instantly, like the transistor radio. (But transistors must be carefully shielded from outside heat.)

The first all-transistor hi-fi amplifier appeared in 1957, a full-power job turning out twenty watts with very low distortion, though in respect to outward control features it was far from a fully developed home instrument. We'll be slow on transistors for a while; but they are on the way and their idiosyncrasies (from the music listener's point of view) are worth knowing about in advance.

1. Transistor preamp circuits (their most likely use) will take any signal of either high or low impedance, without matching problems. Thus you may plug in either a home-type high-impedance mike or one of the more expensive professional low-impedance mikes, without worrying about the expensive matching transformer ordinarily required for low-impedance mikes.

2. Transistor circuits use only the current they need to make actual sound and so when there is no sound to amplify they run on almost nothing. Perhaps seven watts for a full amplifier which with tubes might draw a continuous hundred watts or more, sound or no sound.

3. As mentioned above, transistor equipment runs cool. The ventilation problem is reversed—no undue heat must be allowed to reach the transistors.

4. Transistor hi-fi circuits can be designed to operate on low-voltage DC. Ordinarily this is supplied from conventional house current by the usual transformer-rectifier system. But since the operating DC (direct current) can be made twelve volts, an alternative supply can be had from an automobile battery or even from a group of flashlight batteries, with instant conversion to house current via a separate plug. No inverters, converters and the like. Battery-operated hi-fi is thus soon likely. (But if you reverse the poles of the battery input current you'll ruin the transistors. That will require a very foolproof plug system.)

I mention *printed circuits* belatedly not because they are unimportant but because as far as you are concerned they are mostly invisible and out of your range of direct interest. But these ingenious preformed circuits, "silk-screened," if you will (the process is similar) onto a flat surface with all "wires" and all components (resistors, condensers, etc.) included, have already done marvelous things for hi-fi in the way of compactness, economy and quick repair. Where the old-style wiring systems are essentially hand-constructed, piece by piece, the printed circuits are mass-produced semiautomatically. They take up far less space than the old arrangements and can be replaced as complete units on a virtually snap-in basis.

As ingenuity replaces more and more of the old-time hand assembly with printed circuitry, hi-fi equipment gets smaller and smaller, is made more quickly and cheaply, lasts longer. But printed circuits are somewhat limited by an odd feature—they are necessarily two-dimensional. The printed lines of conducting material can't cross or they'll short-circuit. Designing a printed circuit is like solving a puzzle of the kind where you must find your way through a maze without crossing a line—or, perhaps, like designing a complete traffic cloverleaf without any overpasses! For this reason alone, hand circuitry, in three dimensions, will be around for a while longer. Printed wiring—using conventional resistors and the like—is a useful compromise.

AMPLIFIER KITS. Almost every section of this volume is bound to include a reference to that fascinating term, the *kit*. In case you haven't run into it, the meaning is simple if the carrying-out is not. A kit is a half-manufactured component, delivered in knock-down form with detailed instructions for the rest of the assembly and (usually—not always) all parts included. You may even get tools. Kits sell at ridiculously low prices, or so it would seem—usually about half the cost of the very same item assembled. There may be assorted economic factors concerning discounts and the like involved here; it isn't too easy to say.

Amplifiers in particular have been developed in kit form; many of the very finest models originated commercially in this guise and are still sold almost entirely in the unfinished state. The Williamson-type amplifiers introduced some years back were largely kits; the currently popular Dynakit is perhaps technically the best power amplifier available, according to some engineering opinion. Heathkits, a brand name, have been available for years and have a reputation for thoroughness in the directions and parts provisions; Eico kits, Lafayette, Allied Radio, are others.

Should you build a kit? The best I can do—knowing the variety of talents available among potential hi-fi music listeners—is to suggest that you can, if you are unafraid of (a) a screwdriver or (b) a soldering iron and solder. This last tool seems to represent the dividing line between the can-do and cannot-do souls! If you can solder (and if you customarily repair your own light fixtures, insert new fuses and so on) you can build a kit. You do not need to know anything at all about electronic theory! I know of several wives who have built amplifiers while their husbands were off on vacations or business trips, all unsuspecting.

However, to build a kit is one thing and to test it and correct faults is quite another. In every electronic kit there comes a perfectly dreadful moment when, the work having been completed and minutely checked through all the hundreds of connections, the power is turned on. Strong men definitely quail at the thought. (Perhaps the unsuspecting housewife won't know enough to be afraid.)

Something always is done wrong, somewhere; few of us are methodical enough to make no mistake at all. Sometimes it is a fatal mistake, and things burn up. Usually it is just baffling or annoying. And sometimes the amplifier works, but not very well. All these things are possible, even with the best kits.

The best insurance, in kit building, is to know an expert who can stand by at the fatal turning-on moment (and check the construction beforehand), who is willing and able to track down mistakes by intelligence and deduction rather than painful rechecking.

I suppose I have turned hundreds away from the amplifier kit by this account. Don't be afraid! You save one-half and, after all, vast numbers of kits have been sold and assembled—more are being sold every day. I do suggest, however, that you avoid (a) preamplifier-control kits and (b) radio tuner kits; at least, until you have tried a simpler kit. These last involve entirely too much of the crucial low-level circuitry that produces hum and distortion for any rank beginner to play around with.

The best kit to start on, then, is the *basic amplifier kit*. Complete amplifier kits, as you'll see in what follows below, include the entire low-level control and preamplification circuitry that I have suggested you avoid. Build your own basic amplifier, and make it a good one and powerful. Buy a separate control unit, or radio tuner with controls, to feed it.

8

Controls and Connections

I now come to the control and preamplifier elements of the hi-fi amplifier—and must explain to you at once that, as things stand now, these same controls and preamplifiers are also found separately in their own boxes, as *control units* of many sorts and in several types of compound *radio tuners* as well (to be taken up in detail in Chapter 9). And so, though nominally this chapter continues on the general subject of the amplifier, it will wander afield, to cover much that interlocks with things past and things to come.

TYPES OF AMPLIFIER. Before I plunge into controls—common to so many kinds of units—look briefly at the types of amplifier you'll find lined up for your inspection in stores and catalogues. Again, standardization has reduced their variety, in the large at least, though details are endlessly different. The important outward amplifier distinction is between the *basic amplifier* and the *complete amplifier*. Practically every model you see will fit in one or the other category; the ifs and buts are very minor.

A. *The Basic Amplifier*. This is an amplifier pure and simple, without controls or modifiers of any sort—or almost none. No volume control (though it may have an input level control to protect it from too strong signals), no tone controls, no preamplifier. It simply accepts a low-power signal at the INPUT and delivers a higher-power signal at the speaker taps (described below), its OUTPUT connection.

The basic amplifier is intended for use out of sight and out of mind; the controls and all the preliminary switchings in and out come ahead of it, in control units or in radio tuners. It is solely for the purpose of driving a loudspeaker system; it takes a finished and shaped signal and amplifies it to speaker proportions, pure and simple.

Basic amplifiers come in all sizes and power ratings, from a minimum of about twelve watts up to the popular behemoths that deliver from fifty to a hundred watts of output power. Prices vary accordingly, from $40 to some hundreds. There are basic amplifier kits galore—and, indeed, a great many people prefer to build this type of kit, in all its simplicity, and acquire a ready-assembled control unit or radio tuner. An excellent idea.

B. The Complete Amplifier. This is the other common type of amplifier unit, complete on a single chassis. One end of it is a power amplifier, as above; the other end (usually the left end) has the built-in preamplifier. On the front panel are multiple controls (see below) and on the rear are multiple inputs and outputs (also below). This amplifier is designed as the home center for hi-fi operations, in whatever size and complexity it may offer. As usual, details differ, but the degree of standardization in the main functional areas of control is heartening to any beginner, once the minor but endless differences are absorbed and put aside.

The complete amplifier now shares responsibility with its alternate, the compound radio tuner, as the main household hi-fi control center. One system is as good as another; differences are mainly in respect to personal preferences and convenience. If you use your system basically to play records you'll probably do best with a complete amplifier; if your records come few and far between, or not at all, you'll prefer a tuner-centered control system. The only generalized comment I can make is that a tuner manufacturer may well put more intelligence and better quality into that specialty than into associated phonograph controls and the like, and vice versa; but this is not a principle that can be rigorously applied—it all depends. It won't be easy for you to make this primary decision, as between an amplifier control center and a tuner control center, but when you have made it, the rest of your equipment will fall into place around the type of unit you have chosen.

From here onward I'll be dealing with aspects of hi-fi control that occur in most or all of these varying units, including the compound radio tuners. (Chapter 9.) Look first at the essential for all hi-fi phonograph sound, the preamplifier—which is found in all sorts of units.

PREAMPLIFIER-EQUALIZER. You have already picked up a fair idea of the *preamplifier*—commonly shortened these days to "preamp." It is what its name implies, a preliminary amplifier to boost up the tiny voltages of extremely faint signal currents that come from microphones, tape recorder playing heads, and in particular, magnetic phono pickups. The preamp works at astonishingly low electrical levels. The incoming signals arrive at about a hundredth of a volt and up; the output, after preamplification, is still only about one volt, on a par with a flashlight battery. The preamp is a *low-level system*, its purpose to raise up tiny voltages to a moderate level where they can drive the main power amplifier into the proper large-scale action—to produce sound at the loudspeaker.

Preamplifiers were once widely sold as separate units, for conversion of older phonographs to the low-level magnetic cartridges. The GE preamp was the common model. Though these elementary affairs are still available, virtually all hi-fi preamps are now built into larger units of one sort or another.

The common preamp locations are (a) built in as part of a complete amplifier, along with complete controls; (b) similarly, built into a separate control unit; and (c) similarly, built into a compound radio tuner, equipped, like the complete amplifier, with a full range of controls.

The preamplifier is the right place, electronically speaking, to put the various types of equalization—that electrical alteration of tonal balance that was discussed in detail in Chapter 5. Virtually all the incoming signals that need equalization also need to be preamplified. The preamp section does both at once; it selectively varies its preamplification (as to the balance of high and low tones) according to the control settings. Almost all of these have to do with phonograph records and are marked with the now familiar clusters of capital letters which indicate the various provided curves—RIAA for standard, plus assorted others, LP, LON, NARTB, AES, EUR 78 and so on. As explained in Chapter 5, though they may seem ever so cryptic, you will be able to get along now quite nicely with only a few; three basic positions will account for most LP records, present and past, and a fourth will do for the 78s, with extra adjustment via the tone controls.

Some of the fancier control units (with preamplifiers built in, of course) still offer many choices of phonograph equalization. A few have multiple pushbutton systems, others have separate settings for the bass and treble end of the record "curve." My own feeling is that, except for semiprofessional use, these more elaborate equalization facilities are generally to be avoided; they will only confuse your listening. There is no harm in them, decidedly, and much potential usefulness, in the right situation; I've used them in many vital ways myself. If you like gadgetry; if, especially, you are a collector with a very wide variety of older discs, crying for maximum flexibility in the equalizing—then the complex controls are fine. But for ordinary, sensible home use, mainly with LP records made since 1955 (RIAA) and, perhaps, a few 78s now and then, the three or four positions on the standard type of equalization control will do very well.

THE SELECTOR-EQUALIZER CONTROL. Standardization has now finally reached the common hi-fi control systems available today, for which we may give fervent thanks. The general layout for hi-fi controls is now pretty much the same everywhere, with variations only in detail.

The *selector control knob* that is associated with the preamplifier (wherever it may be) is now regularly used as well for a general-purpose switching center, to take care not only of records but also of the various other incoming signals to be expected. These include signals that by-pass the preamplifier because they are already strong enough in their own right to drive the main power amplifier—signals from radio tuner, tape recorder (assuming that the recorder has its own preamplifier, as all complete recorders have—see Chapter 13), ceramic phono pickup, television and so on.

All these have their place upon the main switching knob, next to the equalization settings, and the only problem is one of semantics—how do we describe their functions? That, unfortunately, still allows for plenty of variation. Thus the alphabet phono positions now usually have more alphabet next to them, and sometimes the strange clumps of letters mean less than nothing at first glance, though anybody can recognize RADIO or TUNER, TV, TAPE and the like.

The fact is that the high-level input signals—those which do not need the preamplifier—are more or less interchangeable among themselves. If you plug your tuner into the TAPE input you'll simply hear it at that position instead of at TUNER; there isn't any difference, ordinarily, except sheer convenience. For this reason—and since the manufacturers can't anticipate your every whim as to signal sources, these high-level positions are often given an indeterminate name. A favorite, that sounds like the honk of a goose, is AUX. Nothing more complex than *Auxiliary*. Some amplifiers have AUX 1 and AUX 2. (The same term is often used for auxiliary power sockets, into which you may plug your auxiliary components—tuner, changer, and so on.) The thing to remember is that, within the "high-level" (nonpreamplified) category, these positions are mostly interchangeable. Not always; occasionally there is a difference. On one GE amplifier for instance, AUX 1 had a level set, but AUX 2 did not—an excellent compromise when a complete array of level sets is too expensive at the price.

On this same control knob there are two other settings that make use of the preamplifier—both low-level positions, one of which is increasingly important and useful. First, if you see TAPE HEAD, you will know that at this position the tiny signals that come directly from the playback head of a tape recorder may be fed into the preamplifier and correctly equalized for top-quality sound. You may read more of this in Chapter 13 (page 184) but at this point note merely that, whereas a position marked TAPE means the conventional (high-level) input that comes from an ordinary tape recorder, which has already done its own preamplifying, TAPE HEAD (low-level) feeds into your preamplifier and equalizes the tape head signal for flat response. Don't confuse the two. Ordinarily you won't bother with TAPE HEAD; its uses are (a) in connection with tape decks that have no playback preamplifier and (b) to by-pass the regular preamplifier in an inexpensive recorder in favor of the better preamplifier in your hi-fi system.

The other possible position, not too common, is MIKE. Suffice it to say though mikes need preamplification, they are flat—and they deal, of course, with actual sound in air, which is totally flat! (Living sound is the original standard to which all in hi-fi is "faithful.") The MIKE input to the preamplifier, therefore, removes all equalization from the circuit; the preamp is used as a straight amplifier within the low-level range. (If your system has no MIKE input and you need a mike, you can have a switch installed without too much trouble that will detach the phono equalization from the preamp and so allow it to be used for microphone.)

You'll understand that the phono equalization and general switching knob we've been discussing is likely to be found wherever there is a preamplifier—whether in a complete amplifier, a separate control unit or as part of a compound (Type Two or Three) radio tuner. It's the same in principle wherever you find it though details in the marking will, as I say, differ. So conventionalized has hi-fi control become, to-day, that just as the automobile accelerator is for the right foot, so this control knob is usually on the left-hand side as you face any hi-fi control panel.

If you will keep in mind that, whatever the details, all such knobs divide their positions into two camps—high-level (by-passing the pre-amplifier) and low-level (through the preamplifier)—you will be able to penetrate the selector control's alphabet jargon quite easily.

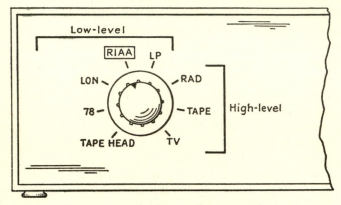

Typical equalization switching control

PREAMP MAGNIFICATION—HUM AND NOISE. Before I leave the vicinity of the preamplifier in this somewhat roundabout account, consider the inherent faults of this useful and necessary section of the hi-fi sound-signal chain. The preamplifier is by far the most sensitive portion of the entire hi-fi anatomy and it is the very first element that should be of concern when you come to acquiring hi-fi equipment.

This importance stems mainly from a factor that may not have occurred to you, the extra magnification that the preamp adds to the power amplifier. Preamplifiers are no more cantankerous than any other amplifier equipment, but thanks to their special position every fault in them or before them is "blown up" pitilessly in the final sound. Magnified distortion is a bad enough problem but the real trouble is with extraneous noise that gets caught in this tremendous magnification. (Electrical "noise," of course.) *Hum* is the worst plague. Less important but annoying are *microphonics* and *tube noise*.

Hum is the bugbear of the hi-fi machine. The power we use, from regular electric lines, alternates in direction sixty times a second. We need only convert a trace of this alternating current ("AC") into physical vibration to set off that familiar faint tone—a B natural—that all of us who have AC in our homes know by heart. (We hear it in a thousand home appliances.) It puts all music into the key of B, which is distressing to say the least. We don't want hum in high fidelity music—but we have the best possible conditions in the preamplifier for exaggerating its presence, through magnification.

Hum is "picked up" via induction through space from any nearby carrier of AC, notably a transformer or motor. The braided metal shielding wrapped around the wire from the pickup to the amplifier keeps it away; without that, your pickup wire would collect a very loud B natural to add to its musical current. At any point prior to the amplifier, where small currents are subject to later enlargement, tiny traces of house current may creep into the signal to emerge, hugely amplified, as hum. Unluckily, the magnetic pickup with its coils of wire is peculiarly subject to hum pickup, furthering the trouble. The whole low-level section of the amplifier must be designed with extreme care to avoid hum. It is therefore a notorious trouble area.

Microphonics, strange ringing sounds that are heard when a preamplifier tube is joggled or tapped, come from within the tube itself; they are microscopic currents inconveniently enlarged. The cure for a microphonic tube is to replace it. Tubes are highly erratic in this respect and tube makers don't seem to be able to standardize their performance.

So enormous is the amplification here that loose electrons in the preamplifier tubes in random movement may be heard sometimes as a continuous sputtering or steady hiss. *Tube noise*. It also varies from tube to tube. Same remedy.

Preamplifiers being as tricky as this, many a commercial amplifier is weak in this department. If you go amplifier hunting, be sure that there is no audible hum or noise or ringing microphonics (you'll hear them when you tap the tubes) in the preamplifier. With a correctly shielded input connection there should be no unpleasant noise even when the volume control is turned all the way up and no record is playing. If there is more than a very slight hum, you have a right to complain.

In amplifiers (and preamplifiers) that are skimpily built, hum tends to increase with age; most cheap home radios and "hi-fi" phonographs are notorious for this, as you must have long since discovered.

Many component amplifiers have one or more small screw taps that may be adjusted with a screwdriver, a turn or so, for possible reduction of the hum. *Hum-bucking taps* is the term. You may experiment with them yourself without undue harm; just turn back and forth until the point of least hum is found.

STANDARD BASIC CONTROLS—"BOOST" AND "ROLL-OFF." There are three more control knobs, usually to the right of the above selector-equalization knob, that you will find pretty much standardized in the hi-fi world. (They are even invading the "hi-fis," when cost allows.) One, usually to the left, is the ordinary *volume control*, which can be taken for granted (but not the loudness control—see below); the others, progressing from left toward the right, are the *bass and treble tone controls*, now an invariable feature of all hi-fi equipment. (Volume and tone controls aren't always hooked into all the various inputs and outputs—for this, see below.) Conventional practice calls for a "neutral" or flat position on each, pointing straight up; turning to the left decreases the lows or highs, to the right increases them.

These controls, bass and treble, are intended mainly for tonal balancing to fit room acoustics—a vital function as you will realize when you get to Chapter 15. Variation from one room to another is often enough to call for the full range of adjustment that these controls provide. They're also useful to supplement the fixed equalizings for records —you can add or substract as much or as little as you want of either bass or treble, to taste.

You'll come to use these tone controls a great deal for variations from one sound to the next, regardless of the source—but, once you have found the best general setting for your listening spot, *always return them to this position*, after temporary changes. Ordinarily, the flat position, in both treble and bass, is the best—it suits average room conditions—and you should stick to it through thick and thin until you are convinced that something different is needed in your room. (You are likely to forget, one day, that the treble knob is set all the way up and thus find yourself listening to inexplicably harsh and tinny music for weeks on end, thereafter!) Make a habit of checking your tone controls the way you check your car ignition.

There are variations from one amplifier or control system to another as to the precise effect of bass and treble tone controls, but in general they conform to a fairly universal pattern—a gradual and relatively mild change, extending from a tonal mid-point all the way up—or down— to the extremes of low or high pitch, gradually increasing the further from the mid-point you go. If you can imagine the graph of response, from bass to treble, conveniently hinged at the middle, you can envision the combined effect of both tone controls as that of a pair of "wavable" wings, seagull style. The controls are continuously variable; a graphic picture represents merely sample settings.

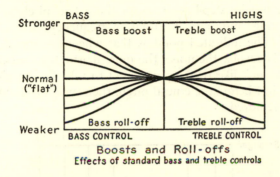

Boosts and Roll-offs
Effects of standard bass and treble controls

The hi-fi names for these gradual tone controls are *boost*, a rise in bass or treble strength, and *roll-off* (attenuation), for a decrease in either bass or treble. The equalization curves for phonograph records involve what are essentially these same adjustments, a boost in the bass to match the record's weakened bass and a roll-off in the treble to match the strengthened high end. (The record itself, of course, is the reverse—it has rolled-off bass and boosted treble.) For this reason, you can do a fairly good job of equalization with your tone control knobs alone and they are well adapted for extra adjustments, to supplement the fixed equalization positions.

CUT-OFFS—TREBLE AND BASS. There are additional tonal controls to be found on some systems which can be extremely useful, if you wish to bother with them. They fall into a more severe class of correction which, in contrast to the gradual, "broad" effect of the boost and roll-off, are "sharp," that is, relatively violent and confined to a narrow area. The appropriate general term, self-explanatory, is *cut-off*, whether for highs or bass.

On occasion you may have to deal with records that are distorted or have severe hiss and scratch, or with noisy radio programs. Such noise is in a fairly narrow band in the upper tonal range. The treble roll-off tone control will reduce it, but you will lose a lot of music too. The roll-off covers too much ground and it doesn't remove enough sound at the noisy high end for such situations. We can use stronger medicine.

The *treble cut-off* is drastic. It cuts out very nearly all sound above a given pitch, very little below it. If you can choose a point just below where the worst noise is you may have a maximum of music up to that point and still get rid of a large part of the unpleasant noise. Cut-off controls are usually step-by-step, with the actual pitch at which they do the "cutting" indicated in vibration frequency; 8,000, 5,000, 3,000 cycles, etc. (The indicated point is that where the sound is already 3 db down.) The worse the noise, the more drastic the medicine. Cut-offs in the treble look like this, as compared to roll-offs—no change in the sound until just before the crucial pitch, then suddenly almost all higher sounds are removed.

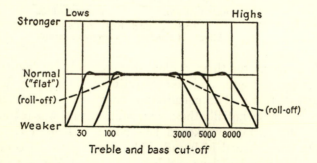

Treble and bass cut-off

What do the numbers mean in terms of music? Fifteen thousand cycles is the top of the average hearing range—very high; 10,000 is practically indistinguishable from it, for most of us. A cut-off at 8,000 removes a bit of noise or distortion and some music—very little. A 5,000 cut-off slices the music down to the level of most older home phonographs; it also cuts out most of the objectionable static or scratch or distortion. Cutting down to 3,000 cycles makes your music sound muffled as though by a heavy blanket.

The most common form of the cut-off control is the *scratch filter* or *noise filter*, sometimes with one fixed position (fairly drastic), sometimes with several choices usually with the cut-off figure in numerical form.

(For the Dynamic Noise Suppressor, see below.) An alternative name is *range control* and, things being what they are, you may find other names as well. This drastic treble tonal medicine is far less important now than it used to be and is useful mainly in the playing of old 78 rpm records and excessively noisy LPs—also for the familiar problem of static on AM radio.

A more important type of cut-off control is the *rumble filter*, sometimes called *bass cut-off*, which "cuts" upward from the extreme bottom, removing a small amount of bass music but a large amount of the low-pitched rumble and thump that is now often heard from phonograph motors (yours or the one that made the record, or is playing it on the air) via the better speaker systems. There isn't any more rumble now than there used to be—there is less. But improved speaker response and improved bass in our amplifiers have between them made audible the low-pitched rumble and thumps that were undetected by older and less competent equipment! For every improvement, a new problem.

LOUDNESS CONTROL. I've spoken casually of the "volume control," as most of us do, as that familiar knob that controls the volume of sound. But many items of hi-fi equipment now include a *loudness control*, which must be sharply distinguished from the volume control though both have to do with the increase or decrease of sound output. The distinction is between volume, sound power issuing from a loudspeaker, and loudness, the strength of sound *as heard at the ear.* The two aren't necessarily the same at all, and the loudness control deals specifically with this last factor, which as you will understand depends on the situation. With the same volume output a given radio may sound extremely loud in a small room but quite faint in a very large one; at a distance a sound is heard less loudly than close at hand, though the loudspeaker volume may be the same. What counts is what we hear, not what the speaker emits—hence, the loudness control.

The human ear responds differently to louder and softer sounds—according to the well-known Fletcher-Munson curves. As sound gets less loud we lose more of our sensitivity to the bass and to some extent the highs, than we do to the middle range. At low levels we are extra-deaf, to low bass, proportionately. Now this is of no great importance in ordinary sound. What we hear, after all, is "right" since it is the natural way for us to react to sound and we can conceive of no other way that might be "more" normal.

It is only when music that should be heard loud is instead heard soft, that we get into trouble. That is a common occurrence in reproduced music. When you play the climaxes of a full-sized symphony with your volume at "background music" level, the bass virtually disappears—because of the ear's poor performance as compared with what it would do at the proper loudness. The bass is there in the sound—but the ear doesn't hear it strongly enough.

The loudness control is a specially doctored form of volume control that automatically changes the balance of sound at higher or lower levels according to the Fletcher-Munson curves so that at all levels you *hear* the correct musical balance, as you do at the music's "real" loudness.

But there is a major disadvantage that you must be prepared for, or you will have trouble with serious unbalance in your sound—muddy, tubby bass, muffled and unpleasant highs. The loudness control must somehow be adjusted to the loudness *at your ear*. And that depends on your location, on the size and type of room you sit in, on how far from the speaker you are sitting.

For normal listening, where the music is about as loud, at your ear, as it ought to be by nature, you need no compensation. It is when you turn your volume down well below normal that you need it, and the further down you turn, the more compensation you need, to bring the bass into balance.

One type of loudness control looks like a volume control. When it is turned full-on there is no compensation at all. But as you turn it down, counterclockwise, the compensation is gradually introduced to match the ear's response, as the sound gets lower and lower compared to normal. Note then that *for all normal music this control must be at the wide-open position*, where there is none of this tricky compensation.

Now how does one set the wide-open position for normal loudness, at the ear, when that loudness depends on so many factors, including the level of the input signal? Suppose the music blasts too loud at the wide-open position?

That is exactly what is wrong with some loudness controls, installed by unthinking makers (economy minded as well as feature minded) who assume that the full-on loudness position will always be "normal"—

for radio, phonograph and all the rest. It seldom is, in plain truth. And necessarily, therefore, you must have some means of adjustment, to set the normal sound where it belongs, before you can use the loudness control at all. This can be done in several ways—but however it is managed, you should be *absolutely certain* that your equipment can accomplish it, or that the loudness compensation can be switched out, before you buy any device with a loudness control in it.

To make that a bit more clear, here are the forms in which this too ingenious loudness control is likely to turn up.

1. The amplifier (control unit, tuner) has a LOUDNESS control on the front panel—the only volume control provided. (It may be marked VOLUME!)

In this case, look *immediately* for two things: (a) a loudness ON-OFF switch, to disconnect the compensation and turn the control into an ordinary volume control; and (b) level controls at the inputs—one or all.

a. If you can safely set the incoming signals at the right volume for the sound to be "normal" with the loudness control knob all the way on, you're all right, whether you do it via input level controls or even by an outside level (volume) control, as on a radio tuner. See below for how to proceed.

b. If you have a LOUDNESS ON-OFF switch (sometimes marked IN-OUT), you can always get rid of the whole business of loudness compensation and use your control as an ordinary, old-fashioned volume control with no more than the ordinary problems.

But if you have a LOUDNESS knob with no switch and no means to set the incoming levels, you are in trouble. With a loud signal—such as most radio tuners provide—you'll be forced to turn the loudness knob back to reduce the excessive volume—and this will automatically "compensate" the sound as though it were soft, making it unpleasantly tubby and heavy in the bass. Inexcusable, but it can happen in numerous amplifiers.

2. There may be two "volume" knobs on the front panel—a loudness control *and* a volume control, side by side. (Cf. the GE amplifiers.)

This is a confusing arrangement but it works well if you understand it. You will find that either one of the two knobs will cut down the volume—which do you use?

a. If you want no loudness compensation, turn the LOUDNESS knob *all the way up* (that removes all the compensation, as already explained)—and leave it there. Use the VOLUME knob for your regular control.

b. If you want loudness compensation, start the same way—turn the LOUDNESS control *all the way up.* Then set the VOLUME control for a comfortable "normal" loudness—as loud as you're likely to want the sound. Leave it there. Now use the LOUDNESS control and your music will stay nicely in balance from "normal" all the way down to a whisper.

You'll have to reset the VOLUME control whenever the musical source changes, or when you change from one signal to another that is at a different level. It is a level control for all channels.

In this arrangement you must be sure to check the LOUDNESS control for position, each time you use the amplifier. If it is turned down, you will get tubbier-than-normal music, especially if you try to bring up the sound with the regular volume control, not noticing.

If loudness is too complex for you on this sort of loudness control, turn it all the way up as of (a) above, and stick a piece of tape over it so it won't move. Then you can forget it.

3. A third and quite simple type of loudness control merely provides several fixed degrees of loudness compensation, which you choose yourself via a switch (sometimes called a *loudness contour selector*). It isn't automatic and it won't involve you in complications. Just switch it out, or try for the best position—being sure that other controls (tone controls, equalization) are rightly arranged first. (Cf. Lafayette's LA-40 Music Mate 15-watt amplifier.) This type is becoming more popular—for good reason.

DYNAMIC NOISE SUPPRESSOR. A brief note about the still useful specialty of the H. H. Scott Company, offered in Scott amplifiers and control units. The Noise Suppressor was once both controversial and famous, in a day when scratch and distortion were inevitably mixed into whatever hi-fi sound was available. Rightly used, it gave us a maximum of useful music with a minimum of scratch. Today, it is chiefly useful for old and scratchy records, and occasionally, for noisy radio conditions. It is definitely worth considering (as a built-in feature) if you have a special problem in noisy records.

The suppressor is a dynamic cut-off filter that closes and opens automatically in response to the volume level of an incoming signal. It works mainly in the treble but also in the bass (to remove rumble).

The idea is ingenious. When music is loud, scratch is safely drowned out and so is not heard, and the same with rumble in the bass; but in soft passages both rumble and scratch show up painfully. The electronic "gates" of the suppressor accordingly open wide to let through the loud passages with their full tonal color, but close down electronically to filter out the scratch and the rumble during the soft passages. The whole operation is continuous and virtually instantaneous—hence "dynamic."

The earlier noise suppressors were hard to adjust. But the suppressor is now semiautomatic and nearly foolproof so that you'll do a minimum of adjusting to get a maximum of use out of your old records.

INPUTS. Finally, after this ramble through the amplifier's middle, we reach the beginning—the *input* section, that array of entrance plugs (and associated switches and circuits) where the various sound signals enter the amplifier (or the control section of a radio tuner—same idea). Here is another practical area that has now been well standardized, after years of chaos, for which we may bless the wise manufacturers.

On present home equipment virtually all input connections are via the universal *"phono plug"* (RCA plug), a small tip with a metal collar around it which slips over an outer ring on the corresponding socket. There is only one possible input exception: a microphone input is often either a screw-down connector or a snap-in type (Cannon plug), according to standard engineering practice. (For types of microphones, see Chapter 17, pp. 246-247.)

This ubiquitous phono plug is actually a nuisance and thoroughly inadequate for its widespread use. It is too small and far from sturdy. It breaks off or mashes flat, and the collar squeezes too tight or stretches loose. Its most common fault is that the braided shield, soldered clumsily to the collar on the plug, breaks away at the slightest provocation; or loose strands from the shield make a partial or complete short circuit with the inner conductor wire. If any incoming signal hums, blats, sputters or goes dead, suspect the phono plug immediately—that's hi-fi's Number One source of trouble.

But—it's standard, this little plug, and so it's worth its weight in peace of mind. Someday, there'll be a universal, interchangeable, compatible improvement. A few phono plugs are already reinforced, for better performance at the crucial "neck" where the wire enters the plug.

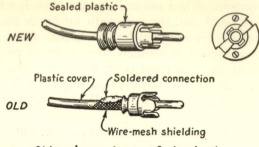

Old and new types of standard
input-output plug and socket

We've pretty well covered inputs in the preceding pages, by implication. To match the TAPE selector switch position on the front panel there must, obviously, be a TAPE input—and so there is, a socket to the rear (usually) that is marked TAPE. Similarly for TUNER (radio). If there is an AUX (auxiliary) switch position there is an AUX input socket to correspond. Simple enough, generally speaking; but you will want to know first which inputs go through the preamplifier, low-level, which by-pass it, high-level. There is often some confusion.

Typical Low-Level Inputs—Through the Preamplifier

Magnetic phono cartridge	MAG, HI MAG, LOW MAG
Tape head input (p. 91)	TAPE HEAD
Microphone	MIC, MIKE, etc.

Typical High-Level Inputs—By-passing the Preamplifier

Radio tuner	RAD, TUNER, etc.
Tape recorder playback	TAPE
TV sound	TV
Auxiliary—general-purpose	AUX

Confusion is apt to show up, as already explained, between TAPE, which is high-level, for a conventional tape playback, and TAPE HEAD which is low-level, sending the faint signal direct from the tape heads through the preamplifier. Also, the new ceramics that are equalized and reduced in output to replace magnetics are, of course, to be plugged into the magnetic input—*not* the ceramic! They have been denatured, these, and so you must conform to their new, synthetic identity as pseudo-magnetics.

The only further item to check in respect to inputs is the presence or absence of level controls—preliminary level-setting volume controls for each channel—and this is an important matter. There isn't any standard place for the level controls; some are mounted right at the input but others may be operated via a screwdriver through a small hole, in the front panel or elsewhere (there's a volume control behind)—wherever space allows. Each level-set should be marked clearly enough. Economy often dictates a compromise, with level-sets on some but not all of the major inputs. This is fine—but calculate what level-sets you may be likely to need. Radio is the most important since radio tuners put out a whopping big signal and don't always have their own built-in attenuators to cut it down to size.

HIGH AND LOW IMPEDANCE. I have avoided an explanation of that cryptic word "impedance" until, so to speak, pressure has built up irresistibly. I don't propose to explain it electrically even now—but you'll need to have some idea of its place in hi-fi—which is important. Speaker circuits are low-impedance, magnetic and ceramic pickup inputs high-impedance, and the difference is great in terms of wiring, hum shielding, permissible type and length of cable. These aspects can't very well be avoided.

You may conceive of impedance as a species of resistance, having to do with pulsing, signal-carrying currents. At *low-impedance* (the signals are less impeded) current flow is greater; at *high-impedance* it is small and tight. Impedance, like electrical resistance, is measured in ohms.

The practical thing to remember is that *high-impedance means high-hum-susceptibility*. Pickups, microphones, at the low-level end of the amplifier, the input end, are mostly in this high-impedance category. The preamplifier itself has a high-impedance circuit. That means very careful shielding of all external wires with grounded metal covering (braided); it means short connecting cables, never more than three or four feet. It means that power lines, transformers and other radiators of potential hum must be kept away. High-impedance circuits are a necessary nuisance—except where medium-impedance can take over, such as the useful *cathode follower* output circuit from radio tuners and control units, which allows for much longer wires and a minimum of fussy shielding.

When necessary, one may convert from one impedance to another via a transformer (expensive); thus a low-impedance microphone feeds into a long cable at the end of which there is a mike transformer to convert to high impedance to match the preamplifier circuit. A high-impedance mike requires a very short wire, like a pickup. Most home-type mikes are high-impedance; no transformer, but you can't run a long wire from them.

Speakers have very low impedance, from four to sixteen ohms in contrast to the thousands of ohms rated by most phono cartridges. The amplifier's output transformer is an "impedance-converter" that furnishes low impedance matching for various types of speaker.

Here is a roster of common impedance ratings in ohms and the hi-fi elements in which you'll find them.

Low Impedance (4-50 ohms):

Loudspeakers (4-16 ohms); low-impedance mikes (50 ohms); amplifier outputs (4-16 ohms).

Medium Impedance (often called *low*):

Cathode-follower output circuits from tuners, control units, amplifier TAPE outputs (200 ohms); some microphones; broadcast connecting lines (600 ohms); TV and FM antenna systems (300 ohms); moving-coil magnetic phono cartridges (300 ohms); some headphones.

High Impedance (10,000-1,000,000 ohms):

Most crystal, ceramic, magnetic phono cartridges; high-impedance mikes (crystal, dynamic); preamplifier circuits and main amplifier input circuits; some headphones.

Matching of impedances means, as you can guess, providing the right type of circuit for each element's impedance needs. A low-impedance microphone won't produce any sound if fed into a high-impedance preamplifier circuit; a matching (mike) transformer is needed. The output transformer, again, matches the amplifier power tube output to the speaker's low impedance. Leave all this to the experts in practice—but retain somewhere in a corner of your memory the general features of high and low.

OUTPUTS. What goes in must come out and there is, on every amplifier or control unit, a set of output sockets. By pleasant convention the inputs are now usually to the right as you look at the rear of an amplifier and the outputs to the left, or at the center.

Outputs are somewhat different in their classification from inputs;

the outgoing signal from an amplifier is one thing and the same from a control box or from a radio tuner quite another—the destination is different. And so we can split up the output area into (a) speaker-bound signals; (b) amplifier-bound signals—from control units and tuners; and (c) various by-pass outputs, to feed tape recorders and the like. The things to know, as usual, are the characteristics of each, where it will go, and (something you may not have thought about) what con-

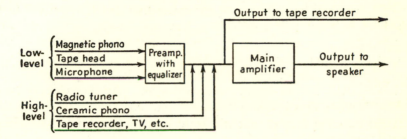

INPUTS AND OUTPUTS

trols it has been through or has *not* been through. Thus, the usual tape output (for making tape recordings) by-passes the tone controls and the volume control, but does include the earlier equalization for phonograph records. It has a fixed output level, supposedly just right for recording, and you can't change its volume, nor its tone except by the equalization phono controls. Useful—but sometimes inconvenient.

A. *Speaker-Bound Signals.* Signals for the loudspeaker emerge from the main power amplifier, wherever that may be, and are fairly potent in both current and voltage compared to the tiny input signals at the other end of the amplifier. The loudspeaker circuit is low-impedance, can be carried by ordinary electric light cord or hookup wire without shielding and to any length desired. This signal is already magnified and there is no further problem of hum pickup.

The power amplifier has a number of *output taps* on its rear, coming direct from the output transformer. They are now invariably of the screw-down type, usually four, of which you choose a pair—one is always the "common" or ground (COM or GND, sometimes numbered 0). The others are the varied impedances for matching your speaker—4, 8 or 16 ohms. No more need be said—except to warn you that the connections are usually so close together that stray strands of wire are likely sooner or later to make a partial or complete short circuit from one to the other. No harm done, but the speaker may produce a feeble, sputtery, bassless sound, or die entirely. This is the Number Two connection to check immediately, when trouble is experienced in the system. (Number One: the input phono plugs.)

B. *Amplifier-Bound Signals.* If you have a separate control unit and a basic power amplifier off by itself, or if you have a radio tuner with controls, you will have an output for connection directly to the power amplifier. It is normally a cathode follower output and so you can use a reasonably long cable. (A few control units may still have high-impedance outputs that require a short connection to the amplifier.) This output is invariably a phono-type socket, just like the rest, and it looks exactly like an input. Be careful where you plug your various cables! Nothing drastic will go wrong if you plug your radio or record changer into the output, but it's better not to tempt fate and electronic flexibility.

Markings for control unit or tuner output are usually just OUTPUT; or if there is also a tape recorder output, MAIN OUTPUT. Note that in this type of main output the signal has been through the volume control and the tone controls—everything. Keep an eye out for an *output level control* here, especially on radio tuners.

C. *By-pass Outputs (Tape Outputs).* On many amplifiers, on control units and on radio tuners you will also find a special output, as described above, that is intended for tape recording. It goes through the phono equalization (so that you may copy disc records onto tape) but it by-passes (1) the main volume control and (2) the tone controls. The output level is fixed, or rather, depends on what goes in at the other end. You use your tone and volume controls, for room sound without changing the standardized balance at this tape output. Thus you may listen or not as you wish, and at any convenient loudness, without affecting the recording that is being made at the same time.

You'll find that many one-piece complete amplifiers have *two* extra outputs. One is TAPE; the other is often labeled PREAMP—that is, it comes directly from the preamplifier, but is before the main power amplifier. It corresponds exactly to the main output of a control unit or a tuner and does go through the volume control and tone controls. (Do *not* use the power output [to the speaker] of any main amplifier for recording!)

And there you have it. I'm sure I've skipped lightly over all sorts of special aspects of the amplifier and I know I have been mum about things that seem terribly important to many a hi-fi fan. If you, the music listener, have found all this a bit more than you had bargained for, I can make you no apologies—except for having missed a lot. It's a complicated world, if a rewarding one when all is said and done.

There are far too many amplifiers now on the market for a detailed listing and evaluation, even in the briefest terms. Factors described in this and the last chapter can help you decide which type and model is best for you. Here are some further general remarks that may help:

The bulk of the good-quality *complete* amplifiers now offered are priced around the $100 figure, in models of twenty to thirty watts. (As always, the mail-order special models—Allied Radio, Lafayette Radio, Radio Shack, etc.—cost less for the equivalent ratings and performance.) Models in this price range will probably be offered you first. But the optimum price-versus-quality values are lower down. Like autos, amplifiers have been getting fancier, more powerful, higher in performance. The "low-priced" ten- and twelve-watt models from *Bell, Bogen, Harman-Kardon* and the like are now about $70 and are excellent values, generally, for most home use. (But for some speakers, notably the inefficient acoustic suspension models, AR and KLH, you may need more power.)

There are still a number of excellent economy models, ten-watt, now in the $45 range; they represent top value in cost versus performance and will be adequate for most musical listening—they are far superior to most built-in "hi-fi" amplifier sections in one-piece phonographs. Leading models are the *Bogen HF10A "Challenger,"* $45; the *Bell 2285,* $49; the *Grommes LJ-6,* $39 and a low-priced bargain. Lower-priced mail-order models also belong in this category. See listings, pp. 268, 269.

Basic power amplifiers, control-less, range from about $45 to $150 or more for the high-power behemoths now so much in demand. *Basic amplifier kits* are reliable and save you large sums. Buy a ready-made control unit to match —don't try the kits for these unless you are experienced.

Separate preamplifier-control units, for use with basic power amplifiers, begin at around $40; the really good ones run from $70 to $100. They are *low-level* devices and are crucial to good sound—more so than the power amplifier. Get a good one—but avoid complex controls unless you are gadget-minded.

9

The Radio Tuner

TUNER-CENTERED HI-FI. I have left discussion of the radio tuner until after both record player and amplifier not because it is less important but because it often includes complete built-in control facilities and a phonograph preamplifier—so that you may use it in place of the amplifier (or control unit) as your main center of operations.

In fact, this tuner-with-extras challenges a long-time convention concerning hi-fi—that a hi-fi system is first of all a phonograph and that other elements are "added."

Many people don't play records, or seldom play them. Those who do usually want radio too and find it best to acquire it right at the beginning. There is plenty of hi-fi on the air today, including vast numbers of records. So it was a brilliant thought to put radio first, to make the tuner the operational center for an alternative type of high fidelity system. (See diagram on p. 115.)

"ORDINARY" RADIO. You may wonder why a radio tuner is necessary for your system, in a household that may already have several sets, not to mention pocket portables and car radios! Still more radio, for the hi-fi system? Yes—and no.

To begin with, you no doubt have gathered that a radio tuner is not a plain, ordinary radio. More expensive than many radios, but also incomplete—just part of a radio. Every ordinary home radio, however small, is a three-part system in itself, a tuner to detect the signal, an amplifier—usually pretty feeble and far from hi-fi—and a loudspeaker. (The smallest transistor portables use an earphone in place of the loudspeaker.) The hi-fi tuner is basically no more than the front end of

108

a radio. Of the three general types of tuner, the third (below) gets as far as an amplifier (much more powerful and of far better quality than in any house radio) but still depends on an outside loudspeaker. The simplest tuners merely "tune"—they deliver a radio signal to your amplifier as an alternative to the record player. They don't even have a volume control.

THE VERSATILE STANDARD RADIO. The ordinary household radio does a lot for us even though its sound ranges from so-so to atrocious and its distance-getting ability and selectivity (separating close stations) is usually punk. In many respects it is far more convenient than a hi-fi tuner, notably in that it is easily portable (the day of the portable hi-fi system has yet to come), turns on and off quickly, gets to work in an instant when you are late for a program. Most hi-fi sets take their time about warming up.

Consider, too, that, in spite of us music lovers, radio exists mainly for news, popular music, baseball, fights and commercials, and it does very well for all of them. Our ears are trained to interpret the strange noises of transistor portables and shelf radios as intelligible speech and music. Distortion means little until the sound is virtually swallowed up in it. At full output, distortion in a good hi-fi amplifier is perhaps 1 per cent. On a small portable blasting away at the beach, it is probably a good 95 per cent! Fantastic—but it is enjoyed, all the same.

There are nice reasons for this. First, our announcers' voices are trained up to a kind of vocal "edge" that can cut through small-radio hash and bring linguistic sense to our ears. Announcers don't talk like ordinary people, as you will find out if you ever hear your own voice dismally muffled by a small radio, as I have.

A second reason is that our popular music styles have been marvelously shaped, over the years, to suit the small, lo-fi radio, as well as the big juke box. No swelling musical climaxes, in popular music, no dying-away-to-a-whisper, a steady thumping pulse that can never be misunderstood and a brassy hardness that forces its way, like the announcer's voice, through the feeblest radio. No question about it, lo-fi sound and popular music are perfectly wedded. I don't mean to be satirical. I have real admiration for the effective sound combination that has evolved over the decades from this odd teamwork between musicians and engineers. I am not a lover of the juke box and the portable myself, but it is clear enough to me that radio's main audience is happy with radio as it is, and rightly. Perhaps you are too.

Hi-Fi Pops. But in the last few years, profound change has taken place, starting with the improved, wide-range recording that came to the pops field with the plastic record. It is now no longer correct to say that pops music doesn't need hi-fi. Without it, the music still gets along nicely—it has to. But popular records and jazz are now recorded with top-quality sound and most newer juke boxes have the "fi" to play them. The old familiar juke-box boom is still with us, but it has been joined by the ting of the cymbal and the swish of the wire brush—sounds never before audible in juke-boxdom! Inevitably, the music itself has already changed. Even the commercials are different, in accord with the improved facilities.

I find myself, a supposedly hard-bitten old classicist, enjoying all sorts of nonclassical sounds these days via my hi-fi FM radio tuner, and so will you. If you have any interest in radio's popular music, you will want it hi-fi. To have it so, you'll need a good tuner.

The Classics. But "classical" music—that conglomeration of all the world's music from these many centuries—still stands well apart in the hi-fi sense. Its almost unlimited variety in providing sound for hi-fi to work upon is the major reason for the espousal of "serious" music by numbers of "hi-fi fans" who never otherwise would have heard a note of the stuff. This is a good thing, for it brings the sound of fine music to areas where it otherwise would surely not have penetrated. The fact that some hi-fi ears are immune to musical sense isn't really disturbing—except when you, the music lover, are directly involved in a hi-fi demonstration!

The classics (including modern, of course) have everything that hi-fi can triumphantly reproduce and "lo-fi" cannot. There is tremendous low bass, shimmering highs, a vast array of ingenious sound effects, huge dynamic climaxes (missing in pops music), unlimited color and mood. Even the unmusical ear can hear the sound values in the classical area.

AM Radio. "Standard" radio, AM, makes use of *amplitude modulation*. The newer FM radio, via short waves measured in megacycles, almost wholly static-free, uses *frequency modulation*. I don't propose a long explanation but a short one will give you an inkling as to the difference. Modulation is the word we need to know about.

MODULATION. Modulation, in either AM or FM, is the impressing of a sound-signal wave, like any of those electrical signals we've already run into, upon a vastly more rapid electrical oscillation of the same sort, a "radio frequency" wave—ranging in practice from about 500,000 cycles a second on up into the millions and billions.

A 500,000-cycle (500-kilocycle) wave may be made to pulse stronger and weaker, say, sixty times a second; in which case it has been amplitude-modulated with a 60-cycle tone. Similarly the radio frequency vibration can be made to pulse—in its amplitude—in the entire pattern of musical sound. Thus, AM broadcasting.

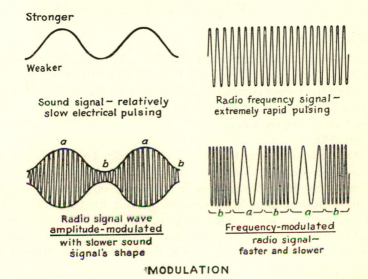

Stronger

Weaker

Sound signal — relatively slow electrical pulsing

Radio frequency signal — extremely rapid pulsing

Radio signal wave amplitude-modulated with slower sound signal's shape

Frequency-modulated radio signal — faster and slower

MODULATION

FM RADIO. FM Radio modulates radio waves in a different way—instead of the amplitude or "width" (strength) of the radio signal varying, it varies in its frequency, vibrating faster or slower according to the sound-signal pattern. An odd way of doing things, but ingenious. Essentially the idea is to send out a signal so specialized that only a device made specifically to "untangle" this particular kind of modulation can pick up anything at all from it; hence static, interference and the rest of the unwanted radio noise is mostly by-passed in FM. It can only hear its own special code. Nature and man create all sorts of electrical vibrations that are converted into meaningless noise by the old AM radio receiver, which cannot separate the wanted sound from the unwanted.

Modulation is done at the broadcast station. The purpose is simple enough. You can't launch ordinary electrical sound currents into the air. But high-speed electrical vibrations, radio-frequency waves, can travel through space and through most objects. Send out your music and speech in this form and it goes without wires. Pick it up, via an interposed antenna (which collects only an infinitesimal amount of the original radio signal); amplify and then "detect" it—remove the slower sound vibrations from the high-speed radio ones by a kind of electrical filter system—and you have a tiny replica of the original sound which can be fed to an audio amplifier as another sound source, alternative to the phonograph pickup. And that is radio—simplified.

TUNER TYPES

The radio tuner is a component that includes some, but not all the elements of the complete radio—it is as silent as the grave until you plug it into the proper complementary sections in the hi-fi home system. The type of tuner you get depends on what else you have, or will have, and vice versa. Let me categorize the tuner in several ways. First, as to FM and AM.

A. The most common type of tuner includes both FM and AM, built together on one chassis, sharing a good many of their internal parts, operating from the same dial. A number of higher-quality FM-AM tuners feature completely separate systems for the two, built together on the one chassis. Some of these can be used to pick up FM and AM signals simultaneously, for stereo ("binaural") broadcasts; they are usually called *stereo tuners*. (But in the future, better stereo will be broadcast via a single FM multiplex signal, requiring a different type of tuner construction.) This arrangement is familiar in FM-AM home radios and it will probably be your choice, unless your needs are more specialized in one way or another.

B. There are tuners for FM alone, dispensing entirely with the AM section on the principle that your AM listening will be taken care of by assorted portables around the house, convenient enough for news and the like. The *FM tuner* is indicated when you are within easy reach of enough major FM outlets so that you can hear everything you want via FM, without resorting to AM. Most larger cities provide you with this FM coverage, including network broadcasts.

C. If, on the other hand, you are located so far from FM—in the country or, especially, in the vast spaces of the West—that you despair of good FM reception; or if you are buried in a deep valley and can't pick up FM, which is like TV in its line-of-sight characteristics, then you can fall back on a high-quality AM *tuner*, which then will make the most of the available AM broadcasts. It can do wonders, compared to standard radios. (But see the section below on fringe-area FM reception before you give up.)

Secondly, tuners come in three general types of component unit: (1) simple tuners without "extras," (2) tuners that include complete controls and a phonograph preamplifier, and (3) tuners that include all this plus a power amplifier as well.

1. THE BASIC TUNER. You may acquire your tuner without controls except for the tuning knob and an on-off knob and you will do so if you have your controls elsewhere, in a complete amplifier or in a control unit. You can spot this Type One basic tuner instantly, on your dealer's shelf or in the catalogues, by its two knobs—no more—one at either end of the tuning dial. (There may be exceptions, but not many.) One knob tunes, the other switches from FM to AM and/or turns the set on and off. This type of tuner depends entirely on the controls found in your amplifier or control unit. It plugs into the TUNER or RADIO input as an alternative to the phono input signal. (You can even plug the tuner power cord into an extra amplifier power socket so that it goes on and off with the system itself.) A true first section, but in its fanciest forms it can cost you a small fortune, though the more inexpensive models run as low as $50.

2. THE TUNER-PREAMPLIFIER. The second category of available tuners, known by various names, is that in which the tuner (usually FM-AM) is combined with a full set of controls and a phono preamplifier—the "front end" of a complete amplifier. You can spot these Type Two tuners quickly by their many knobs—five or more. (But be sure you aren't dealing with the third category, below, which looks superficially the same.) This tuner has everything that the usual amplifier offers—except the power amplifier itself. It has the phono preamplifier, equalized, the dual bass and treble tone controls and so on. In fact, all comments in Chapter 8 on amplifier controls apply to this kind of tuner as well as to the third type, below.

The Type Two tuner does not include a power amplifier and therefore you must have one elsewhere. The assumption is that it will be a basic amplifier—without controls of its own. (See Chapter 8.) In this type of installation, as explained above, you shift the center of operations away from the amplifier to the tuner. The amplifier itself, without controls, may be set out of the way and even at some distance (but be sure it is well ventilated).

You may plug a record player, tape recorder, etc., into this type of tuner via the usual inputs and outputs (Chapter 8) and there are facilities for tape recording off the air.

Note that the names for these Type Two tuners vary from brand to brand. The Fisher 80-T, for instance, is called an *AM/FM Tuner with Controls*. The Pilotuner FA-540 is a Type One tuner without controls (*two knobs*) but the Pilotuner FA-550, same name, has them all (*five knobs*), Type Two. You won't have any trouble with these differences in a hi-fi store, but if you order by mail from a catalogue you must be careful. Printed descriptions are apt to be confusing—hi-fi salesmen aren't writers.

3. THE TUNER-AMPLIFIER. One of the earliest popular component units, long a major seller for home replacements, was a relatively low-priced combination unit that included on one chassis a radio tuner with controls (a few) *and* a built-in power amplifier. It sometimes came with a speaker, unmounted, out at the end of a cable; you mounted the speaker in your old radio cabinet or, failing that, dropped it (more often than not) into the nearest old cardboard carton. This type of tuner unit was often called a *chassis*, an ambiguous name that has since died out. It was not a good bargain because it was too cheap for the numerous elements crammed into the one package. At $40, such a mail-order unit had no more than eight or ten dollars' worth of amplifier and controls. At best, the quality was low—though, I hasten to add, no lower than a thousand standard radios.

Today, this form of compound tuner has come back—at a higher price but with little or no compromise in quality over the same elements in separate sections. Tuner, complete controls and amplifier are all on the one chassis. The cost may seem staggering (Bogan BR-550: $225) but is usually no more than the equivalent cost of separate units, sometimes a bit less due to savings in cabinetry. Remember that you are buying here almost a whole hi-fi system in one "package."

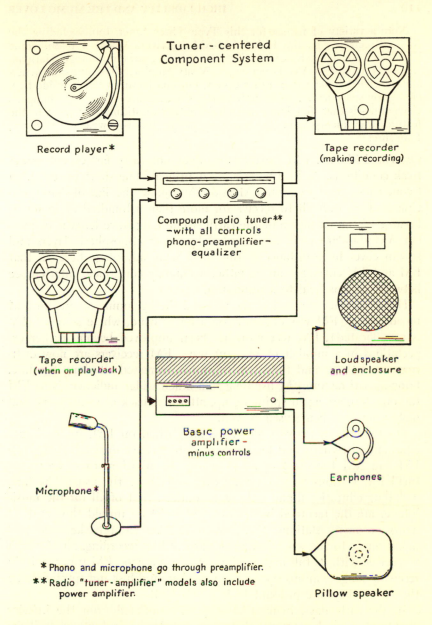

Tuner - centered
Component System

Record player*

Tape recorder
(making recording)

Compound radio tuner**
–with all controls
phono-preamplifier–
equalizer

Tape recorder
(when on playback)

Loudspeaker
and enclosure

Basic power
amplifier –
minus controls

Microphone*

Earphones

Pillow speaker

* Phono and microphone go through preamplifier.
** Radio "tuner-amplifier" models also include
power amplifier.

Note a variety of names for this Type Three tuner, too, including the *Radio Receiver*, e.g., the Fisher FM-AM Receiver, Model TA-500. Some brands of Type Three tuner are self-explanatory in their terminology: Harman-Kardon TA-120 FM-AM Tuner and 20-Watt Amplifier. The units are generally somewhat bulkier than other tuners, but considering what is inside they are clearly space-savers. Their only innate disadvantage—from the shopper's viewpoint—is that they limit your choice rather drastically in respect to the features they incorporate. But for many people this is a welcome thought, I am sure!

ON THE FM AIR. FM broadcasting does not carry far, except under freak conditions. As in TV, this is intentional. The short waves (high frequencies) used in both FM and TV follow the line-of-sight principle and are difficult to receive for more than a hundred or so miles, because of the curvature of the earth. (The long wave lengths of present AM standard radio are reflected by upper atmospheric layers and so can cover huge distances.) But there is an advantage here, in that FM and TV coverage can be rather accurately controlled, interference between regions held to a minimum.

However, since the end of the war and the beginning of present FM broadcasting (FM was originally on a lower band, where some of TV is now located), FM reception has been improved beyond earlier expectations in a number of pleasant ways. FM receivers are now drift-free (see below) and their sensitivity has increased all along the line, bringing satisfactory FM listening to a much wider audience. New FM stations, too, are again springing up, after a setback of some years, and higher power is being used as well.

On the air, all network programs are carried on FM, in the larger cities and elsewhere, and hundreds of stations have dual facilities, both FM and AM broadcast of all programs. In addition, there are many small FM stations to add variety over and above the usual AM fare, including educational and city-owned outlets. Best of all for the music listener are the recorded broadcasts, which fill up untold thousands of hours on many stations, the content ranging from background and mood music to the whole range of classical hi-fi recording, all of which is received with its full high fidelity sound via a good FM tuner (within receiving range), minus static, minus background hiss and sputter. Even the disc jockeys are pleasant to hear, via FM!

In the early days, many FM broadcasts suffered from the inferior quality of network programs that came over land telephone wires. Telephone line quality had been good enough for AM but was sadly under par as compared with the sparkling brightness of full-range "live" or local FM sound. That situation still applies in some cases but things are improving. New microwave relay circuits send programs from one station to another via chains of broadcast towers thirty or forty miles apart. Many telephone line connections are now improved, via new types of coaxial multichannel cables as used for TV. Similarly, the old inferior equipment in many early FM stations has been replaced and studio quality is generally as good as it should be. East and West Coast readers will find themselves favored in these respects, partly due to the density of population in the coastal areas and the consequently better radio coverage. People in the vast central regions will find less to please them in FM, speaking generally—though for many a listener one good FM station will make the difference between satisfaction and despair.

CHOOSING A TUNER. What should you look for in a radio tuner? Your first thought should be to your location. The more difficult the reception in your area, AM or FM, the greater the need for a really good tuner, and for a good antenna installation to take advantage of the tuner's capabilities.

For listening in or near the big cities, where powerful radio signals abound, virtually any tuner will do a fine job for you, often with simple indoor antenna facilities. In this case your decision as to which tuner to acquire will therefore depend on your purse, your taste in programs, and on your associated equipment. Higher-priced tuners, of course, give you more quality in basic respects—longer life via better parts and construction, ultra-low distortion in the delivered signal (and zero hum), high stability—reliability. Nice words, these, and they add up to trouble-free performance over the years. A high-quality tuner is a good investment, allowing for the inevitable geometric progression (Chapter 10) that makes prices for the best equipment staggeringly high. (Fisher Gold Cascode FM Tuner FM-90X: $170). But, on the other hand, the reverse consideration makes the lower-price tuners top bargains in quality versus dollars.

FM SENSITIVITY—FRINGE-AREA LISTENING. For FM reception beyond forty or fifty miles and/or reception in poor locations—behind a mountain, down in a deep valley—you must count on a sensitive tuner and a good outdoor antenna. The combination can do wonders. It's hard to say which is more important—good policy considers both.

FM sensitivity has been remarkably increased in the last few years, to open up quite exciting new distant listening possibilities. Remember that the FM tuner does not reproduce most static and distinguishes sharply between overlapping stations. The main deterrents are, instead of AM's horrid sputtering static, a steady shushing hiss that rises and fades away as the signal varies in strength, plus a curious jumping that may suddenly replace one distant station with another momentarily. (The FM receiver favors the stronger station and rejects the weaker one, rather than reproducing both together, as in AM.) Also an occasional sudden "shush-shush," caused, apparently, by interfering reflections from passing planes and clouds. Moreover, no matter how faint, the FM signal is always wide-range and fully hi-fi and so is easily intelligible, whereas the distant AM signal, static-ridden, is a confused jumble.

Sensitivity in the FM tuner is measured in an ingenious and easily appreciated way. Between stations on FM, you normally hear a loud hiss. An incoming station quiets the noise, if it is strong enough, to the zero point, and you hear only the broadcast program. Receiver sensitivity is measured by the strength of radio signal required (in millionths of a volt!) to reduce this hiss by a given amount, normally 20 db (that is enough to remove most of it), e.g., "2 μv for 20 db quieting." Occasionally a 30 db figure is used—requiring a stronger signal; but the 20 db rating is becoming standard. This rating is not entirely beyond a certain amount of wishful juggling, for better appearance; but in comparison to no rating at all it is useful and welcome. (Note that most household FM radios are described as "sensitive FM receivers"— meaning exactly nothing in the context of conventional publicity.)

You will now find the sensitivity rating of virtually every named-component tuner given in its catalogue description. The figure (for the 20 db quieting of the background hiss) runs from 3 or 4 μv (microvolts) down to a near-ultimate sensitivity of about .95 μv. In other words, the most sensitive tuners are three or four times as powerful in distance-getting ability as the least sensitive. Again—this factor is of virtually no importance in and around big cities, but it can be crucial in distant and poor locations. See below for antenna considerations.

Here is a rough table, for your guidance.

Needed Sensitivity for 20 Db Quieting

For city and suburban listening or within 1-15 miles of station.	3-5 µv (Any tuner)
For moderate distances, up to 50 miles—in favorable locations —flatlands or high and exposed.	2 µv (Preferably with outdoor FM antenna)
For extreme distances, from 100 to 250 or more miles, and/ or in poor locations—valleys, behind mountains, etc.	1 µv or less (Good outdoor FM antenna is absolutely necessary.)

AM—SENSITIVITY AND SELECTIVITY. Because of the well-known chaos in the standard AM broadcast band, extra AM sensitivity is of limited usefulness in serious music listening. (1) AM static is enormously amplified when weak stations are picked up—and it cannot be separated from the signal itself except by "tone control," which removes all the high end from the sound. (2) *Selectivity*, the ability to separate close-together stations, is inversely proportional, alas, to signal tone quality. That is, the more selectivity—sharper tuning—the more restricted is the tonal range of the tuned signal. You may separate out the desired station, but it will sound muffled and dull. Not a thing can be done about this—except via FM.

However, the AM section of the usual FM-AM tuner makes the very best of this situation, in several ways. (The AM-only separate tuner is even more specialized, for last-resort AM applications.) (1) It is, of course, much more sensitive than the average house radio. It has the power—static and interference allowing—to bring you in faint signals on the regular band. There are times, especially when static is low, when this power can be of real use. (2) For favorable occasions, when the AM signal is strong and interference is not in the way, there is a special *broad-band* tuning position. It is less sensitive and much less selective than the sharp-tuning position, *but* it lets through a maximum tonal range. Under good conditions, with a strong local signal and no interference, broad-band AM sound can approach FM in quality, though there is usually some background hiss. In the absence of practicable FM, therefore, an AM tuner can be very much better for music than a standard radio.

(This discussion concerns standard-band "broadcast" AM only. AM short-wave reception has similar problems but the distance-getting characteristics and, of course, the received program material are altogether different. Short-wave reception is beyond the scope of this volume.)

ANTENNAS FOR AM AND FM. AM radio is not very demanding in its antenna requirements. Small radios have built-in antennas. For the AM section of your tuner there is usually one of those coiled-wire-on-cardboard affairs that can be put under the tuner or unobtrusively behind it. For better reception, when desirable, a wire under the rug, or the traditional long wire strung up out of doors (or in the attic) will give maximum useful range. (A good ground will help eliminate may types of static.)

The FM antenna should always be separate. Because FM is short-wave, the antennas are quite unlike the AM type, and closely related to TV, which adjoins FM in the short-wave spectrum.

For strong-station reception a simple 300-ohm *dipole antenna* made of plastic two-cable lead-in strip will do very well. It can be made up cheaply but is often provided with your tuner.

For fringe reception—distant FM listening—you will need a high antenna, like TV, and the higher the better. Outdoors or in the attic, with a 300-ohm "twin-lead." FM antennas, being much like those for TV, have been similarly improved. The best of them, at $30 or more, are mast-mounted and directionally aimed toward the area you want most. As in TV, you can install a rotator for maximum flexibility, and to help separate distant overlapping stations.

A TV antenna will do a fair job on distant FM, but it is designed for a different set of wave lengths and a special antenna is always better. At my country home, a hundred-odd miles from New York City, via my TV roof antenna I could just receive a rather weak New York FM station (WNYC-FM) to hear my taped broadcast. I installed a new smaller, high-gain directional FM antenna, (the FM/Q) and now I listen to the same station with what is called *full limiting*. There is no hiss in the background and I get virtually "at-the-station" quality, only an occasional telltale shush-shush indicating the great distance. That FM tuner (1.5 µv sensitivity), though it is almost two years old and has never been serviced, now pulls in *fifty* or *sixty* FM stations with listenable quality, including many that are well over two hundred miles away. A few years ago, this would have been thought impossible via the FM medium. Readers who are supposedly out of FM areas take note! You may well find that good music via FM is possible, after all, in your location.

FM MULTIPLEX AND STEREO. A subject of immense future interest is the use of a single FM channel to transmit two separate signals, with an "unscrambler" attachment in your FM tuner to separate them. Present stereo broadcasting via one FM and one AM radio station is a mere makeshift expedient and I suggest that you avoid all expensive tuner equipment based on this idea. Before long, via FM multiplexing, a single FM tuner will bring you a full stereo signal, as a single stereo disc or a single tape now brings you the stereo recording itself. The two FM channels will not transmit the "right" and "left" stereo recordings but two combinations of both, called the *sum* and the *difference* (equivalent to the lateral and vertical elements in the stereo disc). The sum signal, right and left *added together*, gives the full standard or monaural effect, as heard by itself, without the second signal. The difference signal, one track subtracted from the other, provides the stereo effect. Keep FM multiplex in mind if you become a stereo fan.

ADDITIONAL FM POINTERS. One of the worst faults of early FM receivers was *drift*—that gradual shifting out of correct tune that turns clear radio music into a horrid blasting, until the set is retuned by hand. Drifting almost killed FM with the general public in the early postwar years—until the problem was solved by AFC—*Automatic Frequency Control*. AFC is not unlike the earlier AVC (Automatic Volume Control) that leveled out the volume between strong and weak stations. It "locks" the tuner upon a strong station like a magnet; the tuning seems to snap reluctantly from one station to the next, hanging on to each tenaciously, as you move the dial pointer. Once tuned in, a station stays tuned with AFC, unless a much stronger station interferes.

For very weak stations that lie next to strong ones AFC must be removed—*disabled* or *defeated* is the graphic terminology. You will find AFC in almost all present tuners and there should always be a disabling (defeat) provision. (Some tuners, presently the H. H. Scott 300, for example, have a wide-band type of FM tuning that makes drift-free reception possible without AFC. In some other models, AFC is variable in strength from zero to maximum.)

The original FM circuit was developed by Major Armstrong, a pioneer in the radio art. His circuit is still about the most satisfactory and "Armstrong Circuit" is a good specification to look for. Among other FM circuits is the *ratio detector*, often used in less expensive FM radios. My impression is that it is not particularly desirable in quality home equipment. (Earlier ratio detectors developed unpleasant double "humps" of tuning for each station, were hard to tune accurately and without distortion.)

A final useful minor feature for ultra-sensitive FM tuners is the *local-distance switch* (e.g., Sherwood S-2000 basic tuner). With a good outdoor antenna and a sensitive tuner you will find that many a station is so strong, even at a distance, that it sprawls over the weaker stations to each side so they cannot be heard without distortion. An alternative is an extra antenna, (a simple indoor type) that will bring them into balance; but the "strong-weak" switch does it better at a finger's flip, by lowering the over-all sensitivity of the tuner to bring the extra-strong signals down to size.

Most tuners of Types One and Two have low-impedance *cathode follower* outputs, which allow you to run the connecting wire to the amplifier over quite long distances.

A useful feature to have in a tuner is an *output level control*. The tuner's signal is often strong enough to overload the first section of the amplifier—even though you may have your regular volume control turned low. The sound is then distorted and blasting. The level control cuts down the radio signal to the right strength. (There may, of course, be a level control at the radio input on your amplifier or control unit, in which case it can do the job.)

Cost. And so you are as ready as I can make you to cope with the radio tuners that are now a major part of every hi-fi display. You must put the facts together in your own pattern to determine what is best for your own good listening. Radio in these hi-fi forms is not cheap, in any case. The first postwar FM tuners sold for as low as $25 but they were simply not good enough for satisfactory reception over a reasonable period of time and prices have since gone upward with the addition of the very features that make FM so satisfactory today. Fifty dollars is a low minimum for a respectable radio tuning section in your home system, and well worth it.

You will note, in conclusion, a rather odd pattern of prices in the tuner area, not so odd if you will think twice. Tuners with both AM and FM radio tend to cost only a very little more than FM-only tuners in the same line. Thus Lafayette Radio's mail-order "Music-Mate" De Luxe FM-AM tuner (Type One) sells for $65, yet the LT-60 FM-only tuner, also labeled De Luxe, is $50 and a simpler FM-AM combination tuner, the LT-25, sells for the same price, $50. Most other brands show similar relationships.

The reasoning is simple. The FM-AM combination is by nature a practical compromise; its design tends to emphasize ingenious simplification, for home use. The FM-only tuner, however, is a more specialized item; a better tuner can be built when the dual-function compromise is put aside, favoring high-quality performance without compromise, and so FM-only prices inevitably are higher for this inherently better quality. Whether you like it or not, then, you will pay for superior performance in the single tuners, FM or AM.

As with amplifiers, there are so many tuners now available that a comprehensive evaluation is impossible. Check the features above according to your own needs and purse. Remember (a) that tuners are not cheap, ever, and (b) that some brands emphasize FM long-distance sensitivity—which may or may not be important to you. Thus *Fisher* tuners are notably sensitive, also *Sherwood*. Others, with lower sensitivity, may be excellent for city or suburban reception of the average sort.

10

A Geometry of Values

Since I first wrote about high fidelity equipment a number of years ago, much has changed. But one aspect, a most vital one for you to understand, has not changed a bit. It never will.

It must have been increasingly clear to you during these last chapters that a large area of the high fidelity world operates under an appalling group of mathematical relationships called *geometric*—where things increase not at a staid and fixed rate but in accelerating leaps, each larger than the last. The geometric progression is the basic term for this kind of relationship, though it has many a close relative—the law of diminishing returns, the logarithmic curve, the law of squares.

The geometric progression is dangerous because in daily life we so often ignore it. It applies to all sorts of things we do. Yet we go right along thinking in the simple arithmetical relationship where, so to speak, a spade is a spade, twice as much sugar costs twice as many pennies, a forty-mile trip is four times as far and four times as long as a ten-mile trip. True enough, you can cite a million and one very proper arithmetical relationships—but what about those that aren't?

What about, for instance, the distance it takes to stop your car at a given speed? If you think that at twice the speed you'll need merely twice the distance to come to a halt, you won't live long; the distance is eight times as far. Is the difference between forty and fifty miles an hour the same as that between sixty and seventy? Decidedly not. With each additional mile-per-hour the life-and-death factors jump upward more rapidly—the number of tons' pressure with which your nose will hit the windshield if you stop dead, not to mention the degree of strain on tires, engine parts, and so on. So, too, in a less grisly way, with power versus speed. It takes enormously more added push from a car engine to jump from sixty to seventy miles an hour than from thirty to forty. The law of diminishing returns works here with a peculiar intensity, in terms of everything from gas mileage to crash impact. Yet plenty of drivers go right ahead driving arithmetically in their minds. Sixty-five and seventy? A mere five-miles-an-hour difference, they'll say. Danger ahead! That is a geometric unit. Look out for the geometric disguise.

The Geometric Unit. The basic misapprehension behind all of these things, and behind an agonizing amount of faulty thinking in the high fidelity area, is our failure to spot a geometric unit when we run into it, to see through the geometric disguise that puts such units into disarmingly sweet and simple one-two-three form. Hi-fi is full of them, in both its musical and technical aspects.

Not that all such progressions are identical. Some, like the increase in hi-fi quality with added expenditure of money, can't be pinned down in any exact way—but the vital thing is to understand that *for each additional rise in quality the cost is greater*, and grows greater at an increasing rate. Divide up your available cash into $50 parcels and each is a geometric unit. The first one will bring you a lot more value than the last. Quality does *not* double for double cost.

Look at a few of the geometric units that we will find in the high fidelity field.

Frequency Response and the Octave. Musical pitch as we hear it is geometric, in terms of vibration speed or frequency. Middle A on the piano is 440 cycles per second; an octave, eight keys above, is 880. Move up another octave and it is 1,760—each rise of an octave doubles the frequency. The next A is 3,520, the next 7,040, the next, 14,080— and if we move up one more octave we jump right out of the range of hearing, to 28,160 cycles. An octave is a geometric unit, and so too, of course, are all the smaller musical pitch divisions down to the half-step and whole step. We hear geometrically in terms of frequency.

Many hi-fi devices are measured or discussed or labeled in frequencies. It is terribly easy to think of the numerical frequency scale as arithmetic, without realizing it, and even the engineers can fall into that error. Look how plausible this scale (a) looks, measured off neatly in thousands.

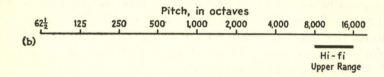

The upper range of tones important in high fidelity music seems to occupy half the scale or more, but when we look at it in terms of the hidden geometry (b), *as we hear music itself*—how insignificant it becomes!

Looking at this chart, you can understand how the fuss that people make over those precious upper highs may sometimes be a bit exaggerated. Not that they aren't important. But the higher you go, the less it matters. The difference between 4,000 and merely 6,000 cycles is large (an interval of a fifth) and indeed quite vital to music; but that between 14,000 and 16,000 is almost infinitesimal—a small half-step in pitch, in a region where many of us cannot hear sound at all! The geometric disguise, again.

DECIBELS. We've already looked at watts of power and found there another geometric disguise. The decibel, which measures sound as we hear it, is not unlike the octave. A decibel (one-tenth of a bel) is roughly the smallest unit of change in sound intensity that we can hear. The range of decibels between the faintest and the loudest sound we can stand comfortably is above 90 db—a big scale. But the geometrical disguise is incredible; for each three decibels louder the sound power must be doubled, and 3 db, mind you, is scarcely any increase—merely another "notch" on the volume control, merely three times the tiniest difference we can hear. Ninety db means *thirty doublings of power!*

Hence our watt-decibel relationship. Twenty watts gives you not twice as much sound as ten watts but merely 3 db more, a trifle; the next 3 db increase requires forty watts, the next eighty. That is the fine sort of disguise offered to us by those deceptive power ratings in watts. The potent new amplifiers take a lot of current, but their out-

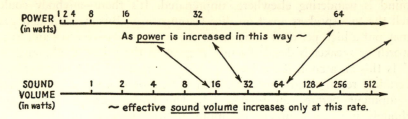

put *in sound* is only moderately greater than the smaller models, and vice versa. Keep that in mind when your hi-fi friends insist that you acquire a hundred-watt monster of an electricity-hog! Ten watts will do *almost* as well.

SILVER LINING—GEOMETRY IN REVERSE. If such extraordinary relationships exist—and they are in every aspect of hi-fi—then it is easy to see why you must spend at an accelerating rate if you want more and more over-all quality in your hi-fi system. It should not surprise you a bit to know that the most expensive speaker systems, the very best now available, run up into the $1,000 range with enclosure, the speakers themselves costing from $200 to $300. So too, with amplifiers; the fanciest cost a fortune. Here is the grand geometrical super-unit, the sum total of all the lesser ones—the cost of top-quality high fidelity.

But perhaps you have not spotted the extensive silver-lining moral of all this. Far too few of us have. What if we reverse our viewpoint and follow the progression downward instead of inevitably, doggedly, up? Suppose we look at the value per dollar as we move down the scale, at the sound per watt, at the octaves of useful pitch per thousand cycles? Strictly practical. The less you spend, the greater value you get, relatively speaking.

Ten watts of amplifier power again, is by no means half of twenty watts—only slightly less. And what of five watts or two watts? Merely a couple of steps less volume. A two-watt amplifier will fill a room with sound and the astonishment of the uninitiated is something to behold. Merely about 6 db less sound than a ten-watt machine, which is not very much. So, too, with all sorts of other equipment.

The rule applies still more fundamentally to over-all performance. Would it surprise you to see a group of experts fooled by a $20 speaker, played on the sly instead of the expected $150 model standing directly behind it? The difference is slight enough not to be noticed when the mind is wandering elsewhere, unprepared. It's there—anybody could tell the two speakers apart on direct comparison. But even though you may put a high personal value on it, the contrast between $13 and $150 worth of speaker is decidedly not as great as the prices would suggest.

Is this an argument for buying cheap equipment? Not necessarily. I certainly recommend a very careful investigation of the modestly priced equipment before you plunge into the fancier grades. Principally, though, it is an argument for more careful judgment of values. Virtually everything you do in hi-fi is in some way tied up to the geometrical progression. Without an understanding of it you cannot possibly make intelligent decisions as to cost versus desirability. It should be a background to all your thinking and evaluating.

11

The Speaker

There once was a time when you bought a speaker—a single speaker —and mounted it in a relatively simple cabinet or enclosure and that was that. No longer. The speaker itself has proliferated in a dozen directions. Speaker "systems" include from one to many individual speakers, sometimes side by side, so to speak, sometimes dividing the tonal range between high and low. There are numerous part-way speakers that are not quite several speakers yet not exactly one, either. And there are radically new types of speaker such as the electrostatic (not new in principle, just new in practice), the ionized air tweeter, the ribbon tweeter, the servo-speaker-amplifier system (Integrand), not to mention the already familiar acoustic suspension speakers (AR and KLH).

All of this expansion is designed to bring better sound to the American home and this it has done, already. Something for everyone. But you, not being everyone, must find your own niche in all this magnificent confusion, and the people who publicize it, who put names to all this equipment, are not out to help you—if clarity and simplicity of nomenclature are any criterion. I wish I could be of more honest use to you than I expect to be. But I am at the mercy of mere words and so I must deal directly with the persuasion—the words that are attached to hi-fi speakers, rather than the speakers themselves.

As you may have gathered, a speaker without an enclosure is like a locomotive without a train. That is one thing that has not changed since I first wrote about high fidelity. Speaker and enclosure are so tightly interdependent that it is not easy to evaluate them separately. The trend today is more and more toward the over-all complete speaker system. When the day comes that the last separate loudspeaker is sold off a dusty shelf and we have nothing but complete speaker systems, ready to play, the following pages will be beside the point. But separate speakers and separate enclosures are still very much on hand and for sale everywhere, and the insides of the complete systems generally include the same speakers or others similar. And so this chapter will look at the many kinds of separate loudspeakers, though not one of them will produce listenable music without an enclosure.

CONES, MAGNETS AND WORK. You may remember from Chapter 3 that the usual loudspeaker is a sort of piston-like motor that converts electrical pulses (from the amplifier) into thrusts of actual motion, forward and back, which are communicated to thin air as sound waves in the pattern of the original—more or less. *The cone speaker*, the most common type among several, is a compromise piston, far from theoretically ideal but highly practical nevertheless, as we know from more than a quarter-century of experience with it. The cone speaker grips the air via its broad cardboard-like pumping surface, as a hand fan pushes air when it is moved back and forth.

The magnet in the cone speaker, and in other types as well (horn tweeters, for instance), is now invariably a *permanent magnet*, nonelectric. Older speakers, before the new potent magnetic alloys were developed, used electromagnets which carried as much as three hundred volts, enough to give you a very unpleasant and possibly dangerous shock. In those days you handled your loudspeaker gingerly—and no wires under rugs and around baseboards. A few of these *electrodynamic* speakers are still used in radios but you won't find them in hi-fi. The electromagnet speaker had four wires and this is an easy way to spot it; there were two for the signal current and two for the high voltage to the magnet. The standard *permanent magnet (PM)* speakers of today have only two wires and are quite harmless. You can run the wires wherever you wish, and the worst that can happen is a short that will make the speaker sputter or go temporarily dead, with no harm done.

Magnets are strange things and interesting in their actions. Science uses them everywhere but some of their fundamentals are still unexplained. Most people are aware of the principle that you can't get something for nothing (the conservation of energy) in such homely matters as gas mileage and electric bills. But the function of a magnet in a speaker is easily misconstrued—the more so since we speak of a "strong" or "powerful" speaker magnet as though it would do work. It does no work.

It is true that the heavier (and more potent) the magnet, the louder is the sound your speaker can make—but not, as you might think, because the bigger magnet has more power. The magnet furnishes no power at all—if it did, it would soon be "used up," like a battery. What happens is that the magnet acts like a chemical catalyst, to promote the conversion of energy though not actually participating itself. A big magnet allows more of the amplifier's electrical power to be converted into actual motion and hence to sound. A more efficient motor.

At best only a small part of the amplifier energy is ever converted. Like most motors, this speaker-motor is wasteful; hence the very low wattage of even a loud sound. But even so, the bigger the magnet, the better the efficiency and the louder the sound. So in effect the weight of the speaker magnet in ounces is a good rough measure of speaker potency.

There's a common misconception right here that may intrigue you. Most people would assume that it should take more amplifier power to drive a big speaker than a small one—as it takes more gas to run a big truck than a motorcycle. But the facts are the opposite. The bigger speaker with its larger magnet allows more of the amplifier current to be converted into sound. The little speaker does an inefficient job with it.

The bigger your speaker (the heavier your magnet), the more sound you'll get for a given electrical input, other things being equal. Other things usually are not equal, but the principle is worth remembering. Bigger magnets, bigger cones, allow for greater efficiency in the use of the signal current.

The loudspeaker's cone is driven forward and back by the voice coil, a ring of fine wire wrapped around the cardboard center of the cone which fits into a thin slot in the magnet itself—an odd-shaped magnet, decidedly. The smaller the gap between magnet and coil in this slot, the more efficient is the sound production and so the voice coil rides just as close to the edges of the slot as ingenuity can manage—but it is limited by the danger of scraping against the walls, which produces a loud buzzing, scratching noise. This inner cone mounting is crucial. There is often a many-legged supporting system called a *spider*, to help hold the voice coil in exact alignment while allowing it maximum forward-and-back motion (*excursion*). The whole system, magnet and all, is usually encased in a dust cover; even a few small grains of sand or dirt can cause scraping in the voice coil slot.

The mounting at the outer edge of the cone also serves a double purpose. It must act as a centering device to hold the cone in place, but it must also be as flexible as though it did not exist, so that the piston motion of the cone is unimpeded. This is physically impossible but many compromise ways of "floating" the edge of the cone have been devised. The usual one is a series of accordion-like ridges around the outer edge which allow the cone to move in and out with considerable freedom. Newer developments that make for even better performance are the *cloth surround,* a carefully tailored cloth edging that is flexible in the right direction, and the recent *foam surround* (note that

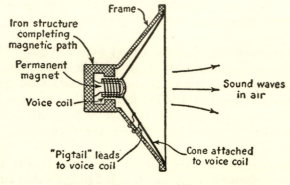

Loudspeaker cross section

"surround" is a noun, not a verb), holding the cone in place via a spongy plastic material. In addition, the edge of many cones is softened by a *plasticizer,* a sticky goo, often silicone; it improves the freedom of motion and tends to damp out various kinds of spurious vibration.

The main area of the cone, in contrast, must be as firm and as rigid as possible—but also very light in weight—in order to act as a faithful air piston. Most cones are especially shaped and the "paper" is far from a simple piece of cardboard; often it is tapered in thickness, more rigid at the center, thin at the edges. Extra supports are sometimes added to avoid the unpleasant *cone breakup,* where the cone breaks away from the simple piston action into its own complicated vibrations, producing sheer distortion.

There's plenty more, but this is enough to give you a sense of the practical complications involved in a very simple theoretical idea, the pushing of air by a straight piston. You'll begin to appreciate the excellence of speakers in general today, after these many years of experiment. The speaker is by nature a distortion-producing device, and only ingenuity and compromise can make it behave.

Thus the best cone speakers today still advertise such figures as "flat within 6 db over the entire range of sound"—which you may compare to "flat within ½ db" for an average hi-fi amplifier. The figure means plus-or-minus 6 db ($\pm$ 6 db), for a total of 12 db variation, either too loud or too soft. That is good—for a loudspeaker. Good even though it represents a factor of *sixteen to one* in the power radiated. (A totally "flat" speaker would radiate the same power, for a given input, at all frequencies or, if you will, at all musical pitches. The plus-or-minus 6 db speaker radiates sixteen times as much power at its strongest points as at its weakest points!)

Granted, this is not so severe a distortion as it seems if we turn to the ear's hearing power. Six db, though equal to a four-to-one power difference, represents only a moderate change in actual, audible loudness. (A decibel, again, is the smallest difference in loudness we can

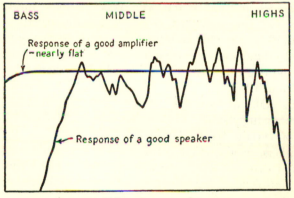

Amplifier vs. speaker

detect.) But even so, a 12 db range of variation from flat response is not exactly perfection—and it doesn't take into account other violent distortions that run concurrently, so to speak, in most loudspeakers.

Speakers distort, then, and far more than any other element in the entire hi-fi chain of operation. But since this same hi-fi chain is inaudible *except* via the speaker, we are plainly stuck with loudspeaker sound as it is, in everything we hear. No wonder the speaker is considered the crucial element in hi-fi.

Yes, we do enjoy reproduced sound and we can enjoy it with a lot more distortion than here described. Our imagination easily makes up for what is missing and what is unfaithful, especially in music. But, as a small indication, you will notice that a plain speaking voice from any loudspeaker and the same voice speaking in person are seldom confused. There isn't much for imagination to work on here and so the objective distortion is immediately apparent. The reproduced speaking voice, even with the finest hi-fi equipment, still sounds "loudspeaker"— and there, if you wish, is a concrete measurement of the lack of "fi" that we live with in all our reproduced sound.

INDIVIDUALITY. Because no two speaker systems produce the same pattern of distortion, no two of them sound alike, given the same incoming electrical signal. They tend to have personalities; they run in families, in this respect—types of sound, like types of human faces, and close-relative similarities, as between various speakers in the same manufacturer's line of offerings. We make a good deal of positive capital out of these differences, and rightly too. We object to some speakers, we like other types, and the preference is personal and subjective. The measured over-all distortion may be roughly the same in two systems but the sound, due to these same infinite differences in detail, can still be utterly unlike and no one can say with finality which is "better."

There is much talk (in which I have joined, I'll admit) of speakers that are "natural," or "musical" in sound, as compared to others that in some tantalizingly subtle way are less natural, less good to music, or to music of certain types. There are "hi-fi" speakers and "classical music" speakers, speakers that perform brilliantly in the showroom and at the sound demonstration and speakers that make themselves wonderfully inconspicuous and useful in the musical home, though they may seem ever so stodgy on the showroom floor.

It is only in very recent times that speaker design has begun to approach that objective perfection that might be called truly and impersonally *hi-fi*, by the unique standard of literal faithfulness to the received sound-signal. The old preferences for "individuality" in speaker sound, for coloration as it is sometimes called, continue to dominate most of us as in the past. We still pick our speakers because we like them as individuals, not because they are wholly "transparent" to sound passing through them, offering no individuality of their own at all. As in the case of amplifiers, every perfect speaker should sound exactly like every other one. Amplifiers do—at least in the basic power stage. Speakers, alas, do not.

Therefore, you may count on choosing yours largely by preference for its special, individual sound (as distinguished from the complex of sound effects that it reproduces for you). And in doing this you run grave risks of misjudgment due to local acoustics as well as to overlooked irrelevancies. (Irrelevancies? As an example, you may dislike a screechy speaker, only to find that the amplifier's high tone control has been turned all the way up by accident.) To the speaker's total individuality you will add such other factors as your budget, the size of enclosure you can accommodate, the type of musical listening you intend in the main to do. For hi-fi railroad records and tremendous percussion bass effects you will want a whopping big system (or an expensive one, in any case) but for Mozart string quartets you may need merely a neutrally accurate and well-balanced system that will deliver music to you without intruding its own presence any more than necessary.

This talk, to be sure, is a beating about many specific bushes, but it is necessary background to speaker thinking. Be prepared to be *wholly* subjective—but be ready, also, to throw in every intelligent check and balance that you can manage, to be sure that what you get is what you want, in speaker performance.

WOOFERS AND TWEETERS. The foregoing account is intended to pave the way for a paradox. I am going to recommend to you, for all modest hi-fi installations, a type of speaker that is clearly limited in certain high fidelity respects and yet, in my experience, offers the very best musical value for the money that you can get, in the low-priced areas. This is the small single speaker, unadorned or mostly unadorned, the type of speaker which has been largely supplemented today, for wider tonal range, louder highs and lows, by the prevalent compound systems. But before I get to the single models, look at the multiunit speakers. They are often better than the single speakers—that is the intention— and in the middle and upper price brackets a speaker system without a tweeter and a woofer is unthinkable. I use 'em myself. They do cost more, and as always, for each rise in quality you pay a greater additional sum, up to positively astronomical levels—say, a cool $1,000 for a large speaker, housed in expensive cabinetry. But the cheapest single speakers that I recommend begin at around $10—and they are amazing, at the price!

A single speaker cannot do an optimum job over the entire tonal range of sound. It is inherently more efficient in some parts of its range than in others. A better-balanced coverage is possible by dividing the sound among several speakers, each designed to cover only a part of the range, at its best efficiency. Slang usually gets into this sort of development before the engineers have so much as finished their work—the big, heavy speakers that take care of the bass range were long ago named *woofers*, the smaller, lighter, squeakier speakers designed for the highs became *tweeters*. These names have stuck even though today the sound spectrum is likely to be divided into more than two parts. New names, not very original, have been added to supplement the woofer and tweeter: *mid-range* in between them and *super-tweeter* up above.

The terms are relative. An eight-inch cone speaker, not specifically one type or another, can serve as a woofer in a small speaker system, as a mid-range in a larger three-way system and even as a quite respectable tweeter in connection with a larger woofer or a large full-range single speaker that is somewhat weak at the high end, as the large ones usually are. The eight-inch in addition can serve by itself (*full-range*) to cover the whole sound range with reasonably good balance and very musical sound—but more of this later. The range of best coverage varies from speaker to speaker and from type to type; in practice it is usually limited, arbitrarily, by limiting the signal that is sent to each speaker. Thus this same eight-inch speaker used as a woofer is fed only the bottom tones and so reproduces only bass; as a tweeter it would be fed only the upper range. The divisions are made electrically by means of devices called *crossovers* or *dividing networks*. There are also many mechanically arranged divisions of labor, as between highs and lows, in compound speakers that involve several radiating elements. Even more frequently, you will find combinations, both mechanical and electrical separation. A "three-way" speaker may actually involve only two voice coils, one of which drives two piston-elements, a larger standard cone for lows and a smaller central dome or hump or conical protuberance for mid-range tones, the top highs being taken care of by the separate tweeter unit. The mechanical crossover is automatic; the big cone simply helps itself to the lower tones, the central protuberance vibrates to the middle ones of its own accord. The dividing line (crossover), always fairly rough and indeterminate, is the point where the two are doing equal work—it may be at, say, 2,000 cycles. Above that point, the smaller unit does more radiating, below it the large cone does most of the work.

Remove the tweeter and this "three-way" system is a "two-way," a single speaker with two radiating parts, and the hump or protuberance or dome that was a mid-range reproducer in the three-way speaker now takes on the whole upper end and becomes a tweeter of a sort, though it shares its main "body," the voice coil, with the large cone.

These are the complications—some of them—which now adorn the hi-fi speaker in its major American lines. I must say at once, at this point, that I am skeptical of many of these values in actual practice. The complications are impressive, the descriptions convincing and the reasoning is excellent. But the sound, to the ear, is not always right. Not for music listening. As far as I am concerned, I don't care a fig whether my speaker is just a "plain" model or a four-way superdiffused what-not with three crossover points, electrical, mechanical and all the rest, if it does not sound good to me—which means that it must do justice to musical reproduction. The complications here described ought to help in this very purpose—for aren't we all after the same, ultimate perfection, which can take only one, unique form, faithfulness to the original sound signal? We are, and they should—but in practice (my opinion, if you wish), they often do not. To be short, many of these complex speakers sound, for my ear, musically worse than the simpler ones.

BRILLIANCE. Now this is, as usual, a matter primarily of taste, this divergence among speakers. There are, to be sure, ways of measuring speaker performance that should in theory be objective and accurate. In practice, as things now stand, these measurements somehow manage to prove what it is desirable to prove. Too many variables, too many subtleties. You will find that virtually every speaker maker will claim his product is hi-fi, that is, flat, faithful to the original sound within relatively small tolerances. I've had the proof shown to me many a time. I prefer to discount it in favor of my ear's preference and so will you.

Ears, remember, are not by any means flat. Ear response is a study in itself, as the hearing-aid people will be glad to tell you. It is possible that my ears and yours are different. I prefer to think, however, that

ear "taste" (we are mixing metaphors here), ear education, is what
really matters. And there we come back once more to the   question
of musical reproduction versus that strange phenomenon, high fidelity
sound.

The plain fact is that a truly flat high-end reproduction is not very
spectacular. Slight high-tone distortion adds brilliance and glitter, and
it increases the impact of the highest sounds (which we hear weakly
at best). For most people, it gives therefore a legitimate pleasure of a
sort, within bounds, just as low-tone transient distortion serves a legitimate artistic purpose in producing the big boom so rhythmically helpful (from an objective viewpoint) in the juke box kind of reproduction!

From whence you may deduce that a "brilliant" sort of reproduction
in the highs can often seem very desirable, especially to those who
either do not know much about the supposed musical original (the
imagined original) or are gently deceived concerning its nature. I speak
in dead earnest. Here, it seems to me, is the core of present argument
concerning hi-fi sound—and at the same time the human motivation
for that hi-fi brilliance that is so successfully promoted in current loudspeaker equipment. It is not for me, this brilliant sound, but people do
like it, as sound if not as music. It is effective, it is stimulatingly sharp,
clear, exciting—or so a million hi-fi fans think. As an afterthought, I
might add that a brilliant sound will always do better in the showroom than an accurate and therefore less brilliant reproduction. But
loudspeakers sell themselves at home as well as in the stores. They are
both doing very nicely.

And so I finally arrive at the discussion I had in mind, to begin with,
concerning the simple, one-cone, one-element loudspeakers of the old-
fashioned sort that, I feel, offer a top bargain in musical reproduction.

It is true that no single speaker can span the entire audible sound
spectrum with impartial and equal response. It is bound to falter somewhere in its tonal range, at one end or the other or both according to
size. The smaller single speaker is deficient at the bass end (compared
to a large speaker); the big single models are fine in the bass but fall
off at the top end.

On the other hand, consider music itself. The extremes of pitch are
of relatively slight importance in music, even on a literal basis. (Given
musical imagination, they are even less vital.) For hi-fi sound, very
low bass and super-high highs are both desirable and enjoyable. In

music they don't amount to much. The highs to 10,000 cycles are vital, decidedly, but those which rise up to 15,000 and 20,000 are a tiny drop in the sound bucket, musically. And as for the bass, below 75 cycles or so there is practically nothing of musical interest. Tones in that sub-cellar region simply do not occur in music most of the time. Why else is there such a frantic search through records for "good bass"—or any bass at all! You will not find a 40-cycle note from beginning to end of most symphonies and even a Bach organ fugue hits the bottom pedal tones only momentarily. On plain statistical grounds, very low bass and very high highs are of little *musical* importance, however pleasant it is to hear them well reproduced.

If your interest is in bass itself, as such, if you must have high highs because you want the best in sound reproduction (and if you can hear and appreciate the best), then you will want a wide-range compound speaker system that responds flat, or nearly so, to *all* audible tones and some that are inaudible. But if your listening is to Beethoven, Stravinsky, Gilbert and Sullivan or musical comedy—to *music*, rather than *reproduction*, your statistical need for the extremes is factually very low.

Much more important for your listening are two factors. First, an unobtrusive, smooth loudspeaker sound that does not get in the way of your music—hi-fi or no. This the single-cone speakers can provide, within their range, with remarkable consistency. Second, you will need *balance*, an equal division of highs and lows, whether the extremes are deficient or not. Balance is such a vital principle in music listening that I must pause to go into it.

BALANCE. The musical ear is satisfied in a profound way with almost any type of reproduction where the higher and lower tones are in balance with each other—even though both may be weakened or totally lacking at the extremes. The ear objects violently to any musical sound that favors one end of the spectrum over the other—either a reproduction that has plenty of good highs but weak bass, or a solid bottom and no highs.

It is an astonishingly demanding principle, this one. You will ignore it at the risk of unpleasant listening. It is often embarrassing to hi-fi enthusiasts—for there are times when you must deliberately weaken a perfectly good high end, or a solidly persuasive bass, to achieve a tonal balance that is even more important than hi-fi "flatness."

You'll remember that a small shelf radio can make good music, even though it lacks practically the entire upper and lower range of sounds—it satisfies because with all its faults it gives you balanced music and so a sense of naturalness even though the sound is very far from hi-fi.

Your ears protest an unbalanced sound by seeming to hear distortion, beyond what is actually present. Listen to a true spectrum of undistorted highs without sufficient bass support and the sound shrieks, seems piercing and unnatural. (Try any tweeter by itself.) Reproduce a full range of low bass without an equally solid upper range of highs to balance it and the music is unbearably tubby, dull, unrealistic.

So to please the autocratic ear we must compensate for every lack at one end by a weakness at the opposite end and we'll do it deliberately if necessary.

Your ear's judgment of balance, by the way, is always affected by listening room acoustics. Hence your amplifier tone controls (Chapter 15) and the balance controls provided on some speaker systems to make over-all adjustments for room sound.

I've already mentioned the single speaker as the best low-priced unit for music listening—now you may apply the principle of balance to its limitations. If we are to lose some of the tonal spectrum in these speakers, clearly it should be a *balanced loss at both ends*.

The singles, euphemistically called "extended range" (they are much extended in range over earlier models of the same sort), come in many sizes, from three-inch midgets for portable radios and the like all the way up to fifteen-inch monsters. They are limited, every last one of them, but differently limited. Unfortunately, the specifications usually given in the sales pitches do not take this into account.

A published range of, say, "30 to 13,000 cycles" merely means that the speaker does produce *some* sound at both these extremes. Just how much, in proportion to the loud middle tones, is not stated—unless the claim is "flat within 6 db, 30 to 13,000 cycles." It usually isn't, because most singles are not at all flat at the ends. The extreme sounds are almost nonexistent sometimes, though there is barely enough to squeeze out a nice-sounding "range" description! What counts, you see, is where the weakness occurs, in what proportion at the two ends.

A large single speaker, "extended-range" type, is almost certain to "droop" far downward in the higher tones, though it may eke out a bit of response to the very top and so rate as "wide-range." It has what amounts to a built-in tone control, reducing the treble progressively as the sounds go higher—but its bass response is excellent. In short, this type of large speaker is likely to give you seriously unbalanced sound, with plenty of bass and weak highs, unless of course, you reduce the bass drastically to match the sagging treble. An assist from a tweeter is the only proper thing. The large singles persist, just the same, and the reason is probably that many people like the discreetly muffled sound they produce. This, again, is a matter for individual taste. But for good musical listening—conscious listening, not background—I recommend that you avoid the big singles, unassisted by tweeters.

The small singles, on the other hand, those smaller than eight inches, tend to throw the balance in the other direction; they are good in the treble (and make good tweeters) but the bass is deficient. Not recommended, except for extreme space-saving.

(Note, as usual, that most "hi-fi" phonographs and tape recorders use one or more of these very small speakers in relatively tiny enclosures. They provide fairly good balance by "peaking" the bass for a healthy boom in the mid-low region. It isn't faithful but it works, as far as balance is concerned. You can do far better than this with a larger speaker and a separate speaker cabinet.)

And so, by the most cogent logic, we arrive at the happy medium in single-speaker design, the size that tends to droop a bit at both ends, but creates a natural and musical balance if it is given half a chance.

The optimum is probably the ten-inch speaker, but that type is not often made in this country though the Europeans still favor it; in America the best bet for good sound at low cost is the modern eight-inch speaker. The ten-inch will not fit in many available enclosures (though you can cut your own hole or have one cut for you) whereas the eight fits anywhere. So does the twelve-inch—but this size is borderline in the single models; it is more effective with help from a tweeter, either separate or coaxially mounted (below), and that puts you straight into a higher price bracket for the same quality of sound. (The tweeter will give you better range but not necessarily better quality.)

The eight-inch speaker is an extraordinary performer. With newly flexible mountings for long cone excursion and with low resonance (from 70 down to 40 cycles) these little speakers can provide flat bass down to within an octave of the very lowest audible tone, a level that covers all important musical sound. In the highs the eight is excellent too, with a slight droop that nicely balances the bass end. The best section of the eight's response is in that vital area of mid-range highs, the so-called *presence range*, where distortion is most unpleasant, where hi-fi brilliance is largely situated—and where good performance makes for musical transparency in the listening. For this reason, eight-inch speakers are often used as mid-range units in multiple systems. The ten has distinctly better bass, but can be somewhat uneven in the high end. Some famous European models of long standing have been tens—the Wharfedale Super 10/CS/AL (now replaced by a foam-surround model) and the Hartley-Turner 215. They cost a good deal more than the eights, type for type.

Single eight-inch speakers come in a few American and many European brands, most of them designed with maximum low frequency response in mind. That means (a) large cone excursion and (b) low resonance, from 65 cycles down. (Big woofers resonate at as low as 30 cycles or less.) A few eight-inch models are still of the cheap radio and hotel-paging sort with poor bass response but these appear in hi-fi catalogues only as bargain-sale items or radio replacements.

Most of the eights and tens are of European origin (some are from Japan), reflecting the Old World's sober appraisal of musical values and common-sense economy. Many are English—fine brands are Stentorian, Goodmans, Wharfedale. (Tens in these brands, at higher cost.) The Norelco speakers are Dutch, the Kingdom-Lorenz models German. American salesmen will do their best to discourage you from buying a single speaker of this sort. The style, here, is to acquire multiple speaker units with crossovers—woofers, tweeters, mid-range, super-tweeters.

Among low-priced eight-inch bargains are the Quam 8A10X ($11), the Kingdom-Lorenz LP-208 ($20), the GE 850-D ($10), the Lafayette SK-69 (Lafayette Radio, $7). More expensive U.S. models are the Jim Lansing D208 ($26) and D216, the Stephens Tru-Sonic 80FR ($32).

European eights and tens include the Stentorians with cambric cones, the ten, HF 1012U ($19) and the eight, HF 812U ($15); the Wharfedale ten, W10/FSB ($42), is especially good at low volume levels; the eight is the Super 8 FS/AL ($23).

Coax, Triax, Concentric. The single speakers, in all sizes, merge into those which on a single frame offer more than one element to propagate various tonal frequencies. We've already looked at the types which use a single voice coil to move two radiators of sound, the large cone for bass and the dome or protuberance (it has many trade names) in the center for the highs, with an automatic mechanical division of sound between the two. These are the "two-way" speakers of many American lines. When they are further elaborated to include a separate small tweeter, usually a small horn mounted within the larger speaker, we enter the *coaxial* area, though that term has been overwhelmed with so many special names that it scarcely is of use now.

A true coaxial speaker is simple enough to envision. It is two separate speakers, a small tweeter mounted coaxially within a large woofer. The woofer is a cone speaker, the tweeter is either a small cone tweeter or a horn tweeter (below) mounted at the big cone's center. An *electrical* crossover network divides the sound between the two.

A true *triaxial* speaker (the term is a trade name of the Jensen Company but has spread to other brands and other types of speaker) is a triple unit, three separate speakers on the same frame, mounted coaxially. There are two crossover networks, dividing the sound signal three ways. Jensen's large and expensive Triaxial fifteen-inch speaker was the prototype and continues the leading model of this sort. There are few true three-way coaxials—the complications aren't worth it except at the top price levels. Other "triaxials" or "three-way" speakers are of the sort already mentioned, with two speaker elements, one a separate tweeter and the other a combined woofer and mid-range.

All of the larger coaxial and multi-way compound speakers are at one important disadvantage, as compared to the separate woofer and tweeter. The highest tones necessarily come from the center of the speaker, which may have to be placed low down in the room, near the floor. Bass tones are best at that level since they roll out in all directions and are not absorbed by drapes and plush and people's trousers and skirts. But high tones are better at a higher level where they can get out to more solid reflecting surfaces and so fill the room. Hence the usual placement of tweeters at the top end of a large speaker cabinet, the woofer near the floor or even at the rear facing the wall, as in the Electro-Voice phased speaker systems.

Cone vs. Horn. You have seen plenty of horn-type speakers in public address situations—in skating rinks, at ball parks and the like. They are useful and efficient but not always practical for music because the bass response of this curled-up and flared tube arrangement depends mathematically on the length of the tube and the size of the outer opening—and for bottom bass tones that opening must be enormous, the flared tube, even when folded on itself, very long. Horns are practical for high tones since the horn required is small. A horn tweeter for top tones is only six or seven inches long; larger models, extending downward into the middle highs, are still only a foot or two long. But as you go lower the horn gets bigger at a fantastic rate.

The horn, like the cone, is a means of coupling a small voice-coil motion to a large amount of air, getting a grip on air itself. The lower the tones (the slower the vibration), the harder it is to grip air and transfer sound-vibration power to it. The small tweeter and mid-range horns are "driven" by a diaphragm unit much like that in a telephone earpiece; the power unit is called a *driver* and the term is often used as well for a big cone woofer that "drives" a huge folded horn enclosure of the sort found in the larger home speaker systems. The cone speaker is, similarly, called a *direct radiator* when it faces directly into the outside air. (Its rear may be affected by numerous types of special enclosure.) The horn appears actively in two areas, then, as far as home music is concerned—the small tweeter horn and the large furniture-enclosed folded bass horn, driven by a cone speaker.

Many tweeter speakers are cones, built essentially like the larger speakers, but ranging in size from eight inches down to two or three. There is no sharp dividing line between types of cone speakers, as I have said; many models serve nicely either as tweeters, mid-range radiators or, in small systems, as woofers. But there are numerous specially made cone tweeters, all of which are direct radiators though they are usually mounted in some form of baffle (below). Horn tweeters include three ranges, overlapping: the super-tweeter, very small, the small tweeter (2,000 cycles or so upward) and the mid-range horn (from 500 cycles or so up), a fairly large and heavy affair and not cheap.

Generally speaking, cone speakers are cheaper than horns in all these areas. Generally speaking, they sound better, too—for the musical ear, as above explained. Nevertheless, horns for mid-range and tweeter purposes are very popular in this country. They provide the desired brilliance and impact for hi-fi listening, they show off well, enhance the sharpness of sharp sounds, bring extra "presence" to the mid-range. And—again for my ear—they give to music a metallic, tinny sound that I find most unpleasant.

It is clear that this is a generalized account. Horns vary from model to model in their coloration, in the degree of metallic brilliance. Side by side, you will find them surprisingly different—which merely indicates the still-continuing lack of that ultimate fidelity which would make them all sound alike! Nevertheless, I think you can confirm these generalities for yourself if you will do some listening on your own.

You will find, I think, that cone speakers used as tweeters generally have less brilliance, are less impressive on demonstration but in the long run are smoother, easier on the ears and, in the last analysis, more ac-

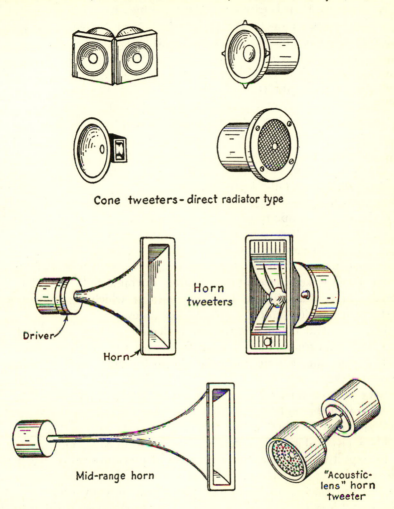

Cone tweeters - direct radiator type

Horn tweeters

Driver

Horn

Mid-range horn

"Acoustic-lens" horn tweeter

curate, more faithful to the original. A vital test of any speaker system in the listening is its obtrusiveness, its transparency to music. Brilliant, horn-type hi-fi sound is obtrusive—often pleasantly so for those who enjoy it. Cone-tweeter sound is less obtrusive, less showy, but it is also more amenable to the musical values that may come through it. You can forget the cone tweeter and concentrate on the music.

The same argument applies to the mid-range speaker, when and if. The mid-range horn is expensive; the mid-range cone speaker is usually a modest, average model, eight-inch or even ten-inch—since the middle range is inherently best to begin with in this type of speaker.

ELECTROSTATIC. A brief look at the new types of speaker, those which are neither horns nor cones in the usual sense. By far the most significant is the electrostatic speaker, usable primarily as a tweeter and mid-range sound-producer. (It must be very large to produce the bottom tones and is difficult to design for the large excursions necessary to push out the low bass.) This speaker is essentially a condenser or capacitor. It generates sound waves directly from two charged, flat conducting "plates" or thin metallic layers separated by a very tiny nonconducting gap, when its high-voltage charge is modulated by the sound signal.

It is an odd property of charged condensers that they can "talk" when subject to the sound-signal's alternating-current fluctuations— they vibrate, to produce sound. You may have heard an ordinary can-type condenser in your amplifier suddenly give forth with faint music when the speaker accidentally became disconnected. This kind of "talk" (in contrast to the big cone speaker which reproduces lows best) is in practice limited to the higher tones.

There are two major electrostatic high-end speakers available today and both are extraordinary. I have lived with the JansZen speaker for several years and it is my preferred choice for music over all standard tweeters; the newer model Pickering Isophase mid-range and treble speaker is also extraordinarily fine in sound, going down lower than the JansZen into the mid-range so that it will operate with a single woofer. (The JansZen does best with a mid-range speaker as well as a woofer.)

These electrostatics are expensive—not far from $200. They are worth it, in respect to that usual tiny increment of precious quality that makes listening better with them. No false brilliance here! Not much, anyhow—a tiny fraction of that which you'll hear in many a horn tweeter. The sound is smooth as silk, or should I say as steam—just listen to the recorded sound of a steam locomotive on one of them if you want realistic reproduction!

Electrostatic tweeters, strangely, are also used in the low-cost "hi-fi" phonographs, the Columbia 360, Philco and many European lines. The basic cost is not necessarily high, but due to problems of impedance and high voltage a separate and compatible electrostatic component speaker is not likely to be cheap. Listen to one if you have a chance. It will at least give you an objective idea of high-quality sound.

RIBBON AND IONIZED AIR. Two other new tweeters, also in the expensive category, use two unconventional principles. The Ionized Air tweeter appears in this country in Electro-Voice's *Ionovac* system, at $150. Inside its narrow horn slot you will actually see the purple glow of ionized gas, which is made to vibrate directly into sound waves. Well worth investigating, if you have the cash. It includes a large power-supply chassis and plenty of high-voltage current.

The *ribbon* tweeter is more widely appreciated in England than hereabouts. It operates on the same principle as the ribbon microphone —a tiny suspended ribbon that lies in a magnetic field and vibrates to the signal current, producing sound. Its quality is very high, its price as usual not very low. You're not likely to run into it in most hi-fi shops.

The *acoustic suspension* speaker is so intimately a matter of enclosure and speaker together that I'll discuss it in the next chapter as an overall system.

TWO-WAY, THREE-WAY, FOUR-WAY SYSTEMS. The coaxial speaker combines two or more separate units upon one frame and on the same axis; the two-way speaker system makes use, in contrast, of two entirely separate speakers, a woofer and a tweeter (sometimes more than one of each), plus the necessary electrical dividing network in a small box, to distribute the highs and lows to each. The three-way system, similarly, has three speakers, adding a mid-range unit plus a dual crossover system to spread the sound three ways instead of two. A four-way system adds still another speaker, often a super-tweeter to take care of the topmost highs that most older ears cannot hear at all. Sometimes the four-way division is spaced so that there is a middle-low and a middle-high speaker, plus the bottom woofer and a top tweeter. In such a system there must be a four-way split of the sound signal and the complex dividing network becomes a very considerable expense in itself.

To complete the picture we must consider the compound speakers already described, which are put to use in all sorts of mutiple-speaker systems—and here we run into another of those linguistic confusions. "Two-way" and "three-way," in present usage, also apply to the one-frame speaker units themselves, those which feature dual-function voice coils (driving two different radiating elements) for a two-way effect. And so we have "two-way" speakers as well as two-way systems with separate speakers.

If I seem to flounder in verbiage here, I am merely reflecting the present state of the speaker art. The best thing to do in all cases is to count the voice coils, count the cones and diffusers and radiators, add up the horns, big and little—and *listen to the sound*. You may find it lovely even at a low price; or you may dislike it intensely, even at the $500 level.

PROMOTION. We can blame a great deal, these days, upon the American system of promotion that sees a good thing and puts it to work—for sales. The intention, as I have said, is to persuade, not to describe. No sooner does an objective term take on some slight merit with the general public than it is snatched up and hitched onto every possible item that might conceivably be sold via its magic. "High Fidelity" itself is the archexample in this field, but practically any other word or phrase that catches on with the public is liable to the same enthusiastic amplification for just as long as it is of any use.

So it is that "coaxial," which has a very favorable sound, and "two-way," which also sounds good, are terms that are now almost indiscriminately used, stretching the basic dual concept to cover virtually any sort of speaker system that can benefit from the terminological boost. Words like these are constantly being upgraded, applied to lesser equipment to give it a lift into seemingly higher areas.

I could quote you dozens of painfully specific examples at this point but I refrain, for reasons of tact. It is not the fault of any one manufacturer after all, but of the entire hi-fi industry and, behind it, the great mass of American selling.

And so I cannot explain to you in words all the hi-fi variables in this area of the loudspeaker—where things are so very fluid at the moment. I have tried, but I can't begin to account sensibly for the existing variations and contradictions, nor can anybody else except in terms of this upgrading sales pressure.

But the names aren't really important—let's remember. Just confusing. Perhaps I need to pep myself up here, as well as you, for it is a nightmare business, this attempt to make sense out of what clearly was never intended to be objectively sensible. We are concerned with the stuff itself and there, as always, I am ever optimistic and full of admiration for the human ingenuity that creates so much of pleasureable and aesthetic value out of electronics and machinery.

SPEAKER "PACKAGES." Inevitably, with so much confusion at hand, the speaker manufacturers have had to take steps to simplify matters for their customers—and for their dealers too. Not in the terminology, which seems to get more complex every year, but in the actual offerings shown in the catalogues and in hi-fi stores. The result is the speaker "package." Like other packages (how salesmen love that word!), these are preselected groupings of components, sold as a lump, the parts ready to be put to work. The price of the package is usually less than the combined prices of the individual speaker components that make it up.

The ultimate package of this sort, to be sure, is the complete speaker system in its enclosure, ready to play. There are plenty of these, too; but they belong in the next chapter. Short of this, the speaker package (speaker assembly minus enclosure) is a useful in-between arrangement, in case you want a multi-way speaker system but are in doubt as to how to choose its parts.

There's no strict rule, but you'll find that most speaker packages of this sort are sold ready-wired, the tweeters, woofers, crossover networks ready to plug together, or furnished with directions for quick assembly. In some lines—not all—the parts are already mounted and wired on a flat board, for direct insertion in a speaker cabinet. This can save you time (no sawing of holes) but the boards are made to fit certain enclosures that, as you might expect, are made by the same manufacturer; they may or may not fit into other models.

There are two common sources for packaged speaker systems. The major manufacturers are one, notably those who offer the numerous and complex models already described. They list a whole series of packages, covering all the various tweeters, woofers and mid-range units. There is much interchangeability; so-and-so package will fit three or four different enclosures and each speaker cabinet will take various speaker packages. Prominent among these is the package that includes the official "insides" of some well-known named complete speaker system—at a budget price, often in conjunction with utility or kit-form enclosures. (See page 168.) You can buy the insides of most of the named models in this form.

The other source of speaker packages, generally at much lower bargain prices, are the mail-order houses. They handle the above packages, but in almost every catalogue they offer several pages of special speaker bargain combinations that are decidedly worth investigating. Many of the components are imports, often the excellent Japanese equipment. (The quality is good; whether you approve of imported goods in competition with our own is up to you to decide.) In addition to numerous inexpensive two-way and three-way systems there are low-priced coaxials, in one piece, assorted dual-cone speakers and plenty of singles—also interesting tweeters.

As usual, keep the geometric disguise in mind when you consider the very low cost of some of these units. Many of them offer really remarkable performance. Listen, if you can, before you buy; but if not, then buy "blind" but with intelligence, using your best judgment as to the type of speaker likely to be acceptable to you, according to your own tastes and budget. If you prefer modest, unspectacular sound, don't buy horn tweeters; if you want full-range, "hi-fi demonstration" effects, stay clear of the simple one-piece speakers.

STEP-UP AND RANGE-EXTENDER. A by-product of the trend toward multi-way speaker systems and package combinations of groups of speakers —woofer, tweeter, mid-range—is the booster kit, from various companies, designed to be added to a simple speaker arrangement to increase its effectiveness and its tonal range. The trade terms vary, of course, but the idea is the same; buy a relatively simple and inexpensive speaker to begin with, then add more to it, in separate units, as your budget allows. Some booster arrangements have been so ingeniously designed that you can add them to an existing speaker system without so much as removing the old equipment. If not quite plug-in, these kits are made as simple as possible. They include all types of speaker from low woofer to high tweeter but in all cases are intended to supplement, not replace the equipment already in use.

The idea is good and, indeed, is no more than a facet of the generally proclaimed virtues of all hi-fi component equipment—that you may add to your system from time to time without throwing out the useful parts you have already acquired. The only trouble is, from the point of view of the music lover, that these kits may not always produce the kind of sound that will best suit your favorite music. Again, it is a matter of taste; but I suggest that an extra forty or fifty dollars for a slight extension of low bass or high highs may—or may not—redound to your greater satisfaction in musical terms. It all depends. Remember that added tonal range is not nearly so important musically as (a) good balance and (b) smooth, even tone quality without harshness.

To aid your thinking on this sort of step-by-step improvement, let me point out to you that every speaker unit, in multi-way speaker arrangements, must be considered from a dual viewpoint. First, its sound quality and, second, the coverage it will have, via the dividing network.

For example, you may be thinking of extending the range of a horn tweeter upward by adding a super-tweeter unit, with its extra dividing network. Consider that this network will divert a good portion of the regular tweeter's range of tones into the super-tweeter unit, changing the over-all tone color of your sound accordingly. The usual small horn tweeter covers the range from about 2,000 cycles (near the top of the piano keyboard) up to the limits of average hearing, beyond 15,000 cycles. This includes most of the vital "presence" range where coloration is most pronounced. Hook up the super-tweeter and the dividing network will divert all tones over about 4,000 cycles to the smaller unit, leaving the regular tweeter with a relatively narrow band of tones to work upon. It may, indeed, be almost superfluous—many woofers can cover the sounds up to 5,000 cycles without too much loss.

As to coverage—don't disturb your musical balance. Instead, aim to improve it, in whatever direction it seems weak—add more top strength or more bass, as the case may be.

There are booster speaker kits to cover every such need, including those which add bottom and top—but no middle—to extend the range of a modest single speaker in both directions. A bass-extender kit naturally involves a fair-sized woofer and requires an enclosure to match. Some booster kits of this type come in their own larger cabinet, designed to be used with a separate medium-sized cabinet to extend the tonal range in both directions, upward and downward.

As always, I recommend to you the cone type of tweeter and midrange unit as generally more musical than corresponding horn-type units; but you must trust your own taste in this as well as you are able. You'll find range-extender units of both types in profusion.

The simplest range-extender units are the small and inexpensive cone tweeters, occasionally with simple dividing networks (allowing for a broad overlapping of coverage—which does no harm); they range in size from two or three inches up to six inches or more in width. In the lowest price range the mail-order houses have interesting values, notably in imported items, often from Japan (which makes extraordinarily good equipment at very low prices).

Lafayette Radio, for example, features a metal-cased cone tweeter at $6; the crossover network costs more—$9; a Danish tweeter is only $4, with a higher-up crossover network for $5; an even higher super-tweeter costs $6. There is a GE five-inch cone tweeter for $8, crossover network $5 more; Sonotone's elliptical cone tweeter is $8.

Better-quality cone tweeters such as the excellent Bozak units sell for $30 for a joined pair ($132 for an array of eight, joined!), the dividing network costing about the same; the Wharfedale Super 3 is $23, network $15; numerous other makes fall in the same range.

None of these should be added to any system that does not already provide full bass power, for proper balance of the additional highs.

Bass extension is possible if your present cabinet will take a larger and heavier speaker; otherwise it involves a new cabinet for a woofer, the old speaker being used as a mid-range unit. An interesting answer to this problem is the Heathkit SS-1B Range-Extending kit ($100), a large fifteen-inch woofer and a small super-tweeter in a modified bass-reflex (rear ducts), with a three-way crossover network included. It complements a smaller Heathkit system (SS-1, $40), the two to be used together; but it should work well with any good eight-inch speaker system.

BIAMPLIFICATION. A new and fancy variation on the multi-way speaker concept is the hi-fi system with two amplifiers—sometimes three—and an *electronic* crossover, a highly specialized amplifier that divides the sound signal between highs and lows, with the crossover point (as described above) variable over a wide range. The amplifiers are standard models, though the one that is used for highs only may be of a lower power rating. Electronic crossovers are increasingly useful and are now available in numerous brands, and in kit form; but the complete two-amplifier or three-amplifier system is probably beyond your interest. It costs plenty.

Electronic crossovers run to about $90—but Heathkit has an electronic crossover kit for only $20—well worth considering, if you wish to experiment with various two-way speaker arrangements, and have two amplifiers.

12

Speaker Enclosures and Systems

The entire preceding chapter was concerned with what amounts to a practical abstraction—the loudspeaker without its enclosure. The unmounted speaker, to be sure, can usually vibrate at the slow speeds necessary for low tones. But it has no traction upon air—it skids, so to speak. Think again of the old-fashioned hand fan as a way to get a push upon air at slow speeds of motion. Without it, your extended palm lacks air traction in the same way as the speaker cone.

The higher the speed of vibration, the easier it is to push air. In the upper range of musical tones, an open, unmounted loudspeaker does a good job, and even a diaphragm-type driver unit will "squeal" out high tones minus its horn.

Moreover, high tones tend to travel straight ahead in beams. Low tones spread out, to fill a room and all its spaces. Thus the higher sounds propagate without trouble from both sides of a cone speaker, but principally the front; their beamlike travel makes unlikely any clash between those from the rear and from the front.

But the larger, slower-vibrating tones in the bass spread immediately around the edges of the unmounted speaker from both front and rear—and meet head on. The result is cancellation. No sound. At best, air is simply pumped back and forth around the edge, like the coffee around the spoon that stirs it.

These effects—beaming of high tones, cancellation of the free-flowing low tones—increase or decrease according to the vibration speed. The higher the tones, the greater their tendency to beam straight out. The lower the pitch (the slower the vibration), the more the speaker waves tend to cancel each other around the edge of the cone—and the

harder it is to get hold of the air in the first place. You can understand, then, that an unmounted speaker sounds thin and tinny. It has
no low bass at all; its power to produce bass drops off steadily as pitch
goes down, until it can send out no sound at all at the bottom.

The *loudspeaker enclosure*, then, is only superficially a piece of furniture, though you may feel otherwise in terms of your own living room.
Its primary purpose is to couple the loudspeaker to the air for the
lower ranges of tone—the highs take care of themselves. An ideal enclosure allows the speaker to send out all tones, to the very bottom, in
precisely their original relative strength, and this has been fairly well
accomplished today, not only in the very large enclosures of the horn
type but also in such new small enclosures as the Acoustic Suspension
type, to be described below. Smaller enclosures, according to this ideal,
fail in two general ways: (a) The bass tones fall off toward the bottom,
with virtually no response in the lowest audible octave or so. (b) There
is an uneven, "peaked" bass response, giving a sense of full bass at the
expense of a boomy, sluggish quality. Nevertheless, this last type of
sound though technically a serious distortion is popular with many people. It is still widely used for juke box tone, and provides an important
musical factor, that of good tonal balance (page 139), even though the
lowest bass is missing. In terms of balance a "boomy" and inadequate
bass can stand in for a smoother, deeper, truer equivalent, and often
does.

Behind the dozens and dozens of enclosures (and complete speaker
systems) available today there are only a few really basic differences in
enclosure design; all the rest is elaboration in detail, or in ingenious
compromise to make the best of practical needs in the home situation.
A look at the basic types is enlightening. Principal types of enclosure
are: the flat baffle and the open-back enclosure, the infinite (totally
enclosed) baffle, the folded horn and the bass reflex; these last variously modified and combined with other types in vast numbers of
recent enclosures.

FLAT BAFFLE AND OPEN-BACK. A somewhat formidable list of names, I
admit. Perhaps the best way to explain them is to use plain logic.
There are two intentions in the speaker enclosure. One, as already mentioned, is to couple the speaker to the surrounding thin air, for a solid
push at low frequencies. An allied purpose is simply to keep the back
side and the front apart—so that the emitted bass waves will not be

able to cancel each other. The very simplest separator, still an effective type of "enclosure," is the *flat baffle*, no more than a big piece of board or wallboard with a hole in it for the speaker. With the speaker mounted in a solid wall such as this, the bass tones from the rear and front are kept apart; the larger the board, the lower are the tones that are separated. An *infinite baffle* is one in which the back and front are entirely separated, as when the speaker is mounted in a wall between two rooms, or in a wholly sealed box that swallows up the rear sound inside. More of this later.

It's surprising how much a simple baffle of the flat sort can do for good sound—though fancier enclosures can do more. In the early hi-fi days I used to delight in removing people's speakers from their phonographs and mounting them in big Celotex squares—the improvement in sound was always gratifying. The *open-back cabinet*, familiar in millions of radios and phonographs of the past, is simply a flat baffle with its sides folded in. Though I have run it down elsewhere in this book (there being better things available), I'll have to stand up for its basic adequacy in bringing out the best part of a simple loudspeaker's potential.

If you stand a flat baffle in an unused fireplace you add a gorgeous resonating chamber that may bring out positively unearthly low-bass effects. That was an old trick, before the fancy modern enclosures came along.

HORNS. All of these baffle variants share the simple intent to separate front and back bass waves and so allow the speaker's natural push to radiate bass as well as it can, without cancellation effects. A far greater degree of bass-range coupling to the air can be had via the *horn*, an expanding tube that flares from the speaker itself out to a very wide exit—the wider it is, the lower the bass effectiveness. But for bottom bass an ideally shaped horn would have to be positively elephant-like in size. It might be twenty or more feet long, its opening big enough to walk into without bending your head! Such horns have been built by extreme enthusiasts, but they are not for you and me. However, the horn is wonderfully amenable in one special respect—it can be folded upon itself and still maintain its acoustical characteristics. (Witness all of the brass instruments in the orchestra.) And it can be compromised usefully in the shape to almost any degree.

Therefore the horn is often put to service for a big-bass speaker enclosure, in its folded-up form, inside a piece of furniture that is, perforce, of "reasonable" living room size—reasonableness being strictly a matter of opinion! The horn shape, within the home furnishing, is a matter for highly ingenious carpentry design; often there are two horns, one to each side of the speaker itself. The speaker may be totally enclosed in the furniture, facing inward or downward; or it may face outward into the room with a horn system at the rear—a rear-loading horn is the common term. (Loading in the electrical and mechanical sense of putting-to-work, harnessing; in loading the horn you attach it or couple it to the air.)

Generally speaking, a good horn enclosure of fairly large size should increase the bass range of its speaker by something like a full octave, as compared to a flat or infinite baffle arrangement.

The principle of the horn appears in three rough forms in our present speaker enclosures, each representing a stage of compromise between the giant ideal horn and the much smaller practical piece of furniture.

1. Semi-ideal horn enclosures, quite large, folded, often making use of a room corner placement with the walls as an extension of the horn itself. The prototype of this kind of construction is the famous Klipschorn, a fairly large and expensive three-way system that has been produced in succeeding versions for many years.

2. Smaller compromise horn enclosures, less efficient in the very lowest bass but still excellent in the over-all ability to propagate the bass range of sound. These range through a wide variety of models, including many designed on the Klipsch principle (using the walls as extensions). They are far from small in size, as present speaker enclosures go. Some are of the popular six-sided "cornerless corner" type with sawed-off rear sides so that the box will fit either in a corner or against a side wall. (The rear of the speaker box is three-sided.) Some quite small horn-type enclosures are built, for use with eight-inch and twelve-inch speakers, the Cabinart Klipsch-designed KR-5, for instance, or the E-V Baronet.

3. The horn principle, which is no more than an ever-widening duct leading away from the speaker's front or back, is often incorporated into other types of enclosure as an added inducement for the speaker to emit good bass. Horn loaded is the usual term; often it is no more than a very slight channeling of the speaker's rear sound; but on the theory that every little bit helps, it is a good idea in principle. (Advertising is likely to make more of this sort of feature than is warranted, horns being much in the public eye.)

BASS REFLEX. Before there were commercial horn-type speaker enclosures available, the bass reflex was the supreme hi-fi speaker enclosure, the prime method of encouraging a speaker to give more bass than it would in a simple flat or infinite baffle. Because this enclosure can easily be made to produce a boom or peak in the bass (and has been deliberately so designed, for many a year) its reputation has suffered recently among hi-fi people, who favor the flat, true bass response of the larger horn enclosure, giant or no. But the idea behind the bass reflex is far too good—and much too usefully flexible—to die; it is with us today more widely than ever before but largely in modified and disguised form, both for better bass response in very small cabinets and for new sales appeal.

A bass-reflex box is basically a closed-in cabinet with the speaker mounted conventionally in front and an extra hole or *port*, placed usually below or to one side of the speaker itself. The rear bass waves of the speaker are directed outward through this port, to reinforce rather than cancel the front waves, thereby making use of both sides of the cone's air-push. The port itself is of a size that tunes the whole box as bass resonator, at a frequency very near the bottom of the speaker's capability.

It was Helmholtz, a long while ago, who investigated this type of sounding box and showed that an enclosed space with a duct to the outside could be tuned to various frequencies simply by changing the size and length of the duct. A gallon jug and a Coca-Cola bottle blown across the mouth are examples of this sort of resonator (nontunable) as is the bass croak of the bullfrog, who tunes his duct to a very low pitch.

Every loudspeaker also has a natural reasonance point in the low range. (Tap the cone and you can hear its low pitch.) At this pitch, other things being equal, there is a natural hump in its response—an area of louder bass; below it the speaker's response falls off very rapidly to nothing. The bass reflex, rightly used, is tuned to place its own extra hump (the resonant pitch of the box) just below that of the speaker's, to bolster the falling response. Together, the two humps in the response curve combine to make a reasonably flat plateau—unboomy and with extended bass. Differently tuned, the bass reflex can cause a double-sized hump—and plenty of boom—by coinciding with the speaker's resonance point, à la juke box. A tuned pitch above the speaker's resonance gives a boom in a region of middle-low bass that is potent in its effect—this is one way in which the many small "hi-fi" speaker systems of today achieve their surprisingly big but boomy, thumpy bass.

A conscientious bass-reflex maker designs his box for a particular speaker; or he provides a means for changing the size of the port, and so the box's tuning, to match various speakers. But that sort of painstaking, handcraft approach is too much trouble for us today. Bass reflexes are generally made on the basis of an average speaker and you will take your chances, for boominess or flat bass response, depending on the speaker you use. (If you make a good deal of fuss, you can determine the speaker's resonance and also that of the box, and it is possible to alter the box for best response.)

The modified bass-reflex enclosures come in more forms than you can shake a stick at—and many of them are in the complete speaker category, the speaker already built in and the whole permanently closed and secure from curious eyes like mine. It is hardly possible to go into much detail, so great is the variety of semi-bass-reflex, semi-horn enclosures on the market. For what it is worth, I mention several special bass-reflex categories. One is the medium-sized cabinet in which (a) the port is made up of various smaller holes, or slots—the *distributed port* principle; or (b) where a port opening is masked by some species of heavy fibrous resistant material, an *acoustic resistance* (ARU). Both of these arrangements offer smoother bass response than the plain bass-reflex enclosure by spreading out the cabinet resonance to cover a larger (and less humpy) area of bass reinforcement. A variant of this type is found in the Bradford Perfect Baffle, a small "swinging door" mounted in an opening, to relieve inside pressure.

Another general area of modified reflex enclosure design is found in many of the small space-saver enclosures, often with tricky modifications to suppress boominess—or even to create it. A big boom will pass for bass when true low bass response is impossible. Hi-fi ears don't like it, but the small-box boom at least provides for the vital musical balance between highs and lows that is even more essential than flat response, as we've already seen.

Still another type of modification on generally bass reflex lines is now increasingly important, the *ducted port* principle. Jensen's *Bass Ultraflex* enclosures are excellent examples, but others use it as well. In this type of enclosure structure the inside space is opened out, either to the sides or the bottom, by a flat slot or duct, occasionally by a round tube (University's Ultra-Linear enclosures).

To be sure, this smacks of the horn principle and it takes only a slight widening slant to the path the sound will take on its way out for this to be classified as horn loading. But the duct, via the old Helmholtz principle, still rates as a tuning device for the enclosure's inside space and to the extent that the hollow is a resonant chamber it is still a bass reflex. A tuned duct instead of a tuned hole or port. (The hole is a duct, but a very short one.) There are suggestions of this ducted opening in many enclosures. The R-J's connection from back to front is of this sort—but there the entire duct system is inside the box. (See p. 160.)

(This is another of those bewildering "if and but" descriptions, yet as usual it simply illustrates the trend in today's hi-fi toward ingenious combinations of various principles, a "juggling" of factors for a tricky and effective result in terms of sound. It's good for the ears, if bad for the eyes and the mind.)

INFINITE (TOTALLY ENCLOSED) BAFFLE. The *infinite baffle* is a fine means of promoting boomless response by throwing out the baby with the bath—killing the entire back wave from the speaker cone's rear by bottling it up inside. No opening. In such a system the front radiation is all you hear and the speaker's efficiency is correspondingly reduced, for less volume. But the endless complications of interactions between front and rear are entirely removed and life for the infinite baffle designer would be simple if it were not for one further trouble—that a totally enclosed box acts as a compression chamber, the air behind the speaker resisting springily against the cone's inward and outward motion. You may have noticed a similar effect when you try to slam an automobile door closed with all the other openings shut tight; it bounces back, or if it closes there is an unpleasant pressure wave against the ears of any passengers inside.

With air compression holding it back, the speaker distorts; the smaller the box, the "harder" the air resistance and the worse the distortion. Therefore a totally enclosed box must be quite large, with copious padding inside to help swallow the back wave. The larger the box, the "softer" the air pillow. (You'll note that bass reflex and horn enclosures both avoid this problem via their openings to the outside.)

Nevertheless, some excellent speaker systems employ infinite baffle arrangements, with various sound- and pressure-absorbing systems within the cabinet.

The *Boffle* (below) is in effect an infinite baffle. The *Sonotone* all-cone Model 220 complete speaker system ($200) is a coaxial speaker in a totally enclosed baffle with special acoustical damping inside.

R-J. Several important developments in small speaker enclosure design have emerged in recent years straight out of this very anomaly—that a small infinite baffle box puts too much springy air pressure on one side of a speaker cone. If the cone could be "loaded" with some sort of equal pressure *on both sides*, distortion would disappear, yet bass response might be greatly improved at the bottom frequencies. And the box would no longer have to be big—that was a major thought.

The first of these new systems, the first deliberately to strike out for big true bass in a really small space, was the *R-J enclosure*, still widely sold for mounting speakers in a space not much larger than their own dimensions. The R-J is patented but its novelty was not so much in the mechanism itself, I would say, as in the enterprising change of attitude that conceived of the need for good speaker performance in a *small* space—far smaller than had been common with earlier speaker mountings, except at a gross compromise.

The R-J enclosure is related to the bass reflex in its use of a tuned resonant enclosure, but it is radically different in that this air space is *in front of* the speaker, which is wholly enclosed inside the box. The front side of the cone is no longer out in free air but must push against a confined body of air, with a carefully calculated small duct opening to the outside. Now the crux of this is that with the front of the cone thus loaded, the rear can take much more pressure from confined air—and so the size of the box can be radically reduced. Equal pressure or resistance on *both* sides of the cone and, consequently, low distortion.

Ideally the R-J rear could be entirely enclosed, an infinite baffle, with the front pressure of the tricky new air space and its duct nicely equalizing the back-side resistance against the cone's motion. Actually, in order to use the back waves too, there is a further internal connection that brings the cone's rear sound forward through an inside duct space to join the front sound, a sort of inner bass reflex. The entire sound emerges through the single small duct, oddly shaped in a diamond-like pattern.

Other types of small box, necessarily avoiding the R-J patented principle, nevertheless were soon able to produce good sound from small cabinets using variously modified horn and bass reflex arrangements. Once the small-cabinet idea caught on, ingenuity was lavished on the necessary compromises. Though I still prefer the R-J to most others of

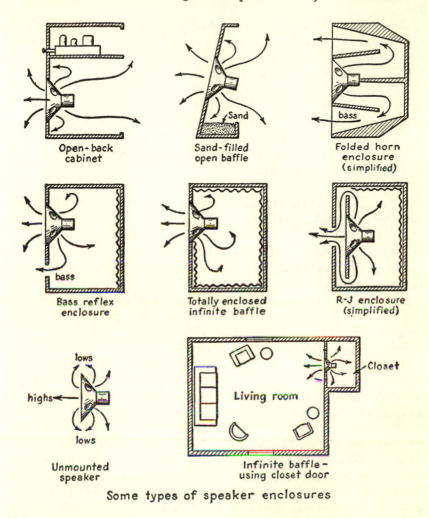

Open-back
cabinet

Sand-filled
open baffle

Folded horn
enclosure
(simplified)

Bass reflex
enclosure

Totally enclosed
infinite baffle

R-J enclosure
(simplified)

Unmounted
speaker

Infinite baffle -
using closet door

Some types of speaker enclosures

the separate cabinets (it is now more sturdily constructed than were the earlier models), I'm the first to admit that the dozens of others do generally a good job, aided by the improved new small speakers that have been tailored especially to make the most of small enclosures. The whole vast movement, toward small space-saving hi-fi enclosures, was set rolling by R-J, back in the early stages of the hi-fi expansion, and now is burgeoning in the complete speaker area (below).

Several years later, the small speaker system principle was carried to a theoretical extreme in a still more radical invention, the AR acoustic suspension speaker. This one was launched not as a space saver *per se* but as a small speaker system that *had to be small*, just as the folded horn is inherently large; it invited competition from the largest and most expensive systems on the market—and it sold (and sells) for a healthy price, about $180. (The R-J enclosures, minus speaker, range from about $50 down to less than $30.) But the AR-1 and its successors, including the recent KLH line, are complete speaker systems and so belong in the next section.

BOFFLES, SAND-FILLED, SPREAD-V. There are a good many other special types of speaker enclosures, minus the speaker, which are of interest but can't be gone into in detail. The long-time *boffle* of Mr. H. A. Hartley, complementing the equally sturdy Hartley 215 single speaker, is an interesting example of another solution to the problem of the infinite baffle. The boffle—why it is called that I could not tell you—is a kind of labyrinth enclosure that, in a relatively small space, is able to present to the back of the speaker cone what amounts to an infinite baffle of large size, creating virtually no distortion. A soft air-pillow, to match the free air on the ouside.

Another Englishman, G. A. Briggs, is the designer of a long series of interesting enclosures many of which stress a point that is usually avoided with care in this country, a solid cabinet structure, immune to spurious vibration.

Mr. Briggs, of course, is entirely right; but heavy cabinet construction costs money and we don't like it. Most of our cabinets, alas, are of relatively light plywood and in many cases there are thin panels that set up buzzing vibrations, or move with the speaker cone to produce serious boominess. Here is an excellent reason, by the way, to acquire an expensive speaker enclosure; it is usually built of heavy wood, thick to begin with and solidly braced at all angles.

The *sand-filled* enclosure seems a bizarre idea at first (and Briggs once was supposed to have imported British sand for his American demonstration!), but it very simply renders an enclosure solidly immovable and unresonant through the vibration-damping weight of a body of loose sand. Solid concrete has been used for similar purposes in some of the more fanatical home-built speaker enclosures, but sand is better because it is totally unresonant; it cannot possibly vibrate and so is able by sheer weight to kill any sort of vibration that reaches it. Let the speaker and the air do the vibrating, not the cabinet. The Briggs sand-filled enclosures are used now in complete, ready-to-play, three-way speaker systems, open-back.

Still another type of special speaker box is the Karlson enclosure, on sale already for a good many years. It is a simple cabinet with an odd spreading V opening in front, behind which is the speaker. The principle is again that of a spreading-out of the bass resonance of the cabinet and speaker; apparently the V opening acts like an infinite number of ports tuned to an infinite number of pitches; the result is claimed to be a smooth coupling of the speaker to air right down to the lowest tones it can handle—the same claim as that of the ARU acoustic resistance unit, above. I haven't actually tried a Karlson, but the fact that it has been sold year after year in the face of the presently growing competition is evidence of good performance.

Other special enclosures continue to appear—but enough. With this much as a background you will be able to absorb the impact of any conceivably newer speaker enclosure without distress!

MULTI-WAY SYSTEM. You'll notice that I have made no mention of woofers, tweeters and mid-range units in connection with these many types of enclosures. The reason is twofold. First, the primary need for a speaker enclosure is to produce good bass—and this involves only the bass-producing speaker, whether woofer or full-range type. I have implied in all the foregoing discussion that the speakers mentioned were bass-producers first of all. Secondly, in most cabinets there is now some provision for the installation of tweeters and, in many cases, for mid-range speakers as well, notably in the larger horn systems. In smaller speaker boxes the tweeter units, if any, are mounted directly on the front baffle board near the larger speaker—sometimes there are holes precut, more often you cut your own hole or have it cut. In larger enclosures there is often a shelflike separate section at the top, usually hidden behind the grille cloth, in which the tweeter and/or mid-range speakers may be mounted.

Remember that speakers for high tones need no more than a small-size and very simple enclosure or baffle. It is helpful to mount the tweeter where it won't be involved in the larger bass vibrations of the woofer proper—hence the isolated separate shelf section in some enclosures. But the same isolation may be had simply by placing the tweeter outside the enclosure, loose in its own small mounting. (Even a cardboard box of small dimensions will do for a cone tweeter mounting. A horn tweeter can be mounted flush with any convenient outer surface.)

A mid-range cone speaker needs a certain amount of baffling but, again, since it does not deal with the crucial low-bass area it needs no special treatment. The simplest sort of small baffle will do, to separate the front from the back enough to keep the middle-low tone from canceling out around the edge of the cone. A foot or so of baffle area is usually enough.

Spend your energy, then, on the bass requirements; let this determine your primary choice of speaker enclosure. The treble will take care of itself more or less, in whatever way seems most convenient or decorative.

ANONYMOUS. After all of this, I must point out to you that a very large proportion of the good-looking small speaker enclosures—and many of the very good-looking bigger and more expensive models (often with names)—are completely anonymous as far as their insides are concerned. So are the "polycabinets" for speaker and assorted equipment now widely sold.

"Sturdily constructed enclosure designed for eight-inch speakers," says one ad, and the picture shows a handsome little box with a grille cloth front. What sort of enclosure? Not a word. And there is no "expert" that I know of in a position to go poking his fingers into the hundreds of such enclosures available today, in order to find out!

Mostly, this anonymity is perfectly honest; the makers increasingly prefer not to load you down with statistics and long words. It is possible that a few anonymous-type speaker cabinets hide features that are better kept hidden—not from you, but from those who might smell patent infringements. I am suspicious of some of these enclosures myself, but I am aware that as far as you are concerned, this is not an ethical problem. Let the industry police itself, if there are infringements. Mostly, the new anonymous cabinets turn out to be just the usual and generally quite useful modified bass-reflex systems (look for the port, or ports) with nothing to hide but the name. But with no outside information to go on there's no way for you to judge values, except in the salesroom—and there you should surely ask for an explanation in detail of any enclosure whose operation isn't clear to you. Look at it, *look in it.*

There were no generally available modest-sized, good-looking enclosures of this sort a few years ago. Now there are hundreds of them. Anonymous or no, they are uniformly superior to any and all open-back cabinets of the sort we used to use and, frankly, I think that as a breed they offer an amazingly fine sort of home component utility, to suit the limited space requirements of the average musical family.

READY TO PLAY

The complete speaker system, ready to play, is the big news in the hi-fi world today and the best promise for its future, as well as the simplest way to hi-fi satisfaction for you. In spite of these many pages of analysis concerning speaker parts, I'm heartily in favor of this new trend. It is technically good for sound and, surprisingly, it doesn't cost much extra.

Buying a ready-to-play speaker, I hasten to suggest, isn't at all like buying a complete ready-made "hi-fi," in case you think I am about to desert my own cause. The separate complete speaker system is still a component in itself, assembled from subconponents as an amplifier is made out of tubes and knobs and hookup wire. As a component, it offers you all the familiar advantages of the breed. Quality-wise, it is far ahead of the speaker sections in most "hi-fis" and costs less, sound for sound. It is more versatile, comes in more forms, shapes, sizes, types, and in common with other forms of high fidelity component equipment is reasonably faithful to the detailed specifications its manufacturers provide, concerning the inner elements and the performance.

Moreover, you'll find that the complete component speaker system in this ready-to-play form doesn't cost much more than the sum of its component parts or their equivalent, bought separately—in some cases it actually costs less. You can think of it as in effect another of the many "package" items in hi-fi, a selected list of components chosen by the manufacturer or dealer and sold as a unit, assembled or ready to plug together. The package deal, as we've seen in other areas, saves time and cash for the dealer and doubtful decisions on your part by deliberately limiting your choice. As with other hi-fi elements, you may have the full range of choice if you wish, strictly à la carte. But if you want you can take the dealer's choice and buy a package, table d'hôte.

(Why not whole hi-fi systems, assembled from named components? That is the ultimate trend—but see Chapter 19.)

Complete speaker systems are hardly new. For many years there have been such systems available though mainly in the larger and more expensive types. Large speaker systems have been sold for years by such reputable firms as Altec, Stephens, Jim Lansing, Jensen, not to mention the leading firms in the multi-way speaker field, University and Electro-Voice. Even in the professional field there have been notable complete speaker systems, ready to play. One in particular, RCA's LC1A system that houses the well-known Olsen fifteen-inch coaxial in a matched bass-reflex enclosure, has been around for many years. You will still find it in dozens of professional radio studios and recording halls (even Columbia Records uses this RCA equipment!)—but it is typical of the rigid conventions in our commercial world that RCA has never sold this model outside the strictly professional area.

The hi-fi demand, then, is the thing that has changed, not hi-fi itself. And this change is clearly occurring in the hi-fi buyer. "He" is more numerous now than he used to be, much less the gadgeteer, more the plain home owner—often the plain music lover. He is likely in the aggregate to be ready to accept more packaged equipment than in the past, to take more packaged advice. He is more interested in the sound of hi-fi than in its equipment; he'll buy it in lumps, wholes, because they are more convenient and do not force him into uncertainties and doubtful decisions.

Nobody can object to legitimate uncertainty on the part of the intelligent music lover—we all can use advice when it turns out to be honestly, helpfully constructive. The trouble with sales advice, well meant or no, is that it leads to false simplification and is small comfort in the long run. This package idea can be carried a lot too far—for your ultimate interest. Don't go all the way and buy a plain, utterly simple "hi-fi"! But, on the other hand, do take a look at the excellent simplification we are now discussing, the ready-to-play packaged speaker system.

COMPARATIVE COSTS. Your first inquiries into complete speaker systems will probably show up some higher prices than you had expected. Think twice before you wince. First, the speaker package includes both the enclosure and the speaker (or speakers) inside, plus dividing networks and the rest, the whole ready-installed. Second, the speaker is furniture-finished, which costs money wherever you buy it.

In separately sold speaker cabinetry you have your choice of unfinished or finished wood—part of the generally wide flexibility of the separate-unit system. In the ready-to-play packaged speaker system you do not (except for an occasional dull-black "utility finish"). Virtually all of them are intended to be good-looking, as is. The difference in cost is easy to illustrate. A recent utility bass-reflex cabinet in unfinished wood (Cabinart) was $39 audiophile net. Its finished equivalent, exactly the same in tonal performance, was $57—which gives you an idea of the cost even of the most economical kind of furniture finishing.

As a matter of fact there is plenty of open and honest comparison available if you are interested, often directly between the various items sold by a single manufacturer. Most of the larger American speaker companies, and some European firms too, now offer their basic lines of equipment in three different ways, with the components specifically named so that comparisons can be made easily enough:

A. *Unassembled separate components*—speakers, dividing networks, enclosures, these last often given fancy names.

B. *Assembled complete speaker systems*, ready-to-play, usually with names.

C. *Semiassembled*, the major components of the above named systems offered separately as subpackages. The speaker packages, used in the complete systems (B), are often mounted on a board ready to slip into an enclosure.

As always, there is a greater choice is the separate components (A and C). Thus there is often a utility or kit-form alternative cabinet as well as the "name" cabinet. (But you can't get this in complete ready-to-play form.) And there is also frequent choice of other speaker arrays, packaged, that will fit into the named cabinet—either cheaper or more expensive. (Again, not available in the ready-to-play form.) According to the very intention of the complete packaged speaker—simplification—these multiple choices are excluded from it.

Plenty of complete speaker systems do not have direct catalogue component alternatives and so can't be so easily compared, section by section, with the equivalent in separately bought parts. Indeed, a good many—among the best—are genuinely one-piece, the speaker and enclosure designed as a unit, the parts unavailable separately. The acoustic suspension speakers, for example, (below) could not be sold in parts even if sales policy demanded it; neither the enclosures nor the speakers can be used with other units. The enclosures of these systems are factory sealed and cannot be opened. In such cases you must judge the speaker system on the merits of its sound, as a complete unit, and as far as I am concerned this is the way things should be.

But comparisons are instructive, if only to give a concrete picture of the cost relationships between component parts and packaged whole speaker systems. I've thought it worth while to pick one such system, arbitrarily, as a specific example of these relationships. The actual prices are not important and may change; the component details also will change. But the general relationships will probably endure, and they apply to many another speaker system.

1. Jensen "Concerto" complete speaker system, assembled and ready to play (B, above):................................. $180
2. "Concerto" enclosure, sold separately (C, above): $80
3. KT-22 speaker kit (used in "Concerto"), sold separately (C, above): $73
4. The two sections, unassembled:......................... $153
5. KT-22 components, sold separately (A, above):
     P12NL woofer $37
     RP102 horn tweeter   29
     A204 dividing network   13
     ST901 balance control   5

KT-22 components, unassembled: total.................. $84
6. Alternative utility enclosure, kit-form: $39
7. Dress-up kit (finished top, bottom, wraparound grille cloth) for same: $36
8. KT-22 speaker kit, plus utility kit enclosure:................ $112
9. KT-22 speaker kit, utility kit enclosure, and dress-up kit:...... $148

If you will study these figures you'll find some strange—but not unexpected—things. Notice that the kit-form cabinet, in this case made by a different company (Cabinart) for Jensen, costs only half as much as the regular "Concerto" cabinet, finished; but the dress-up kit brings its cost up higher than the "Concerto" model by a couple of dollars. In effect, the cost of dressing up the utility model equals the price of a ready-finished cabinet—which is reasonable enough.

Also note that the separate parts of the "Concerto" speaker kit, the K-22, actually cost more than the package K-22 itself, prewired and ready to install. That illustrates rather concisely the fact that packages save the dealer time and money. This kit is not mounted on a board.

The complete ready-to-play system, to be sure, costs the most, $180 as compared to $153 for its two sections bought separately, unassembled. But the installation of the four-speaker units in the cabinet is likely to cost you considerable time and/or money. That could well account, in your own mind, for the $27 difference in cost, assuming everything else to be identical.

Finally, note that there is just one "Concerto" complete package system, without alternatives or substitutes (except a super-tweeter "step-up" kit that can be added for $44). But in the separate forms you have three cabinet choices ranging from the $39 utility model, unadorned, to the $80 regular "Concerto" enclosure, finished. And the speaker kit, the KT-22, will fit a number of other Jensen enclosures, not to mention dozens of enclosures made by other firms; there are alternative Jensen speaker kits that will fit into the "Concerto" cabinet —and so will virtually any other speaker assembly based on a twelve-inch woofer, of any make. The possibilities become astronomical in number, the choice is bewildering! The KT-22 at $73, just to follow up a few more of Jensen's own offerings, can be replaced by a cheaper kit, the KT-23 at $43, in the same enclosures; three different Jensen "step-up" kits can be installed, to expand speaker performance. Alternatively, these two speaker kits, KT-22 and KT-23, will fit into three regular Jensen enclosures and two kit-form enclosures—but enough!

These endless alternatives are typical of component flexibility. The prices are roughly comparable to the price structure found in other major lines of speakers and enclosures and you can apply the general setup here to other makes with some confidence. I can't vouch for every complete system on the market but, for example, you can assume that a complete speaker ready to play at $185 should stand comparison with a component-assembled system costing about $160 in a finished cabinet, not counting the assembling. You can expect a greater difference at the higher price levels (thanks to expensive finish and décor), a smaller difference at the lower price levels. Most bottom-priced complete systems, from $30 to $70 or so, can compete directly with their equivalent component parts in cost and sometimes actually undercut them. If you buy a $1,000 speaker package, you'll probably be adding hundreds of dollars to your cost for the privilege of owning a ready-to-play goliath!

It remains for us to look at a few of the special systems that have appeared in this new area of the ready-to-play speaker, those which in one way or another are more than just packaged and assembled components. Among them are some of the best bargains in musical sound for the music listener. It isn't possible to be comprehensive—new developments are appearing all the time and new twists on the old ones. Yet there are a number of well-established types that I can sample for you usefully.

ACOUSTIC SUSPENSION. I've already mentioned the *acoustic suspension* type of speaker, originally developed and sold by Acoustic Research, Inc. as the "AR" speakers and now licensed to other manufacturers as well. AS is the proper short term for the general breed.

The AS speaker is the ultimate extension of the trend that began with the R-J enclosure (page 160), the hunt for means by which better bass response could be obtained from small cabinets. The AS system is a brilliant variant upon the old infinite or totally enclosed baffle principle (page 159). A special speaker cone makes use of that very springiness of compressed air, in a small enclosed space, to provide the basic restoring force that brings the speaker cone back to its centered position when it is pushed and pulled by the voice coil. The actual operation isn't easy to put into nontechnical language, but you may think again of an automobile (I used the enclosed space of a car body as an analogy to the infinite baffle's "hard" air pillow) and compare the AS to the new air springs used on many automobiles and buses. Replace the loudspeaker's less elastic, more distortion-prone spring material— the stiff cone, the complex mounting at the voice coil and at the outer rim—with a springy pillow of hard, elastic air. That is the basic AS idea. Its special speaker is relatively limp and springless in itself, but can by this very token be made compliant and capable of very long piston-like movements forward and back. The air behind the cone, inside the box enclosure, is sealed tight—no ports, no slots, no ducts— and exerts its full elasticity to hold the cone at its dead-center position even with the most extreme "excursions" forward and back. The most brilliant result of this approach is that the AS speaker box *had to be small*; it was not a compromise to save space. The nature of the air pillow is determined directly by the size of the enclosure; the AS system requires the air stiffness provided by a small box, heavily braced and very solid.

The bass response of the AR-1 model, the original, was far ahead of any other system of even roughly comparable size and outperformed many a speaker system of very much larger dimensions. It still does, though some engineering opinion seems to feel that a really big horn system still produces slightly better response in the lower and middle ranges. Given the small size, the acoustic suspension speaker is unbeatable in sheer bass response.

I must as usual point out that very low bass is not an absolute necessity for musical listening. Nor is bass distortion, including false "boomy" sound, necessarily distressing to the musical ear. There are countless present speaker systems, of all sorts, that do not provide quite the low undistorted bass possible from the patented acoustic suspension principle—or, alternatively, from fairly large systems of the more expensive sort. But the difference clearly has not been great enough to drive them out of favor. Good bass from the musical viewpoint is possible via many different ingenious combinations of speaker enclosure and speaker. Remember that poor bass response does not hurt the ear—whereas distorted top highs and, especially, mid-range highs, are distinctly unpleasant. Nevertheless—the acoustic suspension speaker systems offer top values in low-end sound for the music listener who wants no huge and cumbersome speaker system in his home.

Note that the acoustic suspension principle applies to bass tones only. As in other kinds of enclosure, the treble is taken care of independently by a tweeter, either built in or independent. One of the musical advantages of the AR speakers is a natural and unobtrusive cone-tweeter sound, good for musical listening, and the same with KLH.

A possible disadvantage is the relatively low efficiency. The speakers need plenty of amplifier driving power. With too few watts you may actually overload the amplifier during loud passages—the blasting sound is not in the speaker itself, but in the amplifier. A more powerful amplifier will take care of this.

For maximum low bass, the AR-1 speaker needs at least a 20-watt amplifier, even for modest musical requirements; for hi-fi demonstration sound it should have more, preferably not less than 50 watts to give best transient clarity and definition in violently strong signals. The AR-2, with less bass, requires less power.

The AR-1 complete speaker has a cone tweeter, is about $180. The AR-2, almost the same size (a smaller speaker inside), is about $100, somewhat less for a utility-finish model; it also uses a cone speaker as tweeter. In both there is provision for balancing the highs to room acoustics. The AR-1W is the woofer unit alone, in enclosure. The AR-1 was widely sold with the JansZen electrostatic tweeter, operates best with its own tweeter at the reduced-highs position, to bridge the mid-range area. (AR-1W not recommended with the JansZen.)

KLH acoustic suspension speakers are a newer offshoot of the AR development, licensed. The KLH line covers a wider variety of types, is more modern in styling than the AR line, costs more. The double-woofer complete Model One is $378, $336 in utility finish; a woofer-only model, with space for tweeter, is $197 in a legged floor model, $174 in a "bookshelf" type, similar to AR-1W above. A complete system with cone tweeter, Model Four, is about $225; utility black: $210; Model Six, similar, is in the $125 range.

Eico. An interesting new type of speaker is represented by the Eico Standard, a small vertically mounted system looking not unlike a half-sized grandfather clock. The eight-inch woofer points upward at the top, with a horn loading enclosure below, emitting bass from slots at the floor level; mid-range is via an attached radiator, upward, and the higher highs are sent out upward and in all directions—an unusual feature—by a special "flower pot" of concentric paper cones above the woofer, inside a grille cloth cage. Sound quality is excellent, dispersion and reflection of highs is unusually good; the Eico may be placed on a very small floor space (sixteen inches by one foot) in almost any room location. Should be especially good for stereo in tight quarters.

Two minor disadvantages; the speaker sound is not good at very close range, due to separation of the bass, at the floor, and the highs at chest level—but is excellent at even a short distance; the open top and upward-facing speaker assembly is not very well protected from accidental liquids, ashes and the like that may be put on the open top. Reasonable care will preserve it intact. The Eico costs about $130, complete.

Matching Components. A good many speakers that are available as separate units nevertheless have been designed primarily as parts of over-all complete systems—matching components. A dividing line isn't possible—most speakers, as a matter of fact, are best in the enclosures made by their own manufacturers. But a few examples are worth noting in which the complete system is the important item of interest.

The *JansZen Dynamic Woofer and Enclosure* is a complete woofer system, ready-mounted, that was specifically designed to complement the already-existing JansZen electrostatic tweeter, which requires a solid mid-range as well as low bass to go along with it. (The AR-1W lacks the mid-range.) The new woofer system is sold separately—Model 250, about $175; utility black, $148—for use with any tweeter. Also in a complete system including the JansZen electrostatic tweeter, Model Z-200, about $330.

The British *Hartley 220* speaker, supplementing the separate model 217, is specifically designed for the *Hartley-Luth "Holton"* complete system; but it is separately available. Similarly, the British *Wharfedale AF/12 Enclosure* ($95) was designed specifically for the Wharfedale Super 12/FS/AL 12-inch speaker ($79), though both are sold separately. (However the Wharfedale *Warwick* and *Windsor* systems, with nonresonant sand-filled flat baffles, are sold only as complete units.) There are dozens of other semiunified systems in which the parts are also separately available, as components.

MINIATURE COMPLETE SPEAKER SYSTEMS. A natural trend in complete speakers is that toward ever smaller and ever more ingenious systems, bettering the bass-versus-space ratio. "Small" in separate speaker systems does not mean limited in the sense of a portable phonograph or transistor radio—the hi-fi component complete systems are relatively potent in the bass range and provide a fairly complete tonal coverage that is better than most "hi-fi" sound and, with a good amplifier, a lot more powerful. Two examples of this trend are worth noting as representative of many more.

The small *Hartsdale* speaker system, a modified bass-reflex box with an eight-inch speaker specially treated for low bass response, is about $40 in finished-wood form, $35 unfinished. It makes a remarkably good and loud sound, well balanced if somewhat boomy (due to the small size.) Measurements: 15" by 10½" by 12¼".

The *Holland Standard* speaker is a more expensive unit of similar small size, mounted on long furniture legs; $145 in rather fancy furniture finish. A remarkably big sound for a small unit. A somewhat larger corner model is $195.

MULTIPLE UNIT SYSTEMS—WALL SYSTEMS. Many complete speaker systems include as a matter of course a woofer-tweeter combination or some other multi-way arrangement. A somewhat different principle, overlapping, is the use of several identical speakers, two, three or four woofers, to provide a teamwork-type of large cone area that operates like a big woofer in an economical way to produce large sound volume without strain. Some systems (e.g., KLH Model One/Five) combine dual woofers with a tweeter, or multiple tweeters.

The *Bradford Foursquare* speaker systems combine four single units in four triangular segments of a square, with the Bradford "pressure relief valve" enclosure system at the rear. A model with four eight-inch speakers, two with four twelve-inch, medium price. The *Bozak* cone-speaker systems include a number of models (and speaker kits) with two woofers and one, the *B-310*, with no less than four woofers, one mid-range and eight tweeter cones, at $725.

The Europeans favor a type of wall-mounted speaker system that often fits into a corner, overhead. It is excellent for background music and such uses as restaurant music; but for home listening I do not recommend this type. The bass response is often inadequate for our ears and tastes, as compared with similar floor and semifloor models, but a more important objection is that musical sound coming from overhead sources is poorly reflected, has an unmusical "point-source" effect and is spatially unnatural. This is a matter of opinion, of course; the convenience of this type of mounting may make it worth a second thought.

Two examples of European corner wall-mounted speaker systems are the Scandinavian *Tandberg corner loudspeaker system*, at about $70, and the German *Kingdom Sound Corner*, at $60. The Tandberg, though slim and narrow, will mount alternatively on the floor in a corner. The Kingdom Sound Corner hangs like a picture in the top corner, will not operate on the floor. (Other Kingdom models for floor and table use the same cone speaker elements.)

INTEGRAND. Perhaps the ultimate in advanced unification of hi-fi elements is represented by the Integrand amplifier-speaker system, which not only includes complete speaker and enclosure equipment designed to work together but goes back into the amplifier itself, applying an over-all corrective feedback from the speaker into a special amplifier that is part of the system. Here, the speaker's distortion for the first time is put to work to cancel itself out, somewhat as, for a long while, distortion inside the amplifier has been lowered by feedback.

Like most new developments, the Integrand system is not exactly economical in the buying and isn't likely to enter the low-priced speaker area for a while, if ever, in present form. But the idea is important and worth watching. Before long, the principle of amplifier-speaker integration may be applied in other ways to equipment of more general interest. Any development that forces automatic correction upon the speaker's distortion is of potentially wide importance.

13

The Tape Recorder

High fidelity has been greatly blessed—and greatly complicated—by that versatile machine, the tape recorder.

Stereo, for playback and occasionally for stereo recording, has added much that is new and confusing. Decorator appeal has come to the fore as elsewhere and tape machines come in all sorts of odd and fascinating shapes and sizes. The gap between the simple home machine and the "pro" models has been entirely filled in with equipment that now comes in every conceivable combination at dozens of price levels, from $60 to thousands. And most important for our interest, tape equipment for the home has now been given the component treatment—subdivided into separate sections, tape deck, playback preamplifier, etc. All of which means that we must do a tall amount of categorizing to make sense out of the welter, not to mention some defining of strange terms—like staggered heads.

THE COMPLETE RECORDER. First, look at some already familiar distinctions. Tape recorders come as complete machines, self-contained. Or in component form, incomplete and unit-by-unit. The physical distinction is quite clear though the price differences are not so easy to assess as those between "hi-fi" home phonographs and component phono systems. Most major brands of tape recorders include both component and complete forms, often with the same basic mechanisms.

You will note immediately that the outward arrangements of most one-piece complete tape recorders are more or less like their "hi-fi" counterparts in the disc record playing area. There are the usual handsome enclosures in all the usual forms. But more important, there are the same arrays of built-in "hi-fi" speakers and amplifiers. The difference between one recorder and another is often in this particular aspect, the built-in playback equipment, and the cost may be much greater for one that has a fancy multispeaker "miracle tone chamber" of some sort and a slightly better amplifier to match. The lower-priced units have feeble amplifiers and, perhaps, a single speaker. The basic recording equipment is likely to be virtually identical. Some new models—again like the recent "hi-fi" phonographs—even have separate speakers mounted in a removable lid.

Now if you intend to use your tape recorder on its own, with the built-in speaker system as its main voice, these extras are important. But unless you will depend very seriously on extreme portability, at the expense of good sound (even in the fanciest built-in systems), you will do far better with all tapes—your own homemade tapes and those you buy already recorded—by routing your tape recorder playback through your regular home hi-fi system. The difference is tremendous and no two ways about it.

You will find that most complete recorders provide the means for you to do this anyway, as an alternative to their built-in playback facilities (thereby admitting the outside system's incontestable superiority). You can always, then, take advantage of your own or somebody else's amplifier and speaker, and that includes auditorium P.A. systems and the like, into which you can plug your small machine to give it full auditorium volume.* In this case, you will think of the built-in playback system as mainly for emergency and portable use, and for this it can be essential. You will want to hear your tapes, to find out what you have on them, before you can bring your machine back home to play them with their full hi-fi potential. But if this is the built-in playback's main use, you will not want to waste money on too-fancy tone.

Remember that even the simplest larger home hi-fi speaker system will do a better job of sound producing than the fanciest of the built-in arrangements, with their too-ingenious solutions of the cramped space problem. True, for their size the built-in systems do a remarkable job. But you won't ever find them being directly compared to separate amplifiers and speakers, outside—the comparison would be damaging.

* You will need the right connector cables to do it and you should investigate beforehand. For frequent use in this manner your dealer can usually provide you with a special cable or two with the standard connections to fit most P.A. or home amplifier systems.

Put your money first into the business end of the tape recorder, the part that actually handles the tape itself, for recording and playing, and trust the outside hi-fi system to deliver the best sound that the tape can give. Only when you have tried this sort of playback will you realize how much more you can put down on a tape—even with an inexpensive machine—than any built-in playback system can reproduce.

I am, believe it or not, in favor of the complete one-piece tape recorder, with all this in mind, i.e., its internal playback strictly for portable "monitoring," and the main playback through the home system. Most people who have tape recorders use them away from home as often as in the living room. One of the main features of tape recording, after all, is portability.

COMPONENT TAPE EQUIPMENT. If you acquire a component tape deck or transport, described below in detail, you will depend *entirely* on an outside system for *all* playback, whether via your own system in your living room or some other amplifier and speaker. Aside from earphone monitoring, your tape deck will record, but will produce no sound whatsoever, unless you carry along a complementary amplifier-speaker system to go with it.

That isn't as unlikely as it may seem. It is my own preferred way of doing things. I keep a small amplifier and separate speaker box (only a foot square and with a carrying handle) for this very purpose. The tape playback sound is far better than from any "built-in" arrangement, and the whole thing is easy enough to move about—just two extra pieces. The more expensive recorders in effect do the same for you; they come in two units, one the recorder and the other the playback amplifier and speaker, in its own separate mounting. (The Ampex models are good examples.)

As a matter of fact, you may use such a portable hi-fi sound system even with a complete one-piece recorder, to by-pass its own inferior innards. More flexibility, to taste. A bit more haulage, a lot better sound, on location. In Chapter 17 you will find more about the possible uses of a hi-fi system outside of your living room.

The *tape deck* or *tape transport*, also called the tape *transcriptor*, is the major component in separate-parts tape. It includes the entire mechanical section of the machine and a good part of the electrical, mounted on a flat plate ready to install, either in its own case or into a larger hi-fi system. It is incomplete, but it is also considerably less expensive than equivalent complete tape recorders, and as with all hi-fi component arrangements, it is designed in numerous forms to give you what you need and no more. It is *not* a complete tape machine, any more than a record changer is a complete phonograph. Like the unmounted changer, it will usually stand up in a tottering fashion and may or may not operate that way; but before it can function properly, it must be mounted, if only on three or four books. It is strictly a component—but a very attractive one for the music lover out for budget hi-fi sound.

The tape deck does *not* include an amplifier and speaker for playback—that is the first thing to remember. There may be a socket for earphones and there is always an output arrangement to feed an amplifier or amplifiers (two for stereo sound). There are so many alternative forms that we had best go on to the features themselves; but note one further preliminary warning—tape decks come with or without a highly essential electronic ingredient, the *tape preamplifier,* either for playback alone or for recording and playback (a big difference there). Some decks have a preamplifier built in, and so will play (or play and record) directly; others must have it added, at extra cost—various alternatives, as usual, being offered to taste. While we're at it, remember that all stereo playback requires *two* amplifier-speaker systems, complete, and that includes two tape playback preamplifiers.

PLAYING AND RECORDING. We can slice the tape machine another way and make a distinction that has been thoroughly addled in recent advertising by the introduction of stereo. Most tape recorders are actually recorders and players too. The name is merely shortened for convenience, like piano for pianoforte. Other tape machines are players only— they do not record. Still a third category, which now includes many of the available home complete machines, are those which both record and play standard tapes—but for stereo are *players only.*

This becomes highly confusing when a tape recorder of this last sort is called a "stereophonic recorder"! The plain fact is that it does not record stereo at all, but merely plays it. It can record, but only "monaurally," which is the same old recording we've had all along. Unfortunately, nobody seems to have thought of a nonpolysyllabic name for this popular new type of machine and, in any case, the magic word stereo has such appeal that "stereophonic recorder" is worth cash as a name, even at the risk of ultimate confusion. Virtually all the tape recorders on the market that include the words stereo or stereophonic in their names are of this type, even including the lordly Ampex models and the RCA Victor Victrola Stereotape recorders.

A very few complete tape machines actually do provide for stereo recording—with two microphones, on two channels. These are expensive, necessarily; the cheapest are in the $500 range and the Ampex 600 series semipro stereo recorder costs $1,000.

Most of the component tape decks may be equipped for stereo recording, as well as playback, at the cost of the extra heads, extra record-playback preamplifiers (two of everything), and so on.

For details on the larger stereo picture, see Chapter 16, but note quickly right here that few home recording enthusiasts will want to fuss with stereo recording, even aside from its basically high cost. Stereo is tricky; most home stereo recording experiments will do no more than add grotesque and meaningless double-take imagery (two of everything, one in each speaker) to the sensible sounds that come from one "monaural" speaker system!

Finally, in this particular slicing, we must note that there are tape players for ordinary tapes and players that also play stereo tapes—all *without* the recording feature. Just players. No recording, no erasing. The tape player looks exactly like a tape recorder, whatever its form. The mechanism that moves the tape is the same. It merely lacks some of the innards of the complete machine, and most of them are small. Fewer heads where the tape goes into its slot, and fewer parts underneath the top deck.

Complete tape *players*—that is, one-piece and ready to play via built-in amplifier and speaker—are mainly sold to schools, libraries and the like. You will find very few of them in hi-fi salesrooms and catalogues, though persistent inquiry will usually dig them out.

The lowest-priced tape equipment you can buy is the plain tape deck that plays any standard (half-track) tape, does *not* record, does *not* play stereo. This rock-bottom installation may be worth considering in the component form, for you can always add more components later, to increase its ability in any way you wish. In the end, a $70 basic tape deck may develop into an all-purpose machine that records and plays everything in sight. But don't underestimate the simple forms. If your record player does no more than play discs, then the simplest tape player does just as much in respect to tape.

Yet, as usual, there is one warning here—stereo tapes are taking over rapidly from "plain" tapes. The stereo-tape library is already far more extensive, in the 7½ ips type, than the sound available on half-track nonstereo tapes. It's better to stick to disc records for "ordinary" sound and/or stereo disc, and move directly into stereo tape with your original tape equipment, whatever sort it may be, if tape is your interest.

As usual, note that the one-piece tape recorder is far less adaptable than the tape deck; once you buy it without stereo, or the wrong kind (below), you will have the alternative of turning it in on a whole new model, wastefully, or adding a halfhearted and unsatisfactory stereo "conversion." Far better a tape deck, where true stereo can be added later without loss or obsolescence.

WHERE TAPE STARTED. Before I get into the market scene, you will want to know a bit more, if you don't already, about the tape principle of operation. Historically, tape itself dates back only to the end of the war in this country. It was discovered and developed by the ingenious Germans—they had the idea far back before that conflict but evidently it wasn't advanced in the prewar period to the point where our own people got interested; the perfecting of it took place behind the wartime blackout. We were blissfully unaware of tape until the Magnetophon, the working German model, was discovered at the end of the war and carried back to the United States for amazed study. The Ampex was the first American machine, built with our own enthusiastic improvements. We caught on fast once the capabilities of tape had been shown us.

At first, tape recording was used largely for radio programs, notably by Bing Crosby, who "canned" programs on the first Ampex with remarkable success. By 1948, when the LP record arrived, many broadcasts were already being produced on tape, with such excellent quality and such ingenious sound editing—a wholly new device—that few people were aware of it until they heard the usual "This program was transcribed" or equivalent.

The first LP records were made entirely from older disc record sources, copied to the new medium, but it wasn't long before the phonograph companies saw the advantages of tape for their own art. By the earliest 1950s virtually all original recording was done on tape, to be transferred later to the various sizes and speeds of disc, after editing.

Millions of feet of tape have slipped smoothly through professional machines every year since, probably enough by now to reach to a galaxy and back. It surely won't be surprising to find that our present period goes down in history as the age of tape! No other medium of record has ever been used to such an extent, if largely for preserving information of no great importance to future archaeology.

Home tape? The first of the home tape recorders was the Brush Soundmirror, which came along surprisingly early in the game—it was used for improvised broadcasting before the professional Ampex was generally available. It was a dismally temperamental machine, as I can remember. It had an elaborate tape-threading arrangement, around corners and between posts, and a diabolical system of pushbuttons that often sprayed your tape on the floor in a heap or shot it into the air in tatters—trouble with quick starts and stops. But the machine was certainly on the right track; even in 1949 there were ardent home tape enthusiasts.

Tape records? Newest of the new, you may think, but actually they too first appeared in commercial form in the early 1950s. Prerecorded tape was the term, and that redundant name still persists. (You buy blank unrecorded tape for your home recording; tape sold with music already on it is recorded tape.) Like so many American developments, tape in its home-style aspects began early but languished, glowing publicity notwithstanding. Then suddenly—the rush was on. The high fidelity movement itself, of course, went through the same thing, as you are aware; the year of its turning was 1953 (with a push from *Life* magazine) but home tape took another four years to hit the jackpot. Not so very new. And note that a certain Mr. Poulsen first conceived of the magnetic recording principle a mere half-century ago.

THE PLASTIC MAGNET. In another volume I have spent a good many pages describing the ingenious magnetic method of preserving sound.* Hi-fi is too big, today, to allow such a detailed argument here. The biggest feature of tape is that in the sound storage and transmission— the electrical-magnetic trail of vibrations—there are no moving parts, no mechanical vibrations. Only the steady motion of the tape itself is mechanical. This removes a major and unavoidable source of distortion present in the disc record. Disc sound depends twice on mechanical vibration, in the cutting of the record groove and in the retracing of it by the phonograph stylus. Distortion has been constantly lowered by

* *Saturday Review Home Book of Recorded Music and Sound Reproduction*, 2nd edition, 1956, pp. 60-67.

reducing those bits of matter, the cutting and playing styli, to such a small mass that they scarcely have any weight or mind of their own and so respond almost exclusively to the sound signal. In tape, there is nothing but weightless, spaceless current and magnetism, without substance, undetectable except in the peculiarly useful way reserved for the tape player. There are distortion problems in taped sound, too, but they are within the electronic engineer's domain. They can be minimized, for a close approach to perfection. On professional equipment a tape can be copied and copied, continuing through a half dozen or so "generations," before any audible distortion appears. In prewar disc days even a very first copy (the much-maligned "dubbing") was noticeably inferior to the original recording. Distortion.

Plain home tape isn't quite that good, but it is already far more accurate—more faithful to the signal it receives—then any commercial recording method used prior to the war. (There were special, experimental "high fidelity" recordings made back in the thirties and many early electrical phonograph records, notably those from Germany, were considerably better in quality than the best home equipment then available to play them.)

The magnetic "pickup" is called a head. So also is the recording element—another head. The erase head is still a third, and outwardly they all look alike. Often, indeed, record and playback heads are identical except for internal electrical switchings; in most lower-priced recorders one head serves both functions, recording and playing.

The tape head is a horseshoe-shaped electromagnet, the two poles brought extremely close together—within a quarter of a thousandth of an inch in many recorders. The "gap" between the poles is invisible and the ends look like one shiny, curved piece of metal, over which the tape slides. Around the magnet's middle is a coil of wire to magnetize the moving tape, as one magnet creating another; or, in reverse, it reacts to magnetization on the tape.

How can tape be a magnet? Magnets are made of solid iron, you thought. A *plastic* magnet? That was the brilliant discovery of the Germans. Not all magnets are of plain iron. The first ever discovered were natural iron oxides found in the earth; lodestones. Other substances are varyingly magnetic, the most potent being those alloys of other metals with iron used in our loudspeakers to help create sound, which is motion out of electricity. Aluminum, nickel and cobalt go into such "alnico" magnets.

If you will think of an unfinished steel bridge smeared with bright orange oxide preservative paint, you'll perhaps see how a plastic magnet might be devised. The orange is an iron oxide, rust, more or less, suspended as a fine powder in a paint "vehicle." Grind up a magnetic oxide, then, make a paint of it, coat one side of a strip of flexible plastic tape—and you have yourself a pliable magnet. You can even make a paper tape magnet, though plastic is far more useful in tape recording.

Earlier magnetic recording was done via ribbons of steel, or thin steel wire. It worked, but was hopelessly bound by its own physical limitation, the necessary springiness of the steel itself. Winding and unwinding long rolls of easily snarled wire, that twists and turns on itself (it records only on one side and won't play back at full volume if turned part-way around), that can't be got hold of to reel smoothly along at a steady speed (home wire recorders simply pulled the tape from one reel to another, the speed changing as the reels grew bigger or smaller)—all this and more made wire recording a nuisance at best.

RECORD AND PLAY. The tape recording head receives an electrical sound-signal, and via the microscopically tiny magnetic field between its two sides in the aforementioned "gap," magnetizes the bit of tape that lies against it. As the tape moves on, the incoming signal fluctuates and a varying trail of magnetization is left behind, stronger and weaker as the sound signal itself strengthens and weakens. This is the recording. The trail or "track" need not be as wide as the whole tape. There is room for two tracks, side by side. Hence—dual-track (half-track) recording and, now, two-track stereo tape, and four-track too.

As in other types of recording, the playback of tape is more or less the same process in reverse. The head now serves as a tiny generator. As the faintly magnetized tape passes over the "gap," it generates a trace of electricity in the coils of the head, which fluctuates in proportion to the varying magnetization on the tape—and there is your sound. As you can imagine, the voltages thus created are extremely feeble. But they still faithfully carry the pattern of the original.

The tape playing head thus needs a preamplifier, like the similar magnetic phonograph cartridge. Both produce very tiny voltages that must be amplified to more useful levels before a regular amplifier can even "hear" them. This, as you will have already gathered, is of practical significance when it comes to buying tape equipment, since a preamplifier must be included, one way or another.

Every complete tape recorder has a built-in preamplifier, usually combined with the recording amplifier. The preamp is a necessary "extra" when you buy a tape deck that doesn't have one—unless, as I'll explain in a moment, you can use the preamplifier in your hi-fi system for tape playback.

Equalization is ordinarily quite automatic.* There are no alternative equalization positions on tape recorders.

ERASE. The less said about the erase head, the better—its function is simply to remove whatever magnetic signal is on the tape and this it normally does to perfection. Erase heads ordinarily use a high-frequency alternating current to joggle the magnetic particles back to a random distribution and so erase the recording. Other types (not so good) use direct current, or a permanent magnet. Erase heads come in half-track types, which erase only one track down one side of the tape, leaving the other intact, and full-track, which erase everything on the tape from one side to the other. A confusion between the two can result in assorted disasters.

Whatever the type, a fully recorded track should be removed 100 per cent by the erase head as it passes by, even at the fastest speeds. However, a violently overrecorded signal (such as many amateurs make) sometimes won't erase entirely. That is their fault, for a poor recording job.

TAPE THROUGH YOUR PHONO PREAMP. There is a money-saving reason for knowing that the very faint signals from a tape playing head must be preamplified before being sent on to the main amplifier. The job is ordinarily done by a built-in preamplifier, or by a separate unit in the case of the tape deck. However, any preamplifier will do—if it has the right equalization, the proper "curve" to make the tape signal come out flat and balanced properly. That includes your phonograph pre-

---

* Equalization in tape, as well as in discs, can be done in various ways and there have been arguments in the profession as with disc record equalization (Chapter 5), notably how much should be done in the preparation of the signal before it is recorded and how much afterward, in the playback. Standardization is now reasonably complete, via the NARTB curves and the accepted Ampex-type equalization—at least in this country. European-made machines may conform to another system (CCIR) and many older machines are nonstandard, notably the older Magnecorders, still widely used. Tapes made on any of these machines are perfect when played back on the same machine, but may be variously off-balance in sound on other playback machines. You can use your amplifier tone controls to do a fair job of correction.

amplifier. In every home amplifier or control unit there are already pre-amplifier equalization choices for various types of disc records including the RIAA standard. All you need for tape is an additional position, tailored electrically to fit the tape requirement. An increasing number of home amplifiers and control units now have in addition to the usual RIAA, LP, FFRR switch positions, an equalization position marked TAPE or TAPE HEAD, with a corresponding input connection. That can save you the cost of a special tape playback preamp—quite a sum.

You can buy a tape deck that has no preamplifier of its own but provides connections direct from its playing head, to plug into this home-amplifier tape input (for *playback only*—not to record). This is an excellent way to add an inexpensive tape player to your present equipment, though unfortunately it can't provide recording as well. That requires a special recording amplifier, as found in tape recorders and in separate *record-playback* amplifiers.

You can also improve the playback quality of many complete one-piece tape recorders by feeding the tape head directly to this same input, in your hi-fi preamplifier. It can do a better job with the tape signal than the machine's own cheaper built-in preamplifier. You may have to get help to figure out the connections needed, if your tape recorder doesn't have an output direct from the playing head.

A word of caution here—confusion is again incipient! You now may have up to three different tape connections on your home amplifier; it is unwise to mix them up, though nothing dreadful will happen if you do.

A. The tape output, out of your amplifier, intended to feed into a tape recorder for recording the amplifier's sound. It is usually independent of the tone controls and the volume control, having a fixed level of its own, even when these are changed for room-sound adjustment. (Thus you can play music loud or soft, to taste, and at the same time record it at the prefixed correct volume.)

B. A tape input, corresponding to those for radio tuner, TV, etc., to take the *ready-preamplified* signal from your tape machine, at the higher level the main amplifier requires. This is the standard and familiar way to connect a tape recorder into your hi-fi system for playing tapes. Just plug it in.

C. Now, on newer amplifiers, there is also the special tape head input direct to the preamplifier, with a switch position alongside the phono equalizations—next to RIAA, LP and the like. Sound goes directly from the tape heads to be preamplified by your phono preamplifier.

The separate record-playback preamplifier units for some tape decks (for recording as well as playback) cost a large amount extra. You can save that sum if you merely want to *play* tapes and can use the preamplifier already available in your home system as here described.

TAPE TERMS. Here are a few useful terms concerning tape. We've already separated the tape *player* from the tape *recorder*, and we know of tape *heads*—playing, recording, erase. You'll see them under the cover in the slot where the tape is inserted, between the two reels. They are small enough so that many small recorders have room for at least three and some machines will take up to five or more—if needed (Berlant-Concertone and others). Heads come in various ultra-compact forms, for the usual batch of situations. Note that recording and playing are often combined in one head—a record-play head. Erase heads are different in construction, though they look the same. In addition, note these interesting distinctions:

1. *Full-track* and *half-track* heads (all sorts). The full-track models operate down the middle of the tape, one track. The half-track heads work to one side, on a single slightly narrower track. But change the reels around and send the tape the other way back and you play, record or erase a second track beside the first. This is called alternatively *dual-track* or *half-track* tape. Slightly askew as to strict logic, but the idea is right. Two tracks on one tape, one at a time.

2. *Stacked (In-Line) Heads* (used for stereo). This type of head, which comes in all forms but is normally used in the home only for playing stereo tapes, combines two complete head units in one piece, one mounted directly *above* the other; both operate on the same tape. Stereo tapes marked *"in line"* or *"stacked"* play on these double heads, both tracks being played at once at the same point on the tape. (In-line recording heads are similar.) "Half-track" stereo heads, too (p. 235).

3. *Staggered Heads*. If you are wondering about the other kind of stereo tape, *staggered* or *offset*, it is easily explained. Before the compact double stacked heads were available it was necessary to mount two heads in a row, one next to the other, in order to record and to play two tracks on a single tape simultaneously. They had to be an inch and a quarter or so apart and so the two stereo recordings were "staggered" on the tape, one constantly an inch and a quarter behind the other.

This system is now outdated by the superior stacked-head system. Many record companies do not make staggered tapes at all. I advise you to steer away from staggered stereo, even though many recorders and conversion kits still feature this system.

4. Tape Transport, Tape Transcriptor. These are alternative names, more or less, for the tape machine, the physical moving parts which "transport" the tape from one reel to the other—everything except the electronic equipment. In practice, however, the tape transport may include most of the basic wiring and heads as well, already built in and ready to use. (Magnecorder P-63 Tape Transport, $465.) In fact the distinction between deck and transport is mostly nonexistent, unless perhaps to suggest that a "deck" is mounted on a flat decklike plate. The British speak of a *tape transcriptor*, meaning a tape deck. (Collaro Tape Transcriptor.)

The common denominator in all of these variants is that they are incomplete, without audio playback amplifiers and speakers; all are designed to plug into an outside sound system. You had best take the confusion of terms in your stride.

5. Two-Head and Three-Head. No matter how many heads you can actually observe inside the slot of the tape, where the tape goes, there are two basic tape systems in use in today's machines. One is basically two-headed, the other three. The difference is fundamental and interesting, too.

The *two-headed* tape recorder system is found in most home machines. That includes, oddly enough, many that appear to be one-headed as you look at them. In these, the two essential heads, the erase head first and then the double-function record-play head, are mounted in a single head case, though if you look closely you can see the two bumps where the tape must slide first over one, then the other.

In this type of machine the first head erases. The second combines the functions of recording and playing, via the recorder's switches. During the playback, of course, the erase head is turned off, but in the "record" position it is on, and removes all old material like a preliminary sound-broom, before the tape reaches the recording head. In these machines the amplifying system is adapted to work for both recording and playback. You can listen in on (monitor) the input signal, but there is no way you can hear the actual recording until afterward, when you change the switches to playback and listen to the recording. The head that records the signal also plays it back, and it can't do two things at once.

The *three-head* recorder, including all Ampex models, both home and professional, and virtually every professional machine, is a brilliant if expensive improvement on this system. The three-head machine has separate heads for recording and for playback, instead of one for both functions. Moreover, it also has a complete separate amplifier system for each—and so, in effect, it is two machines in one, both operating on the same tape. (The third head is the erase.)

Now the ingenious feature of this is that you can use both parts at once. You can record through head No. 2 (the first, as always, is the erase) and play the recording through head No. 3 almost simultaneously, only an inch or so away, and the time lag is a fraction of a second. Thus you may listen to your recording virtually as it is being made. A priceless advantage for all sorts of exacting work and well worth the cost of the extra head and amplifier system.

Via switching, you may also listen to what is going into the recording head (the input signal); and so you can compare the "in" and the "out" (the recording itself) by instantaneous "AB" switching back and forth. The two should of course sound exactly alike except that one is delayed, like an echo.

In the three-head recorder system the playback head is *always* in operation. It plays whatever sound is on the tape at all times, whether brand-new recording or old—a sort of permanent playback, to which you may listen at any time, whether you are recording or are playing already-made tapes.

Not many low-priced machines have this useful three-headed system. Too expensive. But a number of fancier home recorders do feature it, notably all the Ampex models. The Concertone ($575) has this feature and most component tape decks have room for the extra head that is required and thus can be had in three-head models, or can be converted to three-head operation. A highly desirable feature, I assure you, and no professional tape recordist would be without it for a moment.

The equivalent arrangement for stereo recording and playback requires a fabulous array of equipment. There must be two in-line stacked double heads (one for stereo recording and the other for playback), plus an erase head, full-track (to remove both tracks at once); also *four* separate amplifying systems, two for recording and two for playback. It's no wonder that the Ampex stereo portable recorder Model 601

2PF—with all of these features—costs around $1,000, twice the price of the ordinary Ampex 601 that makes a single, monaural recording. This is why most of the advertised "stereophonic recorders" do no more than play stereo tapes.

6. *Controls* on home tape recorders have been boiled down to a fairly uniform system, with wide variations in detail. Like record changers and automobiles, they all operate about the same way. Two general types of control are now available. The *one-knob* arrangement performs all major functions via the single large control handle. The *pushbutton* system—with varying numbers of pushbuttons—has an interlock arrangement so that you will not be able to do two things at once. European-made tape recorders tend to have less uniform controls. But this is a minor point; you can learn their ways fast enough.

Basic controls are simple. Fast forward, fast reverse (rewind), play, and record. In the playback position the erase head does not operate and the circuits are connected for the record-playback head to pick up the recording already on the tape. In record position the erase is on (beware!) and the same head makes the recording. (In three-head models the controls are the same, though record and playback heads are separate.) Usually there is a safety button to press in order to start recording—to save precious tapes from inadvertent erasing. A few recorders have trick extra controls such as a stop that keeps the recording circuits going—you may stop and start up again without recording a large audible plop on the tape. Very useful if you can't edit out noises.

Tape counters are useful if you incline to that sort of thing. I find that a glance at the relative size of the two reels gives as good an indication as you need, most of the time. You can supposedly locate any passage in a recording by such a counter, if you have it set correctly, but I am skeptical. It is in the nature of tape recording for things to get lost in that long quarter-mile of tape on each small reel!

Level indicators (for their use see Chapter 18, pp. 252-253). One small pinkish light or green "eye" is the minimum; two are better, since one serves as a warning and the second is a danger signal—too high volume. The more expensive recorders have a meter level indicator—the professional type is called a VU meter (volume units), with the danger area marked in red. All professional machines are so equipped.

7. *"No Reel Turnover."* Webster-Chicago is one of the few makers of home tape recorders that still provide the convenient but expensive

two-direction recording. The Webcor tape machines record through to the end of a reel and then, in reverse, back to the beginning via a second record head mounted so as to make a second track in the normal position. The advantage of this system is that you don't have to remove the reel at the end and rethread the tape for the second track, as in other half-track recorders; the disadvantage is the extra cost involved in the required two record-play heads and the more complicated erase, and the other reversible features.

8. *Cartridge Tape.* It has seemed for a long time that tape in "plug-in" cartridges would be a fine idea—no threading, no rewind—but the practical difficulties are immense and the cartridge has had only a limited application. Wilcox-Gay makes a home cartridge recorder, the Jet ($130) and provides the special tape cartridges (not generally available); a number of miniature professional "snooper" recorders of the pocket type use cartridges. The main problem is getting back to the beginning of the tape from the end. A loop system is the only way, but though it may be done in a small space, there is apt to be much sliding of one layer of tape over another—and a snarl of any sort is fatal! Better stick to the thread-it-yourself system unless you convert to "half-track" stereo, which uses a "cartridge" with two reels (p. 235).

TAPE ALIGNMENT. This is a crucial aspect of tape recording which, if you are lucky, you will be able to ignore. The tiny gap in the record and play heads, less than a thousandth of an inch wide, must be precisely "square" with the tape that moves across them. Normally, the heads are adjusted at the factory and, barring severe bumps and jars, will stay in this alignment indefinitely. Adjustment is usually possible, however, and directions are provided, but for a good job a special alignment tape ($6) is best, and a meter as well, for accurate measuring. But the job can be done on a rough-and-ready basis simply by listening to the playback of a known correct tape—any commercial recorded tape, for instance—and adjusting alignment of the head by ear for the best sound, i.e., that with the sharpest, clearest high tones.

The principle behind alignment is not hard to grasp. The recorded "track" or magnetized trail of recorded sound is left behind by the tiny, straight "crack" of the gap itself—less than a thousandth of an inch wide—and it is oriented to that gap. If the head that plays the recording is set at a different angle, even by a tiny bit, the two will not match. A possible analogy is an out-of-shape box top, that won't fit over a square box. If the playing-head gap exactly lines up with the gap that made the recording, the tape plays perfectly.

What is an out-of-alignment sound? The audible effect is a drastic loss of the shortest wave lengths, in hearing terms the brilliant higher tones. The worse the alignment, the greater the loss of highs—as though a treble tone control had been drastically turned down. The sound is muffled, dull, peculiarly lifeless and dispirited. When alignment is corrected the high tones jump back and the sound comes to life.

The trap in alignment, a serious one, is that you may not know your machine is out of alignment, perhaps for months or years, until you try to play tapes made on other machines. Then—trouble, and it is almost too late to repair the damage. You may, you see, make a recording with a head seriously out of alignment (not square to the tape) and, if *the playing head is at the same angle of misalignment*, the tape will play back perfectly. Now this is precisely what happens in the average home machine, since the recording head is also the playback head! No matter how far askew it gets, the tapes you make will sound fine when played back equally askew! You'll never know the difference —until you play somebody else's tapes, or worse, you try that fine new Beethoven Fifth Symphony that you have just bought on a commercial recorded tape. Being in perfect alignment (that is, its recording head was rightly aligned), this tape will come through with unutterably dull and unhappy effect on your machine. Play your own tapes again, and all is well once more.

You have a choice to make, in this case, between two evils. You may play your own tape, or the commercial tape, but not both.

You can understand that if there were no particular standard of tape alignment, you could always play back any tape on its own machine but each machine would be a law unto itself and tapes would not be interchangeable. Some fixed angle must be agreed upon and the obvious one for a standard is at exactly right angles to the tape itself, 90 degrees. All tapes made with heads aligned to this angle are interchangeable; their magnetic tracks match all correspondingly aligned playing gaps.

There are, then, several dire possibilities for "out-of-alignment" sound:

A. You play a correctly aligned tape on your out-of-alignment machine; they don't match. Dull sound.

B. Your machine has correctly aligned heads but is playing a tape made by a head that was out of alignment. (Maybe it was yours.) Mismatch, and the same dull sound.

C. Your wrongly aligned machine plays a tape made on a *differently* misaligned head. One is as bad as the other but they are different—hence, dull sound.

As you can see, once the head is out of kilter and you have made tapes with it, you are in trouble. Because when you put the head back in proper alignment, though it will make correct tapes from thenceforth and play them correctly, it will no longer play the old tapes!

First Aid for Misalignment. But what can you do? Suppose the damage has been done and you now have a priceless collection of tapes, every one of which is out of alignment? Worse—suppose you also have other tapes, differently aligned?

In an emergency, on most machines you may deliberately misalign the playing head, to match it up to any given tape. Tape machines in this respect are wholly unethical. Right or wrong, they will play any tape to which they are exactly aligned. As long as the tape and the playing head match, the sound will be fine.

(Warning: Do *not* experiment with three-head recorders, including Ampex, unless you are very familiar with the rather complex procedure necessary to get the separate recording and playing heads into correct alignment, or can arrange to have a competent person put these heads back in order after you have finished tampering with them.)

To play an out-of-line tape, locate the alignment screw on your record-play head (*not* the erase) and then screw it back and forth, preferably while the tape is playing, until the sound is right. (On some machines you may not be able to change the head alignment at all.) The effect is easy enough to hear—a tiny adjustment will bring a dismally dull sound back to crisp clarity. You'll probably have to take off the cover that protects the heads, but this shouldn't be more than a moment's work. See your instruction book.

You may, indeed, be so delighted at the improvement in your out-of-line tapes that you'll be inclined to forget that in the end you must get the head back to correct—i.e. standard—alignment, or your trouble will be compounded. The simplest way to do this, again, is to play a commercial tape and readjust the head by ear for optimum sound.

But, you'll say, you can't go on readjusting your tape heads for every tape you've made, *ad infinitum!* Alas, you may have to, if your tapes are variously aligned, unless you copy your old, out-of-line tapes onto new tape.

It takes two machines; you hook one to play into the other. The idea is to deliberately misalign the *playing* machine, matching the tape you will copy. The machine that *records*, of course, will have its heads in perfect alignment—make sure of that. (Test it via a commercial recording.) Make copies in this fashion and your new tapes will be in standard alignment and interchangeable with all other correctly made tapes. Well worth the trouble of copying, if you have precious older tapes that suffer from this serious defect. (P.S. Remember to realign your machine to the correct standard after the copying is done!)

STEREO. I have been talking obliquely about stereo throughout this chapter and, at this point, you have an idea of the technical requirements in the way of extra heads, dual preamplifiers, dual complete amplifier-speaker systems. Rather than continue with that subject here, I'm setting aside Chapter 16 for stereo in the large and I refer you to that section for details. I have only two negative suggestions to emphasize here. First, my best advice is to avoid staggered-head stereo equipment in any form. The staggered-head arrangement is already obsolescent. Pay a bit more and get in-line (stacked) heads for your stereo equipment.

Second, and in a similar vein, be chary of the stereo conversion outfits now on sale, to change your recorder from monaural to stereo, or from staggered stereo to stacked. (The only exception is in the case of tape decks where alternative equipment is easily installed.) These gadgets will work—if you manage to acquire all the extras that aren't always mentioned. But they are makeshifts, pure and simple, and unless you are in a terrible hurry, they should not tempt you far. Better a new model, with the stereo heads already built in, where they belong.

So much the better reason, you see, to buy component-style tape equipment. As always, obsolescence is slower, replacements and additions can be made as you go along without junking a whole machine, and in the long run you will find yourself happier. You can add stereo heads and preamplifiers to most recent tape decks not so equipped, and they will be as up to date as a new machine.

For *microphones*, see Chapter 17.

VALUES. Like everything else in hi-fi, tape comes in many price ranges, with the usual geometrically increasing cost for better and better quality.

The first principle to remember is that tape is inherently more expensive than disc—even without stereo. More expensive by the minute, in commercial tape records, which cost about twice as much as an equivalent LP disc for the monaural tapes and up to four times as much in stereo. More expensive, too, in the tape recorder-player equipment. Also more complicated.

As a rough rule of thumb, I suggest that in acquiring tape equipment you multiply the cost of a disc player two or even three times in order to decide what a roughly equivalent tape recorder might cost. That includes the recording feature as well as the playing of tape—more value for the money. But even a tape *player*, minus recording, costs a lot more than its quality-equivalent in standard disc equipment. The recent Pentron TP-3 Tape Player sold for $100; a roughly comparable Allied Radio four-speed changer for $50.

Tape isn't cheap but its values are high. Don't underestimate them. TV, after all, costs as much or more. Tape is well worth what it costs and the more enterprising you are (see Chapter 18), the better value it will be.

When you buy your recorder, insist on a trial. Play a record "out loud," then record some of it on the machine and have it played back through the same loudspeaker system. Or, alternatively, use the machine's own built-in speakers; listen to a record as it is played into the machine, then compare the sound with the same as recorded on the tape. There should be virtually no difference.

The lowest-priced tape recorders, one-piece, in the $100 range or less, are roughly equal to the budget portable phonographs that are sold widely (for a good deal less) and which do a good job, with moderately good sound and a very moderate life span. It is better, if you can, to move up at least one peg and buy your tape recorder, minus stereo, in the $150 range. That opens up better quality in the machine, in the sound, and in the range of features as well as probable durability.

The $200-$300 range of recorders give more in several directions: (a) stereo, which adds to the cost in various ways; (b) fancier décor; (c) considerably greater versatility, in controls, inputs and outputs; (d) fancy built-in playback speaker systems (but see page 176); (e) last and most important, better quality, notably in some of the durable, well-built European models. Extra cost won't necessarily bring all of these things at once; they are points to check avidly.

At around $350 you begin to edge into semiprofessional machines, in two ways, not necessarily commensurate: (a) still better quality, and still more useful features, notably the three-head recording system (page 187), which is necessarily quite expensive. Also such advantages as built-in mixers, to combine various sound sources, panel meters instead of the simpler neon bulb or flashing volume indicators, (b) and/or professional-type features that may be undesirable for home-type recording—watch out for these. Thus, machines like the Concertone, the Tapesonic and the Presto tape deck take the large 10½-inch professional reels of tape but are in consequence very bulky and clumsy. Some machines in this range may have unwanted and overtechnical broadcast-style controls and electronic features—no use going into details; they will suggest themselves when you investigate.

From $500 to $1,000 and more there are semiprofessional machines to be had, often highly desirable in a really first-rate home hi-fi installation. The little Ampex 601 (and its stereo partner, a bit larger) is the smallest and most convenient but others have other appeals, including the large reels—if you need them. Enough—for most readers will by this time be far out of their depth!

The above discussion concerns complete recorders, one-piece, including playback speakers. (Speakers are occasionally separate.) But before buying any recorder, look carefully at the *tape deck* (*tape transport*), the component tape equipment. It offers the greatest flexibility and lowest obsolescence.

Tape decks come without case, or mounting, include heads (varying configurations) but no preamplifier. The simple playback-only preamps or, alternatively, the more complex and expensive record/playback amplifiers, are sold as separate units—but fit into ready-made spaces in the tape deck, adding no extra bulk. (The controls fit into knock-out panels.)

Your tape deck alternatives are (a) in the heads and (b) the preamp or record/playback amplifier—two for stereo. The simplest head arrangement is a single head, playback only (no erase). More complex arrangements include several heads, for conventional erase, record and playback, or for combined stereo playback and conventional record/playback. (Stereo *recording* not generally recommended.) Leading brands in the U.S. are Viking, Bell, Pentron. (Revere sells a complete recorder minus case, for hi-fi installations.)

Note that a single head serves for both recording and playback (unless you order special three-head configurations, as described above). Sometimes the erase head is combined with this record/play head in one physical unit. For all tape *recording*, the more expensive record/playback amplifier is necessary; but for tape *playback only*, the simpler playback preamp suffices and may be replaced by the TAPE HEAD position in your hi-fi amplifier, as explained above. Here are some typical tape deck costs:

Simplest basic tape deck. One head, no preamp. (Will play standard monaural tape through TAPE HEAD input on tuner or hi-fi amplifier.) Viking: $78. *Bell:* $98. *Pentron:* $85.

Tape deck for monaural record/playback and in-line (stacked) stereo play-

back. Viking: $113. Bell: $118. Pentron: $110 (requires one playback preamp, one record/playback amplifier).

Playback preamplifier for above decks, to mount integrally. Viking: $30. Bell: $30. Pentron: $40.

Record/playback amplifier for above decks, to mount integrally. Viking: $78. Bell: $59. Pentron: $80.

Rough cost (minus amplifier and speaker—use your hi-fi system) for standard tape installation, recording and playback: $150-$165. For the same plus stereo playback (requires two amplifier-speaker systems): $200-$230.

14

Hi-Fi Housing

DECORATOR CASES

These days, you are as likely as not to acquire your entire high fidelity system ready-housed, each section in its own handsome modern cabinet. The day of the out-in-the-open amplifier, with tubes and transformers projecting at the top, is over except for the biggest and most functional power amplifiers. Sleek, slim casings now cover most of the amplifiers on the market and radio tuners and control units as well. Hi-fi units are clearly meant to look handsome (and sell handsomely) without further mounting, though the working insides can be had minus case (or can be removed from the case) if you prefer to mount your system inside a piece of furniture, or in wall cabinets or the like. Even your loudspeaker is now likely to be a complete system, ready-mounted. Only the indomitable record changer still comes cabinetless, though it is often mounted on a base.

There is no advantage in sound quality or performance to be gained from the new decorative amplifier enclosures. In fact they have a major disadvantage that hasn't always been successfully met—overheating. I once had an early enclosed amplifier that burnt out when I left it on by accident for two or three hours. Not enough ventilation for the red-hot power tubes. You'll note that the new amplifier cases are literally full of holes; the assorted metal mesh or perforation makes a handsome part of the décor yet provides the needed ventilation too. Take this as an important hint: wherever you put your amplifier, *be sure that it is well ventilated.* The same applies with lesser force to radio tuners and control units, where the tubes generate less heat than the amplifier's big power tubes. Transistors produce barely a trace of warmth.

"Sections 4 and 5." You cannot go about choosing actual components for a hi-fi system without taking practical account of two extra "sections" not basic to the main three of Chapter 3, the working parts of the system, but vital for good sound even so. The first, subject of this chapter, is the housing of the system. It affects the sound in more ways than you may think, since it determines much concerning your listening habits, the placement of your equipment and of your speaker —very important points. Second is the listening room itself, its acoustics and furniture arrangement. So important is this that it goes into its own chapter, the next one.

Before you make so much as a tentative plunge in the direction of a given amplifier, record player or speaker, consider your preferences in the way of nonmusical housing. The variety of approaches is immense and people's inclinations are equally different. So is the cost, over and above the cash spent on the basic units themselves. It may be virtually nothing and, if you so desire, you will not have to do any onerous installation work. But you can easily keep yourself busy for months of carpentering and painting if you enjoy it.

I might add, parenthetically, that your home system will be shaped in the buying and installing by certain other practical factors, not always considered with enough gravity: Neighbors. Thickness of apartment walls. Children and dogs. All can be coped with, if you begin at the beginning.

This book is not the place for detailed drawings and plans as to possible hi-fi layouts (nor for pretty pictures with human models sitting cross-legged on stools looking at hi-fi). You will find quantities of such information in the hi-fi magazines and in much helpful literature issued by the various high fidelity manufacturers; also in assorted hi-fi year books, special newspaper supplements, feature articles in the slick-paper magazines. High fidelity, remember, is big business now. My purpose, as usual, is to give you a background and perspective, from our special point of view, the music lover's. The best thing I can do right here is to make you a bird's-eye survey of possibilities, from one extreme of housing to the other, so that you may place yourself solidly in the right context.

The Simple Approach. What with the above-mentioned decorative cases plus prewiring and plug-in connecting, you will find it hard to make an old-fashioned messy hi-fi installation now! Still—for those who enjoy it the gadget approach is always possible. The male side of many a family, if I know anything about it, will fight for this just as long as he can get away with it. Put everything out where the guests can see and be in awe. The more wires and tubes and transformers, the better. Plenty of living rooms under this persuasion look like laboratories of the more casual sort. Best of all, it's cheap. Put the speaker in a plain, unfinished box whose very ugliness proclaims the spirit of utility—the most music for the least expense. Set the record changer on a table or handy shelf. Trail wires to the amplifier, on the floor under foot, behind a chair or beneath a side table. Run an ordinary electric-light cord (it is as good as any) to the speaker enclosure, off in the best part of the room for good listening.

If you go in for this happy extreme (happy for the man whose pride of ownership is involved) you'll take only one or two mild precautions. As to placing the speaker, see the pages to come. But note that your record player must be close to the amplifier into which it feeds (or the control unit—or radio tuner), ordinarily within three or four feet. The cable (which the dealer can install for you) must be shielded and not more than the standard three feet or so in length; if it is too long, the pickup circuit being high-impedance, there will be a serious loss of high tones, as though you had turned down your tone control knob.

Most radio tuners now have the useful cathode follower output that allows as long a connecting cord as you wish to the amplifier and without special shielding, but you should check on this; if not, the tuner will also have to be close to the amplifier. The speaker can be set at any distance, via that ordinary lamp cord. (Note that most separate control units also have cathode follower outputs and thus can be placed as far as you wish from their basic power amplifiers.)

Whatever your casual layout, be sure, again, that all units containing tubes, and especially the power amplifier, are well ventilated. This should be no problem in an out-in-the-open installation.

ORDER FROM DISORDER. It is so easy to make improvements on this rough-and-ready hookup that you will surely make them at once, unless you are the type who doesn't make beds and leaves the dishes unwashed. You already have a set of reasonably attractive cases with the working parts inside; progress from this point is mostly a matter of straight lines and proportion.

Clear away a foot or two of shelf on a bookcase and stand the amplifier in the space, convenient to your hand for manipulating the controls. Run the necessary wires perhaps behind books or neatly tacked down with insulated staples, instead of just dangling them. (Don't place the amplifier too near the shelf above. Four or five inches is safe clearance.)

Find a neat and well-proportioned space to stand the record changer in its own wood or metal base ($3 to $5 extra). It will fit on a wide shelf too, or a window seat (but not on top of a hot radiator!) or side-

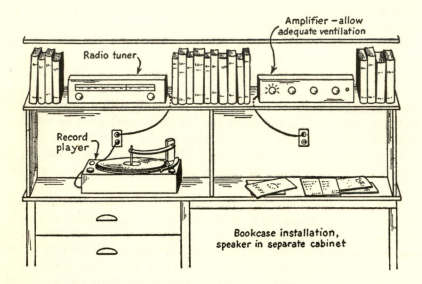

Bookcase installation, speaker in separate cabinet

board. It can even stand unobtrusively on the floor near an armchair and within reach. A radio tuner will go very neatly into most bookcases and will look well even in the "chassis" form (the insides and dial minus outer cabinet). Again, the lead wires can be run behind books or fastened down. Everything, of course, will plug together, except, perhaps, the speaker connection to the amplifier, which connects with two screws.

If you are not up to installing switches, run all the components' power cords to a triple plug at the wall socket, or to an extension cord. It is a good idea to arrange for a "master switch" so that one action turns off everything. You are likely to have one cord for the changer, one for the amplifier and one for the radio tuner. Most amplifiers have extra power sockets connected through the on-off switch, to take care of these.

You can run your speaker wire under a rug, though it is better to run it around the side of a room at the baseboard. The problem is the same as with the usual lamp cords—except that the current in the speaker wire is not enough to cause danger in the way of short circuits.

You can also take advantage of small cabinets or niches, that are handy as improvised but effective housing for some of the units, dust-free. (But be careful about ventilation!) Your amplifier can be set inside a cabinet or bookcase with front doors if you leave the doors open when the system is turned on. (A trick is to put in a refrigerator-type switch, so that the system turns off automatically when the doors are closed.)

The chances are good, now, that your speaker system will be complete in one piece; you will simply place it where it sounds best. (Chapter 15.) A separate speaker can be mounted for you in its cabinet enclosure by your dealer if you don't relish the job yourself.

I emphasize this type of installation because it is not usually featured in hi-fi ads, nor in the magazine and book accounts, which run to fancy decorator suggestions or to the build-it-yourself type of arrangement. You do not have to cater to either of these viewpoints unless you want to; you don't have to spend extra money on housing. Via the simple approach you can easily have a respectable hi-fi installation that will credit you with good taste in looks as well as in sound.

SHELF AND TABLE CARPENTER. If you are a shelf and table builder, if you like to saw up wood and construct simple living-room conveniences for yourself, you can go a good deal further in this direction, still without buying outside equipment. At this point you should begin to consider the array of semicomplete kits now available, as well as helpful small gadgetry for mounting changers, speakers and the like; but stick to home building for a moment. As long as the loudspeaker enclosure itself is not involved, amateur cabinet construction will not directly affect your music.

You can mount your changer or manual record player into any top recess, perhaps with a lid that comes down over it. You can buy hardware for the sliding, pull-out changer shelves that open outward in many phonograph cabinets. The changer's mounting hole, in any flat horizontal panel, is a problem; a paper diagram (template) is provided, but the cutting is a jigsaw job, difficult if you're not accustomed to the work. Obligingly, the hi-fi dealers sell ready-made panels with the proper hole precut, for a few extra dollars.

As an alternative to setting your amplifier on a shelf or inside a cabinet (the best plan, to my way of thinking) you can mount it in any vertical support with a suitable panel in front; bore holes for the projecting controls and mount the knobs and escutcheon plate outside. Most amplifiers include detailed instructions for this type of mounting. (Again, there are hundreds of cabinets and cabinet kits available—see below.) A two-unit amplifier can be separated with the power unit down below and out of sight, the control unit mounted on a convenient panel. (I still prefer it on the loose and movable.)

If you plan this sort of installed system, do your home designing *after* you have bought the equipment. You'll save agony by working with the parts right in front of you where you can measure them. You're likely to miscalculate on measurements if you trust catalogue descriptions.

Don't try to build your own speaker enclosure unless you are a fairly experienced woodworker. The enclosure is a part of your sound system. Measurements must be exact (and according to a prepared design —not via guesswork), the parts close-fitting and solidly put together. Even with extensive help from printed instructions, this is not simple carpentry by any means. It's better to buy a ready-made unit, unfinished, if you want considerable savings. Speaker enclosure kits are a good compromise saving you even greater sums, and they now come with their surfaces finished as well as in the unpainted, unfinished form (below). But be prepared to glue and clamp and nail.

Finished woodwork isn't necessary, but bare wood does pick up smudges and finger marks. The simplest finish is rubbed-in furniture wax, put on with a cloth and polished, in several coats. (Sand off smudges and marks first.) It gives a rather handsome blond satin surface to most cheap woods, dust and finger-mark free. Shellac, "antiquing" paint and the usual stains and varnishes will involve you in more work and mess—if you want it.

A prolific source of ideas for hi-fi cabinetry is in the existing furniture around your home, especially the sort that has outgrown its original usefulness. I have seen systems with the loudspeaker installed in an old-

fashioned washstand commode, where the pottie used to be. Everything from office desks to shoemaker's benches can be used. On a more pretentious level, there is much handsome antique or modern furniture that can be adapted to carry some or most of your high fidelity equipment, with grace and charm. If you have a built-in cupboard with doors of wood or glass, or a china closet or knickknack cabinet, you may have a ready-made spot for keeping your equipment both handy and dust
' free. . . . So it goes. There's room for a great deal of pleasure of the home-fixing sort in this settling of your hi-fi system into the existing surroundings of your home.

READY-MADE HI-FI CABINETRY. If you contemplate buying ready-made furniture you have a bewildering choice before you. Furniture to house hi-fi in style is an extensive business with burgeoning catalogues of woodwork, now available in every form from "kits" of unassembled lumber to the most elaborately finished and decorated quality cabinetry. You can get it in all the usual ways, via mail order or on the sales floor.

Speaker enclosures from good to terrible are included in this furniture. Often there is not so much as a mention of the type of enclosure provided, as though it were scarcely important. It is. Handsome cabinets with the undesirable open-back speaker mounting may be described evasively—"Takes twelve-inch or fifteen-inch speaker," without a word as to how. The old familiar custom of including the speaker in a one-piece cabinet along with everything else is still catered to and must be shunned. You should resist temptations toward this false kind of simplicity if you want your music well reproduced.

Don't expect to get finished cabinets without paying a good solid sum. If you want budget-priced music you will buy unfinished wood as a matter of course—or you will pay more for the cabinet than for all the insides put together. Good looks are to be had, even unfinished. With fair home craftsmanship you can work up one of these unpainted units into a satisfying piece of furniture; or you may save via the new finished-wood kits.

Cabinetry to house the entire home system comes in a number of general types, worth categorizing in your mind even though they overlap in many ways.

A. Equipment cabinetry, fairly large and with numerous internal compartments, often to order, plus one large section designed for the loudspeaker, used alternatively for storage.

B. Equipment cabinetry designed to take all components *except* the speaker—lacks the large speaker compartment.

C. Matched cabinets in pairs, one for the loudspeaker (check on the type of enclosure!), the other for the associated equipment.

D. Various smaller cabinets, for records, record players, etc.

E. Preassembled modular cabinets, separate but designed to be placed together like building blocks.

F. Speaker enclosures.

Once again, I recommend that you put out of your mind all thought of a cabinet where the speaker is housed along with other components, like an old-style phonograph. The speaker should be *separate*, and preferably at a distance from the control center for best listening. (Even the new "hi-fis" now tend toward widely separate speaker cabinets, influenced in part by stereo and its need for two separate speaker outlets.)

Categories A and B above are closely related—the difference is simply that in Type A there is a large space for the speaker, or for storage; in the smaller Type B there are only the compartments for various smaller components—amplifier, tuner, etc. You will find an astonishing variety of cabinetry under these rough headings! In usual hi-fi style, there is flexibility too; many models are available in several different internal arrangements, to your choice, right-handed or left-handed, sidewise or upright, with or without short legs.

Type C is very popular—the two matching cabinets are invariably pictured in the ads side by side, for a handsome effect. However, you will be wise to separate them, though even side-by-side placement, simulating one piece of furniture, is an improvement over the single cabinet. The speaker's vibrations are still not likely to be carried to the pickup—the unpleasant *acoustical feedback* that so often makes one-piece phonographs shake and buzz.

Type D includes everything from simple bases for changers up to more elaborate boxes with lids, for the same and for the larger "professional" arms and turntables, plus record storage case and even built-in bars! Type E is similar except that these modular lines usually provide small units to take all types of equipment, including separate boxes for the speaker.

All of these (leaving aside the speaker enclosure, F) come with simple blank panels, vertical or horizontal, designed to be cut or holed to fit individual components. The makers of the equipment do not as a rule do the cutting—there are too many different sizes and shapes needed. (But they often sell separate precut panels for specific changers, etc.) You can usually have the work done by the dealer who sells you the cabinetry, before it is delivered to you (and he will also mount the components, if you insist).

The cabinetmakers now build to suit the increasingly standardized dimensions of the common hi-fi components and so the task is not difficult, in any case. Component makers, too, provide detailed facilities and instructions for this type of mounting, this being a major part of their business. The hi-fi dealer himself is in contact with both component maker and cabinetmaker, and is thoroughly accustomed to the installation job.

You can do it all yourself, of course, if you are adept at simple hole boring and sawing. You may have to do it if you order components by mail, from the big mail-order houses such as Allied Radio in Chicago. These large firms don't like to bother with boring holes and putting in wires—their business is too big. Take this into account, if you plan to buy hi-fi by mail. This is one good reason to patronize a local hi-fi store where you can go in person, even though prices may be a bit higher than via mail. You can settle these things there on the spot, and quickly.

SPEAKER ENCLOSURES. Never forget that we must treat the speaker enclosure first as an acoustical chamber and secondly as decorative furniture. Many of the separate speaker enclosures are, rightly, sold by firms that specialize in enclosure design and speaker manufacture but unfortunately, not all. There is still much fancy cabinetry with the old-style open-back enclosure, definitely not recommended for best sound. Numerous other enclosures are of the bass-reflex type, variously modified. (See Chapter 12.) Generally speaking, these bass-reflex cabinets do a satisfactory job, since they are designed for "average" speakers and yours will probably not be too far from this norm.

Four forms are available among separate speaker enclosures. (1) The kit, to be assembled by you from precut unfinished lumber and glue and nails; (2) the prefinished kit; (3) the complete utility model, assembled but unfinished, and (4) the finished, ready-to-use enclosure. (By "finish," of course, I mean the outer surface of the wood.)

The price differences are significant here. A kit (1, above) costs about half the same enclosure in its assembled unfinished "utility" form (3), and the new prefinished kits (2) fall midway between these. Completely finished enclosures (4)—the same models, with identical acoustic characteristics—cost nearly four times as much as the unfinished kit models (1) of the same enclosure. (Similar differences apply to amplifier and other electronic kits.) This certainly puts a premium upon home construction!

Nevertheless, I advise you to avoid the kits unless you can cope with the gluing and nailing that generally has to be done—these kits are not the sort that you merely screw together. Investigate before you buy, and more power to you if you can save successfully in kit form.

Fancy enclosure furniture is increasingly a matter of décor as the prices go up; the quality of the emitted sound isn't necessarily better, either—it can often, as I say, be poor. If you are sensible you'll avoid the top-bracket hi-fi furniture and put your money into more musically productive elements.

Keep in mind the double purpose of all such cabinetry and don't be misled by beauteous wood and metal. If you can, give your prospective cabinet a good knocking and shaking, look at the material, the reinforcing, the method of joining the segments. Even if you are no woodworking expert you can get at least a comparative idea of values on this score. A loosely or weakly built enclosure will vibrate when it should not, adding resonant peaks of distortion; sometimes a whole panel will buzz loudly at certain notes.

Finally, don't look askance at plywood—it may be good. The modern synthetic lumbers are less likely to cause vibration trouble than solid wood itself. Materials such as filled board made from compressed sawdust and resin are excellent acoustically as well as good-looking if well finished.

CUSTOM DESIGNS. As you can imagine, the custom hi-fi builder, whose specialty is hi-fi to individual order, is usually a cabinetmaker of no mean ability and can turn out practically any sort of furniture you suggest to him—or he to you—with emphasis, needless to say, on the more expensive concepts. But most of them supplement their own handicraft with ready-made furniture of the sort already described, which they will adapt for your special needs. If you want custom work and still would like to save money, it is advisable to start from ready-made furniture that approximates what you have in mind, rather than building from scratch out of raw lumber. Only detailed study will tell you which way is best for you.

The principal inspiration to be found in the custom builder's shop is in the way of suggested design and layout—he fairly bristles with ideas as to chic and ingenious hi-fi installations in your particular situation and, of course, he will do the actual installing right in your home. Worth cash on both counts, for many people.

An increasingly prevalent hobby, in this time of quick building operations, is the planning of a hi-fi system as part of a house before the house is even built. Some people go so far as to design their houses around their hi-fi, though to my way of thinking this is more likely to lead to extravagance and to poor listening acoustics than to hi-fi satisfaction. (It is *not* a good idea to build your speaker into a wall or into a permanent unmovable enclosure and even less wise for two-speaker stereo.) Plans for such installations look intriguing on paper. But a design on paper is one thing and a good acoustical listening spot is quite another; too much depends on the subsequent arrangement and quality of furniture and of drapes and rugs—and on architectural intangibles that can't be accurately forecast. Too much, also, depends on the musical ear of your hi-fi architect-designer, who probably makes no pretense at all to being a musician! Be wise—and wait until your house is built before you try to locate the best place for your loudspeaker.

But this belongs in the next chapter.

15

Living Room Acoustics

The most crucial aspect of the entire home music system as far as your direct listening pleasure is concerned is the listening room and its arrangement. Crucial because few listeners have the slighest conception of the tremendous effect *the room itself* has upon the reproduced sound that you hear—after it has left the loudspeaker. After all, our music obviously comes to us from the phonograph loudspeaker; and so we assume, with the greatest of logic, that its qualities are determined in the machine or in the recording or broadcast we are hearing.

The trouble is that most of us never actually come to grips with our room acoustics. We confuse the room with the machine—and it's not at all easy to separate them, in the listening. Normally, most of us listen in a single situation. We don't move our machines around and we thus very seldom have the chance to hear them in differing acoustics. Our own listening spot's sound becomes so familiar to us that it blends itself into a background and we are not consciously aware of it at all; there is no dramatic way in which its contribution to the musical sound may suddenly be made clear to us.

And yet think a bit. Perhaps you have had the significant experience of playing a familiar recording on someone else's phonograph in another house and finding the sound quite unlike that which you know in your own room. It happens often. Of course it would not occur to you that the difference might be other than in the two machines themselves. Why should it? We all know how differently our various phonographs perform. And if by some very unlikely chance the two machines in this case were identical, you would still naturally assume, with a million other people, that something must be wrong with one of them to account for the difference. There would not be one chance in a million that you would pursue a further and rigorous line of inquiry— and *trade machines*, just to be sure.

But if you did, then at last you might discover for yourself the amazing fact that the two phonographs were indeed as exactly alike as two copies of the same record, and that the differences in the sound were entirely a matter of room acoustics.

I myself first discovered these things fortuitously during a series of lectures in which I carted the same phonograph equipment and the same records from one place to another, into plush home parlors, churches, bare school gyms, college common rooms—and in every one I produced the same sounds on the same equipment. I could scarcely believe what happened. In one place the machine would unaccountably lose two-thirds of its voice; in another the bass sounded utterly feeble, the high tones harsh and screeching (which annoyed me as thoroughly as it did the audience)—but before I could make any change in the machine itself I would lecture elsewhere, only to find that now the highs were as smooth as silk, and the bass quite normal! There were rooms where the bass boomed, or where a sofa cushion seemed to have been stuffed into the loudspeaker. My fond arguments in favor of high fidelity were in one place effective and, in another, distressingly unconvincing.

Many home listeners, then, fly off on wild goose chases looking for trouble in their machines where there is none, reordering parts, invoking guarantees, turning in amplifiers, speakers, cartridges, for others more costly, distributing cash and tearing hair. A considerable segment of the hi-fi business is supported on this basis, you may be sure.

And, conversely, there are many inexplicably lucky souls whose rooms happen to be acoustically ideal, to the bafflement of their friends. Any old machine will do for them and the sound, strangely, is always musical. Indeed, the machine itself seems minimized; the music comes forward unimpeded. Record scratch, pops and clicks, static, distortion, all seem to take care of themselves; the music is not too soft, or too loud, it is "right" at almost any volume you choose. And you will note that in such a room the sound always seems *musically big and full*, even from a miniature radio, and *its source is not easily determined* by the ear, whatever the eye may see. These are telltale signs of good listening acoustics. You'll want to strive for those effects yourself.

PORTABLE RADIO TEST. If you have a portable radio you can demonstrate some of this for yourself. (Any machine that you can move about will do, but a portable is easiest because of absence of wires.) Turn it on, preferably to some good music, then walk from your living room into a tiled bathroom. The loudness will suddenly increase and so will the sense of "presence," the realness and immediacy of the imagined musicians. But take the machine into a coat closet full of clothes and the music will be small, dry, close, the brilliance gone, the orchestra bodily shrunken.

Set it in the middle of your living room on a table or chair, with space around it on all sides. Then move it down to the floor against a wall (at a place where there is no rug), and you will notice an immediate increase in the depth of the bass. The actual power factor in this can be as much as six to one! A horn effect.

Move your portable from side to side and corner to corner, stopping long enough to listen critically at each likely spot. Compare the sound at the corners and the sides of your room for any pronounced difference. Try the radio at head level and at floor level—for you may find that this makes a difference in your particular situation.

Once you accept the principle that different positioning of the speaker in the same room may radically affect your musical sound, you can make all sorts of fruitful experiments, if not with the radio then with your system itself when it arrives.

You'll find that the corner is the best place for power, with the walls acting as a horn, in which you are situated. Corners bring out the best bass, too. But unfortunately many corners are not clear of furniture and even when they are, corner listening is not ideal, especially for large orchestra sound, which does not like being confined to a narrow source. Better a wide wall and proper general sound reflection, for best orchestral "width." If your corner works, there are large numbers of corner speakers designed specifically for use in it—but be sure, before you buy.

HIGHS AND LOWS. We can analyze these over-all acoustic differences into a number of specific effects. Take pitch. High tones and low tones are quite differently affected by your room.

Very high tones, as we have seen, tend to move straight ahead in a beam, in the manner of light rays. They are reflected from mirror-smooth surfaces in the same angular way that light is reflected. And irregular hard surfaces break up a sound beam, spread it about, as light is broken up and diffused by rough surfaces.

High-pitched tones are easily swallowed up by soft materials like upholstery, clothing, drapes, or by porous substances like cork or the "soundproofing" used in much modern room design. These materials act upon high sounds as dead-black surfaces do upon light.

Low-pitched sounds, on the other hand, are not easily absorbed by soft materials. Hence when you "deaden" a room with absorbent surfaces, drapes, cushions and rugs and people, you actually change the balance of highs and lows in the music, as specifically as though you had turned down a tone-control knob on your machine. Very important to know.

You'll also remember that low tones, unlike high tones, tend to fill a space uniformly with sound. A loudspeaker aiming out into the room will send a wide, rolling tide of low tones to every corner.

STANDING WAVE. Another unpleasant room phenomenon is the standing wave. It occurs when two large surfaces are exactly parallel to each other—as in virtually all our living rooms. At critical points in the low register the sound waves are the right length to resonate in our rooms, which become giant booming organ pipes, the waves piling back on themselves so that in effect they stand still, with very loud spots in one part of the room and "dead" spots in others. The room space itself is thus resonant to certain frequencies. These low-pitched standing waves can wreak havoc with your music. The extreme resonance involves a large transfer of energy, and the entire system may be affected right back into the electrical circuit—the amplifier is often severely overloaded.

As usual, most people blame these sounds on the machine or the recording. I've seen this many a time and was guilty myself once of such mistaken judgment. I discarded a speaker because of what I thought was very boomy bass response; it was then set up in another room in a nearby house while I got a new one. To my chagrin, the old speaker was fine in the new place but my new one produced the same "faulty" bass as had its predecessor! Standing wave.

You can cope with standing waves in many cases simply by moving the speaker a few feet back and forth or from side to side; the boom may disappear in a slightly changed location. Furniture or anything else that breaks up the smooth parallel surfaces of the walls will also help. (Fancy radio studios are often designed to be dead at one end and live—hard and shiny—at the other, on similar principles, and you will note that few studios have parallel walls.) It is hardly practical for us to redesign American architecture away from parallel walls but we can do a lot to break up the surfaces, and if conditions are really bad we can drape or soundproof an entire wall to kill the standing waves.

One of the most prolific demonstrations of standing-wave trouble is in the hi-fi store's demonstration room, which is often no more than a converted office space, minus rugs and hangings. Even worse are some of the uncompromising hotel rooms that are used for sound demonstrating at the hi-fi shows.

A good audible test for room resonance of this sort is the quality and direction of any booming effect you may notice. A standing wave has a peculiar "feel" to it; it seems to come from all sides, in the air itself; it is almost an ear pressure. Not easy to describe, this sensation, but you may be able to spot it in your own room if some of the very low tones are peculiarly unpleasant.

REFLECTIONS AND THE POINT SOURCE. The most vital room effect of all is that of reflection. In order to be natural, reproduced sound must approximate the reverberation or liveness the original music might have had. Think about this a moment. In the original hall this reflected richness of sound came to the mike not from straight ahead but from behind and from the sides and above, reflected from the hall itself. It was a live "room sound," essential for a musical effect.

In your own room, those same sounds issue one and all from the loudspeaker—both the original music and the multiple reflections, the liveness. It should be clear to you then that it is highly unnatural for this reverberation to come from a single point, the loudspeaker, where in the original hall it came from all directions. The ear confirms this.

Moreover, it is also unnatural for a symphony orchestra to be compressed to the width of a loudspeaker—a mere foot or so! Because we like to look at our phonographs, we have developed the bad habit of facing the speaker, sitting directly in its beam. You'll do much better, looks or not, to conceal its location from the eyes as well as the ears. You'll want to spread out the apparent sound source as widely as possible in order to come somewhere near the actual effect of the original music as we hear it "in the concert hall." As a matter of fact, music for ensembles smaller than the symphony orchestra must be considered in the same way, for we sit much closer to it in a real performance and so its apparent width to us is often even greater than that of the orchestra.

We must hear music not from a point then, but from an area, the larger and wider, the better. And, therefore, we cannot have natural-sounding home music without a large proportion of reflected sound reaching our ears indirectly rather than straight from the loudspeakers.

Luckily this is usually accomplished for us automatically more or less by accident, thanks to the normal reflective powers of home walls, furniture, floors, ceiling. Out of sheer habit and association you probably face your speaker and imagine that you hear the entire sound directly from it, but you're wrong. Don't believe it? Try the hands-behind-the-ears test. Cup your hands (eyes closed), first forward, then backward, and you'll find very little difference—i.e., as much sound comes to you from the rear (reflected) as directly from the speaker.

IMPROVING YOUR REFLECTION. Poor home listening rooms are often too dead. Too many drapes, bookcases, sofas, too much plush upholstery and soft carpet. Reflection doesn't have a chance in these surroundings. Point-source music, music beamed straight to the listener from the speaker without adequate reflection in the room, is extremely unpleasant, no matter how expensive the high fidelity equipment. Too-live rooms, on the other hand, make for oversimplified "mirror" reflections.

School classrooms, large lecture halls and institutional chambers of all sorts are almost always too live for good listening. Not only too great reflection, but too simple. In such rooms the plane surfaces, flat parallel walls, smooth floors and ceiling, geometrical tables and desks, all add up to so many sound mirrors, reflecting the speaker beam much too faithfully. Standing waves are likely if the size is right. (The larger the room, the lower the pitch of the standing waves; a large auditorium puts them mostly below the range of audibility.)

What can you do then, to improve your listening situation?

Perhaps you are not even sure what your situation is. You may not have had a chance to make comparisons. A good test is to measure the beam effect of your machine at a fair distance from the speaker. If at from five or ten or fifteen feet you can walk in and out of what seems to be a narrow band of loud, strident music, or if when you stand at the side of the machine the sound is very noticeably different from that directly in front—then you have reflection trouble.

If you are not satisfied with your room try these things:

1. If it is too dead, brighten up the room's sound properties. Move out some of the soft plush and draperies; put in harder furniture, allow for more open wall and floor, fewer rugs. If too live, vice versa. You will want *irregular* reflecting surfaces. Every bit helps—crockery, china, glass vases, framed pictures, polished wood, metal. Good sound reflection actually is diffusion, the breaking up of the beam into hundreds of complex blended reflections. Look out for large flat surfaces, especially two parallel walls or floor or ceiling. Try to break them up with hard furniture, ornaments, or china, or deaden them with drapes or an ornamental rug. (You can afford to sacrifice some of your total liveness in the interests of removing a bad flat surface.)

2. Go over all possible new locations for the speaker, trying them out for sound. Move a chair or table out of the way to try a doubtful location even if it is not "available"—it might be the perfect spot, in which case you will move your furniture or lose your sound.

3. Break up the speaker's actual beam—interpose irregular or curved, hard and shiny surfaces—table legs, china bowls, chairs, directly between the speaker and your listening spot. (Get away from that idea that you must face your speaker and look at it with an unimpeded view! It has no intrinsic musical interest.) A curving piano frame at eight or ten feet, in the speaker beam, will diffuse part of it nicely, let the rest go on to still more distant reflecting surfaces. But avoid flat, mirror reflections close to the speaker—they leave the beam intact, merely change its direction.

Keep in mind that reflecting irregularities even in the farthest reaches of your room will affect the sound. Everything helps, each surface according to the sound that reaches it, either directly or from a prior reflection. It all adds up, as inevitably as weight. (Sound moves so rapidly that a zigzag reflection from a dozen surfaces will reach your ear only a microscopic fraction of a second later than the direct beam. Residual reverberation, the sound that is left to die out after a sudden noise like a clap, is no more than these weakening reflections, zipping about the room in thousands of paths diffused into one general noise.)

4. Experiment with your speaker's aim. Direct it here and there, against different parts of the furniture and walls. You will probably find that the best sound is heard when the beam is aimed off to one side of your listening spot at a slant rather than directly toward you. Move yourself from place to place in the same way, testing for the

most natural listening spot. The greater your own distance from the
speaker, the better your chances for good reflection. Often the best
place of all is in another room, especially if there are big double doors.

5. Point it away. It is worth while, especially in a smallish room,
to point the speaker away from the listening spot so that you receive
none of the direct beam at all. This plan saved an earlier small listening room of mine and I have gladly used it for years in several other
rooms without finding a better solution. It works beautifully in many

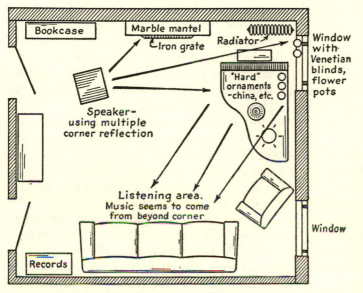

Corner reflection in a small room

places where direct-beam effects are noticeably unpleasant, and it can
make a very small room seem large.

Aim toward a corner first, one that is free of deadening materials;
take away the plush chairs and put in wooden ones; avoid heavy window
drapes. Don't clear the corner out entirely—far from it. The more
irregular reflecting surfaces in it, the better the effect. Venetian blinds,
iron radiators, furniture legs, curved wood or metal surfaces, scrollwork
—all are excellent for reflection.

If you find the right setup, you will hear the music not from the
speaker at all but apparently right out of the corner itself, or better, in

a broad area along the wall and into the corner. Realism will be greatly enhanced. Musical performers will seem suddenly to be larger and more lifelike.

If the effect is not right at first, don't give up until you have tried various aimings of the speaker beam. Move it up or down. It's best to aim it off to one side of the corner instead of right into it, to get a more complex reflection.

The effect can be quite astonishing, especially if you will disguise the speaker with a covering drape plus odd records and the like on top. People enter the room and look for the speaker—unable to find it. The actual box is usually not noticed—for the sound doesn't appear to come from it. By easy test—turning the speaker about to face the listeners—this arrangement can be shown to enhance the naturalness of almost any music; with it an orchestra seems full-sized, a chamber group apparently is playing about twenty feet *beyond* the corner on the other side of the wall, in plain sight, so to speak.

Yes, I realize that this advice flies straight in the face of normal procedure. What! Look at the back of a speaker with a perfectly good-looking front grille designed to please the eye? The rear or, at best, the side is what you'll have to see in my recommended system. A happy development: some speaker makers have seen the light and now offer their smaller speaker boxes with all four sides finished. (E.g., KLH, Eico.)

By good luck, the new small speaker boxes, now becoming widely popular (Chapter 12), are very nicely adapted to this procedure. They make handy tabourets, TV side tables, cocktail and ashtray holders (with a doily or mat on top), general-purpose catch-alls, and you will soon find yours quite indispensable for these purposes, entirely aside from the sound it produces. A first-rate new idea, this, and you'd better think about it.

TONE CONTROLS AND ROOM LIVENESS. Use your tone controls! We have already gone into the matter of equalization for "flat" response; every bit of that still applies to every record you play, anywhere. But having settled equalization, we now encounter the room. And so in addition to our manipulations of its furnishings, as above, we use the tone controls as is their intent, to balance the sound as it exists *in the room*.

How much adjustment? The maximum adjustment on most amplifier controls is from 15 to 20 db or more boost and roll-off, in both bass and treble range. I've found that in many very live "hard" rooms it's necessary to use the full range of the treble tone control to bring the shrill-sounding highs down to an acceptable balance. In a very dead room you may have to boost them by several "hours" on the tone control to override the plush and the pillows.

Bass adjustment is less important in itself since the bass tones are less affected by the room. You can, however, seem to increase or decrease the *highs* by changing the bass—the ear being easily fooled. If in a very live room, a school gymnasium or classroom, you can't reduce your highs enough to get rid of the piercing, shrieking quality in the music, then boost the bass a bit too. It will help the balance. Conversely, if yours is an extremely dead living room and you find that with a good boost in the highs your music still seems muffled, cut down on the bass. Your highs will be in better balance and so will seem more brilliant, though actually they are unchanged. A good trick to know.

But isn't all this a gross distortion of the music, this extra boosting and rolling-off? Yes, you have deliberately destroyed the literal balance of sound—at the speaker. But what does that matter? What counts is what we hear, at the ear. And that is conditioned by the listening room. I don't mean to suggest that correct preliminary "flatness" of reproduction is not absolutely essential. It is all the more important that we begin with an electrically balanced sound, the exact reproduction of the original as it reached the microphone, before altering it to suit the listening room. We must keep the two functions, equalization for the deliberate imbalance in records, and tone control for room characteristics, quite separate from each other in our minds, as they now are on our amplifier controls.

16

Stereo

Stereophonic sound! The exclamation itself conveys some of the excitement that has been generated by this new form of double reproduction: two sound-signals made simultaneously at two (sometimes three) different points in front of the music, brought to your ears through two amplifiers and two separate loudspeaker systems spaced apart on each side of you.

Stereo *discs* have now brought this fundamentally new way of listening into an area where it may be considered by the great majority of record collectors—for stereo disc equipment is relatively simple and inexpensive, the compatibility between standard and stereo discs very high (they are practically interchangeable on the same machine) and conversion problems are far less complex than in the earlier change from 78 records to LP. Stereo *tape* has been the de luxe stereo medium, though in its new "half-track" form it is competitive in cost. (See p. 196.)

When stereo tape recording first appeared, back in the early fifties, I wasn't very enthusiastic about it. "Binaural" sound, as it was more often called then, was not convincing in the early demonstrations for those of us who wondered what it could do for music. The sound was spectacular, grossly exaggerated, noisy, unmusical; the recorded material was mostly of dubious value. Promotion pushed hard at the corniest and most transitory aspects of stereo: roaring jet planes, Diesel locomotives, racing cars, ping-pong games (enormously magnified), not to mention blaring "hi-fi demonstration" music.

The hoopla has certainly not diminished in recent times—but along with it, stereo has been showing its true values for serious musical listening. From a doubter I have been converted to a stereo fan and the cause is strictly in stereo music itself.

Stereophonic recording began largely outside of the standard record business. The first commercial stereo tapes were of fitful interest and not really competitive with the music on disc. But, as interest in stereo possibilities spread, the record companies themselves began to experiment. It seems clear, at this point, that the record industry as well as the hi-fi business looked to this new medium as a future stimulus, when LP should have run its course and new excitement would be needed to keep us buyers buying—both records and playing equipment.

Now this has caused some cynical eyebrow-raising among record buyers, I'll admit. Another new system forced down our throats! Undoubtedly, this aspect of stereo has its importance. But if the innovation is a good one (as was LP, in spite of early objections) then we will take it gladly.

In any case, for some years now all recording has been done in both standard and stereo versions, for future reference. A good many stereo recordings have been released—but the number of tapes thus held in reserve, for wider stereo use, is astronomical. This in itself is an important factor.

STEREO FOR MUSIC. The fact that I am devoting a chapter to stereo indicates my belief that it does offer the sort of permanent musical values that are worth considering, so to speak, at any price.

The days of zany stereo are about over; the serious values are emerging—and I suggest that you can now simply forget all about the past and look at stereo as a mature, reasonable aid to home music listening, on the highest level.

The more perceptive are your musical senses, the wider your understanding of the larger world of music, then the higher are the values in stereo for you, the greater the subtleties. This may be a surprise; but stereo publicity has not been aimed toward you, the serious listener, except in the vaguest of snob-appeal superlatives. Most stereo demonstrations are dismally unsuccessful as far as musical values are concerned. The stereo effect in its really musical aspects is neither obvious nor blatant—and it is often missed entirely on casual first hearing.

THE SOUND CURTAIN. Is stereo "more realistic"? Yes, if by that you mean that there is a better *illusion* of naturalness and immediacy.

Stereo is no more literal than standard recording; its effect is just as much an illusion and requires as much good imagination. It merely adds one single new factor of perception to those already present in standard recording—a small but significant degree of side-to-side separation, often so slight as to be barely perceptible. And yet that extra bit of sound-information, having to do with the apparent source of the sound, can make a tremendous difference to an active musical imagination—given a well-made stereo recording.

Stereo has also been called 3-D. In plain fact it is no more than 2-D, two dimensional. Ordinary recording is actually one-dimensional, as we have seen in Chapter 4.

The stereo recording improves on this situation in a small way—but it represents the difference between something and nothing. In "live," natural music (and other sound) the sources are as varied in direction as in quality; they come from wherever they are, from a dozen or a thousand different points. Moreover, their reflections, the liveness or echo of a concert hall, reach you similarly from a million different shades of direction—and the two ears on your head detect those endless subtleties of directional source and blend them together, into that over-all sense of living music that is our supposed ideal for recorded sound. The standard recording brings this sound to you from a single source, the loudspeaker, and though you may break it up into a new pattern of reflection in your room the truth is that you can never, by any conceivable means, actually separate one sound from another as in the original music. Spread out the orchestra over your living room wall and you spread the soloist too.

The ideal stereo recording would pick up sound at an infinite number of different points. You may perhaps be intrigued by the theoretical "sound-curtain" that engineers invoke to bolster this concept. Imagine a vast curtain in front of the music; one side is an infinite number of microphones, the other an equal number of loudspeakers. In theory, every trace of sound hitting the curtain on the mike side would be transferred to the loudspeaker side and the net result would be sound-transparency. A nice idea though impractical! If an infinite number of tape recorders were put to work to take down the infinite number of sound-points, we would have a species of *literal* recording in space.

In practice we have reduced infinity to the smallest possible number that gives dimensionality at all—just two. A reduction from the theoretically perfect, you'll admit. And yet "something" is so superior to nothing at all, in dimensionality, that the vividly imaginative human musical ear can "hear" a really fabulous degree of side-to-side realism under good stereo conditions. It is easy to understand this if you will keep in mind that the pleasures of standard recorded sound have always been enjoyed without a trace of literal side-to-side information. If no sidewise directionality can be as good as it is, then by the same token, some directionality, even of the vaguest and most incomplete sort, can be even better—with imagination, a lot better. That is the key to stereo listening.

Home stereo, then, is a compromise. Instead of a sound-curtain of an infinite number of points there are only two. The technological development that made stereo practical for home use was tape; two simultaneous recordings could be placed side by side on a standard tape to be played simultaneously. More recently the two recordings are heard via a single stereo disc.

If your ears are rightly teamed with your imagination, you can re-create in your mind from these two discrete sound-points (they are actually no bigger than the microphones that picked them up) a single, over-all sound picture that seems to stretch bodily from one side of your room to the other, between and behind the two speakers. You imagine a very real space—considerably more real than in the case of standard recording—and within it you can actually hear, in a vague sort of way, that certain parts of the music are in one area, others in different areas. Now this is so obviously an illusion that you can judge the stereo effect as a whole by it. There is no sound-source between the speakers—you are being induced to hear one there, by the curious interaction of those two point-samplings, each one of which is giving you part of the sound. Strange, to say the least, but aesthetically very useful in terms of musical reproduction.

Stereo, of course, can be very bad as well as good. Stereo technique is a matter of controlling illusion, of learning to create useful effects and avoid false ones. That is not very different, when you come down to it, from the requirements for good standard recording. In these terms, stereo is a subtle art. It is easy enough to force a literal directionality, to record a musical instrument or a railroad train so that it is violently directional—its sound comes blatantly out of one speaker and not the other. That effect is interesting, but limited (and so are the many "demonstration" tapes that exploit it for stereo sensationalism). The far more tricky bridging over of the space *between* your two speakers offers the really valuable potential in stereo, and it demands subtlety in the sidewise placement of the musical sounds—vagueness, if you will. A musical instrument too obviously near to one of the two microphones, too violently "in" one of the two speakers, will quickly kill the less positive directional effects that re-create the middle area, between the speakers.

Admittedly, there are times when you need no middle area. Stereo is fine for numerous close-up jazz and chamber music sounds where the individual instruments may be heard straight out of one speaker or the other. But as we well know, most musical illusion in the home has to do with sounds that are bigger than your room can hold and farther away than your living room wall. For all such music—and that means most of the music we hear—you will need a powerful sense of illusion; you will want to recreate the sense of imagined space, as you do in standard recording.

STEREO DOUBLING. If the illusion of continuous space is broken, you suffer the bugbear of all stereo listening, the double image. You then have two separate sound-sources; you hear two orchestras, there are two soloists although only one is playing. The double-image effect is the sure sign of stereo trouble; it is the technological opposite of that effective sound-curtain that joins the two speakers' sound into one tonal picture, within which there are separate sounds.

Doubling is not always as bad as it seems for, after all, your "two" soloists play the same music; but the effect is false and therefore actually less realistic, less satisfactory than the ordinary one-directional sound of standard recording. Fortunately, there are other things about stereo sound that can make it attractive even though a slight degree of doubling is almost always present. You can learn to ignore this quite easily, in favor of things more helpful to the musical illusion. And though there may be two soloists, there is usually but one orchestra. The doubling effect may apply only to some sounds, not to others.

Liveness has much to do with stereo impressiveness. Big, live stereo sound, in huge, live halls, is the most effective to hear. (Conversely, small-scale, close-to, "dry" stereo recordings are only mildly exciting in the stereo sense.) Stereo, oddly enough, does more for the hall than for the actual music, but the music benefits indirectly in astonishing ways. A drum roll, for instance, is often startling in stereo, even though the loudspeakers reproducing it are far from hi-fi. The effect is not in the drum itself but in the reverberation, the almost instantaneous side-to-side "wall-bounce" of the sound, reflected from the sides of the auditorium, first one and then the other. These sounds are in all recordings, of course; but in stereo they take on very nearly their literal effect for your ears.

One more aspect of stereo sound is worth thinking about before we move on. At its best, stereo clarifies musical sound to the degree in which it is able to separate the sound sources from each other. The separation is vague—but again the aesthetic effect is relatively large. Orchestral sound takes on a new transparency, a quality of lightness and aliveness. The whole texture of the music becomes curiously more comprehensible, more fathomable to the ear. (That is, of course, if the ear is able to understand the music in the first place—for these things are quite lost on the nonmusical ear!)

Work to find a really good place for your stereo listening—it can be crucial. Choose your stereo recordings carefully—you must be choosy; stereo is more demanding, more tricky than standard recording. Then let your stereo sound take its own time to grow upon you. Give it a long while before you come to any final conclusions.

STEREO TAPE EQUIPMENT. Tape stereo equipment is in all its aspects merely an extension of normal equipment, the usual players and speakers doubled. Remarks that apply to regular equipment are thus good in the main for stereo tape as well. You will find full information on stereo tape equipment in Chapter 13.

First, I offer as a principle that *no stereo is good unless the two channels are heard on roughly comparable speakers*—comparable in respect to expense, if you wish, but more vitally, comparable in their general coverage of the sound spectrum. Identical speakers are not necessary, but are desirable—on the simple principle that differing characteristics, especially in the ultra-noticeable high range, will add irrelevancies to your sound. Speakers of the same brand often have a family resemblance in sound.

Here are the essentials for tape stereo:

1. Double "stacked" (in-line) tape playing head, for standard 7½ ips tape; double offset head and adapting equipment for 3¾ ips "cartridge" tape (p. 196).
2. Two tape preamplifiers, equalized for tape head playback. (One

may be your phonograph preamplifier, if it has a TAPE HEAD position.)

3. Two complete and separate amplifier channels, high-level. They may be built together on one chassis, or built into a complete recorder; or one may be your outside hi-fi amplifier.

4. Two separate speaker systems in two enclosures. (They may be suitcase models, or removable lids on a tape machine, or two enclosures of larger size and better quality.) As above, the two, whether small or large, cheap or expensive, should sound alike, or as nearly alike as possible. Do not plan to use one table-model built-in speaker (in a tape recorder or "hi-fi" phonograph) and one larger hi-fi speaker.

For room requirements, see below.

Note that in most stereo tape machines there is provision for one-channel (monaural) recording, as well as all forms of tape playback, both monaural and stereo (Chapter 13). This means that one of the two built-in preamplifiers is also a recording amplifier.

STEREO DISC. Stereo disc is newer, trickier and of much wider interest to music listeners than the more elaborate stereo tape. It's worth looking at in detail.

Yes, the two separate recordings that make up any stereo reproduction may, indeed, be cut into a single record groove. That, at first thought, seems an impossibility to most of us. (Emory Cook's "binaural" discs of a few years ago did have two separate grooves, an inner band and an outer band played simultaneously by two pickups side by side.) The now-standard one-groove system, the so-called 45/45 (Westrex) system, is an improvement upon an earlier system that was brought to an advanced stage of development, the lateral-vertical stereo disc. Both systems, closely related, include the cutting head that makes the master record, the disc itself and the pickup cartridge that plays it in the home.

Every stereo disc, then, is two recordings in one, both engraved in a single spiral groove, played by a single needle. The two recordings are neatly separated and sent respectively to the two stereo loudspeakers, to right and left of your listening place, just as in the case of stereo tape.

Look first at the lateral-vertical system, forerunner of the 45/45. The first recordings of all, Edison's on tinfoil, were cut with vertical vibrations ("hill-and-dale") impressed or embossed by the stylus. The old cylinder records and the later thick Edison disc were vertical-cut; the playing stylus moved up and down in the groove rather than from side to side. Later, the electrical process was adapted to vertical-cut, high-quality radio transcriptions. Dual pickups that would respond either to lateral or vertical vibrations were used for years in radio stations until the end of the Second World War.

Experimental work on a stereo disc record began a long time ago, back in the thirties. For years there had been two groove systems, lateral and vertical; if the two could be combined, and a way of cutting the records and playing them devised, then two recordings could be

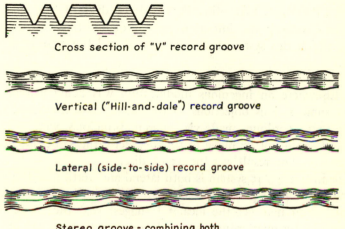

Cross section of "V" record groove

Vertical ("Hill-and-dale") record groove

Lateral (side-to-side) record groove

Stereo groove - combining both

The record groove

cut at once—one of them in terms of lateral, up-and-down waves in the groove as in the old Edison records, the other in the conventional side-wise or lateral groove motion. A reasonably good 78 rpm system was actually worked out—but the times weren't right. There was little interest in the idea and the war put a quick end to it.

After the war, however, came tape recording and "half track" home tape, with two recordings side by side on a single tape. The intention wasn't stereo at first; the two recordings were played one after the other, through the roll of tape and back again, to save space and expense. But the application to stereo, the two tracks playing simultaneously, was irresistible. Soon after 1950, "binaural" tape recordings were demonstrated, followed by the gradual introduction of commercial stereo (a later and better term) tape recordings. Stereophonic sound in the movies, at the time, gave home stereo a big boost though the two are only distantly related, in practice.

But stereo tape was quite expensive. The new wave of stereo interest revived the idea of a universal and cheap stereo disc, which now could be made in much-improved form on the new plastic long-play record.

In the spring of 1957 the first complete publicly demonstrated stereo disc system appeared in England, the Sugden, but other firms were also en route. In the fall English Decca showed its own complete system, along with a series of remarkably fine stereo discs, pressed in standard LP format. Like other British stereo discs of that time, they were lateral-vertical; the intention was to demonstrate the advanced stage to which this system had been carried and the records were not for sale.

45/45. Elsewhere an ingenious modification was being worked upon to meet some serious objections to the lateral-vertical system, mainly that the two recordings, made via different principles, were inherently unlike and could not be made to sound exactly the same, nor to wear evenly in use. The result was the 45/45 disc.

The definitive 45/45 system is both lateral and vertical in the groove, but each recording is *part lateral and part vertical*; the two are opposite but equal. You may get the idea if I suggest that the entire pickup system is tilted a quarter-turn—at 45 degrees—so that instead of lateral motion and vertical motion we have two diagonal motions, 90 degrees apart. Each recording, in effect, is at a 45-degree angle to vertical or lateral. If you are of a mechanical bent perhaps you can visualize, for analogy, a sawed-off V-8 automobile engine with two cylinders in the form of a V, opposed to each other at the diagonal. Substitute for them a pair of magnetic pickup coils and attach each "piston" to a phonograph stylus that will move up and down or from side to side—lateral and vertical motion.

If the two coils push their "pistons" simultaneously, the stylus motion is downward; if one coil pulls and one pushes, the motion is sidewise at the stylus tip. If either coil operates by itself—corresponding to one of the two stereo recordings—the diagonal motion will move the stylus diagonally, that is, partly vertical and partly horizontal. Every possible motion of either side is translated into a combination of vertical and horizontal movement of the stylus.

This is the way a 45/45 stereo disc is cut, speaking in very rough analogy. The playback of the disc is the same in reverse; the same mo-

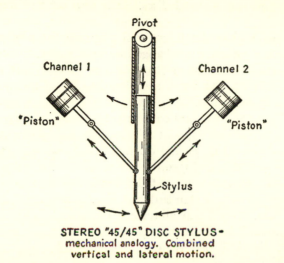

STEREO "45/45" DISC STYLUS -
mechanical analogy. Combined
vertical and lateral motion.

tions are transmitted by the playing needle to a similar pickup mounted in the same V formation, at the diagonal. The two channels thus have identical characteristics except that one is "right-handed," the other "left-handed."

In this stereo disc, the lateral, side-to-side element in the groove, it turns out, contains the essential monaural information in the recording, the "standard" sound, just as in an ordinary recording. The vertical element, the up-and-down groove wiggles, contain the subtle differences between the two stereo recordings, that give the essential stereo effect. Likeness and difference, if you wish, and the technical terms for the two are sum and difference.

Stereo 45-45 discs look like standard discs and are scarcely more expensive to make. They can be pressed exactly as standard records are. They play for the same length, type for type, since there is the same groove length.

PICKUPS AND COMPATIBILITY. The brief RCA-CBS battle in the press that raged a few months before the stereo discs appeared served only to suggest that stereo might mean another major upheaval in home equipment. Actually, the extent of compatibility between stereo and standard disc recording is astonishing.

1. As above, stereo discs have the same speed, size, groove, playing times, appearance as standard discs. Same size needle point will play either type.

2. All stereo pickup cartridges will play any microgroove record, either stereo or standard, interchangeably (except 78). Stereo cartridges are interchangeable with present cartridges, in all types and price ranges from top to bottom. Quality of sound varies—but is not compromised by stereo's seemingly greater complexity. Some stereo cartridges are even better than their standard counterparts—for all records of any type.

3. Thus you may use present phonograph equipment for stereo—everything but the actual pickup cartridge. And you may use all stereo equipment to play standard records, as well as or better than at present.

A. As a first step, you may install a stereo cartridge in your present arm as though it were a standard cartridge. (Connect the two stereo outputs together.) It will play all records, stereo and standard, as though they were standard discs, via the equipment you already own. You can collect stereo discs and play them as standard ones.

B. With the required dual amplifier-speaker system (your present equipment can be half of it) your stereo cartridge, in any arm, will play stereo records with full stereo effect, through two speakers; it will also play standard records through the same two speakers, with enhanced realism, though without the stereo effect.

Only one extra wire is needed in the pickup arm. (Many changers with detachable heads already have an extra connection, which can be adapted for this.) All newer equipment will be wired to take either stereo or standard pickups.

There is only one serious incompatibility. You cannot safely play a stereo disc with most present standard pickups, due to their lack of vertical compliance, up-and-down flexibility in the needle tip, needed to ride safely over the up-and-down bumps in the stereo groove. (It was here that the CBS "compatible stereo disc" would have allowed complete interchangeability, by reducing the vertical component of the groove so that standard pickups could play it.) A very few highly compliant lightweight standard pickups will track the stereo disc safely. Not many. (Such fancy models as the Grado, Volpar, Shure Dynetic and some cheaper models.)

Incompatibility—and potential damage to the stereo disc. But once you have acquired a stereo cartridge, the incompatibility departs. The stereo needle moves as easily up and down as it does sidewise.

Here are safe rules for pickups:

A. Use a stereo pickup on *all* microgroove records (LP, 45, 16).

B. For 78's, use a stereo-78 turnover cartridge; or a separate 78 player or arm.

C. Do *not* play stereo discs with a standard cartridge. Keep the two apart. Beware of unknowing users of your equipment!

The playing problems, you see, are no greater than with present discs, of different grooves and speeds.

Stereo cartridges, newly developed, are generally high in performance at the price, especially in the low-priced ceramics. In fact the ceramic is a "natural" for stereo, and cartridges of excellent quality can be made very simply and cheaply. (They bend in two directions, instead of one.) Magnetics are relatively more complex, with two sets of coils to produce the two stereo signals—but quality also can be very high, without compromise. Most ceramics have three contacts; the outside pair are the two channels, the middle is a common ground connection (shield). Magnetics may have four contacts; but the two ground leads can be joined. Mounting is the same as for standard cartridges. Prices are generally only slightly higher.

Stereo "hi-fi" phonographs are necessarily two-piece at a minimum, because of the two speakers that must be separated in the listening room. Likely common forms: (a) a phonograph box, table-style or on legs, and a duplicate box containing the second speaker. (b) Similar, but a tape recorder in the second box; you may play either tapes or discs, through both speakers. (c) Console phonographs with an extra speaker in a second cabinet. (d) A phono player unit and two separate speakers, mounted in two lids, the whole fitting into one piece for portability.

Component hi-fi equipment for disc stereo is, of course, full of variety—and flexibility in the adaptation. You may install a stereo cartridge in any player arm. You will need two amplifiers (alike if possible), two speaker systems (alike). Use what you have.

Various *stereo adapter units,* for tape and/or disc, are now available—dual stereo preamplifiers, dual radio tuners, FM and AM, dual control centers, etc. Their common denominator is "ganged" controls—one control for both channels together—plus switches and adjustments for various alternatives; most units provide one or more of the extra components you need to round out a dual system. Useful when you are joining up your components for stereo, each with its own independent controls and facilities, or lack of them. An inexpensive example is the *H. H. Scott Stereo-Dapter,* $25, a common control center and switching unit for two separate amplifiers used for stereo and other purposes.

Phasing is a major problem in stereo, and is not always taken care of automatically. (If one speaker's signals are reversed, the speaker "pulling" while the other "pushes," so to speak, the stereo sound is divided in the middle, the blending destroyed. Phasing may be (a) reversed on the tape (rare, but possible), (b) reversed in the speaker connections—change one of them around the other way; (c) phasing may be reversed by some amplifiers—if you use two different models, beware; (d) it may be reversed, inadvertently, by some magnetic stereo cartridges. Best insurance is to have a permanent phasing switch that reverses the connections to one of your two speakers—or simply pull the wires off and change them around.

To check phasing, (1) play a stereo tape or disc and stand midway between speakers; move your head sidewise back and forth. If the sound seems to jump from one speaker to the other, if there is poor blending at the center, reverse one speaker's connections and listen again. (2) Play a test record or tape (monaural) with a low-pitched tone signal, or hum, through both speakers. With right phasing, lower tones are strengthened when you stand at the mid-point. With wrong phasing, lower tones are weakened.

THE STEREO ADVANTAGE. From Chapter 15 you'll remember that a good listening situation contributes so much to the illusion of naturalness and immediacy in music that the equipment itself seems to be improved. The principle applies to any factor that makes for better listening, and stereo is decidedly such a factor. Put it down in your mental notebook, then, that stereo seems to enhance the quality of modest equipment, sometimes quite astonishingly. It is true, unfortunately, that you must have two of everything for stereo sound. Two amplifiers, two speaker systems. Double expenditure would seem to be indicated and in fact most of the ardent hi-fi stereo fans will tell you that you must have the very best of everything, if you want "real" stereo. Triple, quadruple cost, that is the hi-fi stereo implication. But if you'll consider the above point, you'll understand why I suggest that from the music listener's viewpoint stereo needs *less* fancy equipment than standard hi-fi sound, speaker for speaker, amplifier for amplifier.

I still am using one of the first home stereo tape players, a very modest outfit, because it offers such revealing evidence of this. This machine is housed in two table-style boxes, on legs; each has three little speakers in it, of the smallest size, and the "enclosure" is no bigger than the tiny space at the front of most portable phonographs. Two little amplifiers provide about three watts of power for each channel, six watts in all. The whole thing amounts to a pair of standard low-priced "hi-fi" table models, hooked to a stereo tape player. Yet the sound of this machine playing a good stereo tape is a revelation for hi-fi skeptics. It is incredibly better than any single "hi-fi" phonograph —as I can easily demonstrate by disconnecting one of the units, letting the other one play by itself. If this machine can be as good as it is for music, then stereo is in truth a heartening development and the stereo advantage, as I describe it, is worth dollars and cents in terms of greater musical enjoyment for a given quality in the equipment. If it sounds better, it *is* better, musically speaking. Here is a major point to think over, if you are afraid stereo is too costly.

STEREO AT HOME. I can give you a few general hints as to the best way to set up stereo for listening at home—assuming that you have read Chapter 15 as a general guide to all music listening via the loudspeaker. They are simple enough, and are mostly concerned with symmetry.

1. As above, *buy symmetrical stereo.* Be sure that your two "channels" are reasonably equal and alike, on whatever level of excellence they may be. Do *not*, except for strictly temporary use, pair off your big hi-fi speaker system with some pipsqueak built-in "hi-fi" speaker in a small machine! Better two pipsqueaks of equal sound—better for the music.

2. *Choose a placement for your two speakers that is as symmetrical as possible*, with the same general wall and space configurations on each side. This is vitally important. If there is an open door or hallway on one side, there should be a similar opening on the other side. A cleared corner to the right should be balanced with a similar corner to the left. If not, your stereo sound will probably be thrown off balance.

I don't suggest that you rebuild your house to fit the stereo needs. Just look carefully for a good spot; try several before you make up your mind. You may have to fill in a door or an open area of some sort by placing a reflecting screen behind one speaker, to accomplish a balanced symmetry. I have done this very thing in a New York apartment with excellent results. (Any solid or cardboard screen will do, but not a cloth or openwork one.)

3. For general orchestral listening, *place the two speakers from a quarter to a third of the distance from the corners*, in the long end of the room. Exact placing depends on the local acoustics and on the recording and the music. For smaller ensembles—piano and violin, for instance—you will want to move the speakers closer together. In some

large-hall orchestral recordings you can move them farther apart for a grand effect.

4. *Avoid all types of built-in stereo,* no matter how tempting from the decorative viewpoint! I appreciate the good looks of those large, one-piece stereo consoles with the speakers built into the two ends (and special doors to reflect the sound forward) but I distrust their adaptability to stereo's notoriously touchy needs. Speaker systems built permanently into a wall are even more likely to fail in their main function. You will always be better off with two movable speakers, however simple, however fancy.

5. By all means *avoid the single corner,* for one of your two speakers. (Two adjacent corners sometimes give a good stereo effect, though generally speaking, a placement along the wall is a better bet.) Many a listener has been disappointed in the well-meaning attempt to save redecorating headaches by keeping the old speaker in its corner, adding a second speaker against an adjacent wall. Lack of symmetry is the fault. With such radically different acoustical settings, even two identical speakers will fail to blend into stereo realism.

6. Check your completed stereo system for *speaker phasing,* as above.

7. *Balance your speakers' sound for equal volume.* This isn't always easy to do since music at both speakers tends to fluctuate in volume, sometimes louder on one side, sometimes the other. Some stereo recordings provide a steady tone for balancing; set the volume so it sounds the same in both speakers from your listening point. Failing this, listen carefully to music and set volume levels so that the average sound is neither too much on one side or the other—allowing for the sense of the music itself.

Apparent loudness is strongly affected at each speaker by its situation in the room. If you have a door or hallway near one speaker and a solid wall behind the other, the loudness is certain to be different, even at the same actual volume output. Most stereo systems have an adjustment somewhere for this. A few have no adjustment; you will have to adjust the room, via a reflecting screen or other changes—or try the speakers in a different location.

8. Be ready to *change the speaker spacing frequently,* from one record to the next. There is a surprisingly varied range of best spacing from one kind of stereo sound to another, according to circumstance.

9. Finally, *listen actively to stereo!*

Stereo sound is singularly unadapted to background listening. One of its biggest virtues in a purely musical sense is that for best listening it requires real attention and considerable moving about to find the best listening spot. Experienced stereo listeners have a peculiar way of walking around, restlessly, as the music plays—the habit is catchy. Somehow the dynamic quality of stereo sound demands this reaction and I find it rather pleasant, for a change.

You can hear stereo music well enough in a supine position. Naturally you can relegate it to any sort of background too, if you wish—but the stereo effect will be lost, the sound no different from ordinary one-channel sound. If you are going to pay extra for stereo, you might as well give it your full attention.

M-S AND THREE-TRACK STEREO. You will undoubtedly have heard some of the publicity concerning three-track stereo recording as currently used by a number of the larger recording companies. You may well wonder just how three stereo channels can be played in your home on only two tracks, from two speakers. How can one convert three separate recordings into two?

Real three-track stereo in the home—with three complete player-amplifier-loudspeaker systems—would be a marvelous thing if it could be made practical. It is much too expensive for general use, yet oddly enough, some of its benefits can be transferred to the two tracks of a reasonably inexpensive home system.

First, there is the third track for the virtuoso solo. Three-track stereo is made on a special machine using half-inch tape instead of the standard quarter-inch size. Instead of mixing the soloist's private mike directly into the stereo channels, it is fed directly to the third track, simultaneously with the other two, which are taking down the over-all stereo picture of the orchestra. In the final processing, these three tracks are played into a mixing gadget that can add any desired amount of the solo third track to either of the others, or both, for the final home stereo tape. Thus the technicians can juggle the sound about to suit themselves, long after the original recording session.

This is the three-track technique first publicized by RCA Victor. That company not only makes two-track stereo home recordings from its three-track originals but also combines the three into one for standard recordings.

The other use for three-track stereo is actually an extension of the same principle, minus the solo aspect; it puts the third track on a par with the other two for balanced three-track recording, the musical coverage divided equally between the left, center and right. The brilliantly ingenious aspect of this technique is that the triple-track coverage actually can be brought to your ears via two loudspeakers, when the center track is mixed half and half into each of the side tracks. (The same sort of mixer device is used, copying the three-track sound onto a standard two-track tape.)

It works this way. A simple listening principle says that if two loudspeakers send out identical sound, *the ear places the source of the sound exactly halfway between the two.* If our center stereo track is fed equally onto the two tracks of a home stereo recording, it should seem to originate precisely *between* the reproducing speakers—in the middle, and indeed it does, given proper listening conditions. Moreover, this will happen even if we mix it right in with the sound of the outside two tracks of the recording—for the ear can separate mixed sound waves, no matter how complex.

Therefore if your home stereo tape, or disc, has upon it (a) two "outside" tracks, one for each loudspeaker, and (b) a third "middle" track blended in equal proportions into the outside tracks, you *will actually hear all three tracks, in their original relationship,* spatially spread out before you into the single, over-all sound-curtain of good stereo. If you don't quite understand—read the beginning of the paragraph above once again. The third track is a very real illusion.

Mercury was an early proponent of this type of three-track stereo recording, especially in its "classical" releases.

In practice the solo-third-channel technique (RCA) can merge nicely into the over-all technique (Mercury) that uses three equal recordings. Just move the middle mike a bit farther from the soloist, to take in less of him and more of the surrounding orchestral sound, and you begin to approach the straight three-track principle. Still farther and the middle mike's sound merges into that of the outside microphones on a basis of equality.

A brief word, finally, about stereo technique that is at loggerheads with three-track recording because it requires a two-track system from beginning to end. "M-S" ("middle-side") is one rather clumsy name for it, though there is no accounting for possible trade-name descriptions that may in future be applied. Whatever the name, this technique picks an entire *stereo* recording from a single point over the center of an orchestra. Its microphone is a double one, in a single frame;

one of the elements faces directionally straight forward and picks up
mainly the center of the music, the other element takes in the sides.
These two tracks, interacting, produce the same sum and difference
effects, the likeness and the stereo difference, that we find in the stereo
disc groove; by an electrical change of phasing they are converted into
right and left stereo channels, to please the credulous ear.

All of which can do no more than to persuade you anew that stereo
recording—and indeed, all recording—is extraordinarily subjective and
remarkably little concerned with objective realism. I can't help feeling
that this is a useful idea for any music listener to ruminate upon. And
so, if you wish, stereo sound is today's great illusion. But don't forget
that there is always a wealth of "standard" hi-fi illusion to fall back
upon; and if that isn't to your liking, there is still the kitchen shelf
radio and, before that, the old wind-up phonograph in the attic! All
of them have given us great musical pleasure at one time or another.

"Half-Track" Stereo Tape. Things move fast these days. While the
stereo disc was being readied for commercial release, the stereo tape
people were hard at work on a radical new tape stereo record, that would
allow four times as much music per given tape length as the standard
stereo tape and thus could compete price-wise with the inexpensive
stereo disc. At least one major record company was adapting it to a
"cartridge" tape record, for near plug-in simplicity in the playing—but
the need for new-type playing heads and associated circuits in home
tape players was bound to slow its introduction on a wide scale.

The new stereo tape has four tracks on it, two in each direction. The
tape is played through twice, just as in ordinary half-track home recorded
tape. The speed has been halved, to 3¾ inches per second, but thanks
to immense technological progress in tape recording (in industry—
automation, missiles, electronic calculators, telemetering, etc.) the
sound quality at this slow speed and on four narrow tracks is acceptable.

Details on this development will have to await my next edition. If
you are doubtful, I suggest sticking to the already proved values of
stereo disc.

Stereo on the Air. As explained already, I am not enthusiastic about
FM-AM stereo broadcasting; it is a temporary and unsatisfactory expedient. FM Multiplex stereo, described on page 121, will bring full broadcast stereo benefits—"live" or recorded—and I suggest waiting for it.

17

Hi-Fi for Your Friends

What will you do with your hi-fi system when you have put it in
final working order? The very flexibility of a separate-unit hi-fi system is
an invitation to put it to wider use than the conventional home phonograph (or radio), which sits solidly in one place, turning out background or foreground sound.

The hi-fi system, to be sure, isn't nearly as convenient in the handling as the small radio—though I'm hoping soon we'll see some of our
main hi-fi elements, at least, transistorized to real portability—but it can
be put to use, whole or in parts, with a great deal of operational flexibility. And the more easily its separate components come apart, the
better will you enjoy these side uses.

For this very reason, I prefer a system that remains physically in
parts, even though the cabinetry may seem to unify the whole. The
speaker enclosure, if a space-saver type, will slip into the trunk of your
car or lie on the back seat along with the removable amplifier; the record player and the tape machine, separated from the central ganglion,
can be carried about quite easily. And you can always leave at home
those parts of the system you don't need. The whole affair, in such an
arrangement, can be plugged together or unplugged in a few minutes
with no wires to tear out and resolder when you get back.

There's plenty to be done with a hi-fi system right in your own front
parlor. But there are other things, even such minor enjoyments as com-
paring your outfit with your neighbor's, *in toto* or section by section.
And the ardent hi-fi bug, I suggest, practically keeps his system or systems in the trunk of his car, year in and year out. Even a non-hi-fi bug
(such as yourself) can find intelligent, useful, interesting things to do

with a reasonably movable arrangement of parts and the living room may be served in a conventional style in the days or weeks or months between sorties.

THE RECORD CONCERT

Whatever the music, a concert is a concert, you may be inclined to say—but there I will disagree. Even in the "live" music area, these days, concerts are beginning to diversify. The old rigid ways, where people sit in rows with printed programs (mostly in Italian), in silence (except for coughs and sniffles that reflect the state of boredom or interest of the given moment!), listening to black-coated musicians who play but never speak—these occasions are now being sharply modified in all sorts of ways to suit a new age. Thanks to radio and TV, we are accustomed to informality and, shall we say, vocality—informal, genial talk—however foolish and uninformative. Surely no harm can come of it all if through informality of any sort we can come closer to an understanding of music and musicians.

More than TV and radio, more than jazz (which has its own concerts), records have changed our music listening habits. The change, of course, has been away from the formal concert in every applicable sense. And the central location of that change has been the family living room, where recorded music meets its enormous audience in conditions utterly remote from the concert hall.

Where else, then, can we expect new listening habits to show themselves most profitably? A concert at home can be defined, in these new terms, as a listening session with somewhat more plan to it and a larger "audience" than an ordinary, casual record playing session. Just where to draw the line, if a line is needed, is not possible to say, for one man's concert is another man's jam session, or (bless my soul) hi-fi demonstration.

But it is not of the hi-fi demonstration that I'm speaking. You'll have to invent your own rules for that—I am not interested. (If you are a hi-fi gadgeteer, you'll ignore anybody else's demonstration suggestions anyhow.) What if you want to play records or tapes to friends, and make the best possible musical effect? Perhaps one or two friends, or even a half a hundred: a recorded "concert" in this new sense can encompass these extremes, over and above ordinary and private home listening.

A GUEST OR TWO. First, consider the smaller evening of records, for a guest or two or three, in which the machine stays put where it ordinarily lives and the whole affair is strictly *in situ*. My only suggestion here is to follow your normal listening habits, politely but firmly.

If you are a person worth your friends' time and interest, then so are your pursuits and ideas at home. If you are an habitual boor, I suppose your playing habits will be boorish, you'll blast the ears and bore the minds of those who visit you. But, in any case, don't give in to *their* boorish habits, if and when; keep things, as I say, politely but firmly under your own control, change records when you think best, for your own and your guests' pleasure, rather than according to somebody else's suggestions. Be tactful, but run things as you want them to run.

But what of the larger record recital, where a number of people are invited, perhaps quite a crowd, and things must be done in a more organized way? Here I can be more specific.

THE SMALL EVENING GATHERING. There are two crucial aspects to a good evening with records, among friends. First is the listening situation, second is the listening procedure. The more people you have in your living room, the trickier is the listening problem and the more you must go out of your way to see that all are pleased, nobody blasted in the face, nobody left out. If you have followed my suggestions as to reflected sound (Chapter 15), you will have a less difficult problem, for the spread of sound will already be more or less equal, in various parts of the room. If your speaker points out, from a side wall or from a corner, you will have to be firm and forcible with your guests—and mainly *before* the party gets under way. Once down on their bottoms, your friends won't budge if I know them, even if it means physical pain for them in the listening. A crowd of already seated people is as unwieldly as a herd of elephants, when it comes to rearranging them—and remember, they will never understand your reasons for it as you do. Aunt Mamie will insist on a comfy place two feet in front of the loudspeaker (she's big and she'll block the sound), whereas neighbor Bill will take a stance offside by the mantelpiece, and the kids, if any, will prefer cushions on the floor where they'll be mowed down by your loudest passages.

So—set the chairs and sofas up beforehand and with forethought. Not in rows—by all means avoid that—but in seemingly casual distribution around the best listening area, with the poor spots conspicuously minus any seating facilities. This shouldn't take you more than five minutes, but it can save an evening.

And if there are too many even for this, if you bring in extra chairs, then consider moving your loudspeaker, strategically. You may have to involve yourself in new experiments in reflection, to find a good place for the speaker where more people can listen with comfort. But since you're moving furniture anyhow, you might as well do a job.

Don't let people sit close to the loudspeaker or straight in front of it. This is the usual tendency—people act invariably (and you'll have to stop them) as if the loudspeaker were a long-distance telephone and a very faint one at that! They feel strangely as though they must crane their necks toward it, as close as possible. Probably a leftover from the old days when phonographs weren't so loud and (more significant) didn't reproduce the high tones that give color and presence and sense to music.

Here are some hints for communal listening. (They'll apply to large informal concerts too.) Talking—an immediate problem. Yes or no? Take a strictly in-between position about talking.

1. Do *not* expect people to maintain a religious silence. A few would love this, but most would be variously uncomfortable. They'd privately assess you as a fanatic. But—2. Do *not* allow people to talk irrelevantly and loudly about other matters than the music for more than a few minutes, when music is actually playing. (That is, unless you are prone to background effects. That is another matter altogether—I'm talking about records for the sake of what's on them.) On the other hand, do allow some conversation to build up (this of course via the tactful host's or hostess' gentle leadership)—if it is more or less concerned with the music that is playing, if it springs from the music, keeps the music in the mind and alive as it plays.

Now this may seem to be an impossible distinction and a much too arbitrary rule, but I assure you it works—if you are any good as a practiced host. You're the boss, you sit by the record player and do the playing. You make the final (tactful) decisions as to what comes next, whether the mood is good or the interest palling.

So my rule (which you must never, of course, put into words in front of your guests!) is really quite easy. Play records, let people talk about them quietly—you talk first, pointing out this and that detail as the music plays, and so you set the procedure yourself. If people are listening, if the talk isn't wandering too far from the music, keep on playing. But if the chatter begins to drown out the phonograph and a gentle upping of volume (on your machine) merely makes them raise their voices higher to drown it out—then quietly fade down the record, or wait for a good stopping place—and stop. If nobody even notices, then you might as well call off the records for the time being. Often happens! But wait your chance to begin another piece—sometimes you'll want an interval before the next item starts in any case, during which conversation has a chance to erupt and boil itself away. Don't use force, but use constant persuasion, *and never play music unless it's being listened to.*

There are likely to be two extreme types of listener in respect to loudness. Be middle-of-the-road with both. One type, probably Aunt Mamie, will insist the music is much too loud, even when you think it is a whisper. Most annoying, especially when the work is, say, the finale of the Beethoven Ninth Symphony or the "Sacre de Printemps"; music which dies a thousand deaths at low volume! Be firm—and turn the volume down a wee, wee bit (and, after a while, judiciously turn it back up again, keeping a wary eye on Aunt Mamie for the effect). She may not even notice it, once she gets used to your hi-fi sound.

The other type, probably neighbor Bill, wants his hi-fi high—in volume. He'll reach for your volume control and blow you out of your own house, if he can manage it. The thing to do is to plant him as close to the sound source as you can. That'll keep him happy. Turn it up—a bit—for him. But not too much. Remember, a full symphony orchestra in a concert hall is not really very loud *at the listener's seat.* Mostly it plays very faintly—just try rustling a program in your living room as you listen, if you want a rough concert-volume gauge.

Finally, as for the music, the best plan is to have in mind in advance a number of things you'd like to play, but not to stake out a program or any special order of events. Instead, let one thing lead to another. Use the "Oh, that reminds me—" technique, tying one thought to the next, or (equally important) pointing up refreshing contrasts. Lay out casual piles of the records you like, as bait for the curious. But be ready to dive resourcefully into your shelves for spur-of-the-moment ideas.

THE CONCERT. There may well be occasions on which you wish to show off your records and equipment to a sizable gathering—too big for the family living room. You'll have to find yourself a "concert hall," then, and it had better be a good one. Take care! Such bigger events must be organized with proportionately greater skill. You must first have a place for your audience and then work out a good listening arrangement where everybody hears, nobody is blasted, and finally you must decide on procedure for the concert itself.

Think, then, on these pointers for success. First, if possible, avoid straight rows of chairs. If the seats are already in place, as in a lecture hall or folding-chair setup, then do *not* aim your loudspeaker from the center of the stage straight at the nearest rows! By all means, instead, use reflection for your sound, spreading it out for naturalness. Set the speaker up *with its back facing the audience*, and aim it if possible into one corner, or sidewise, turned in toward the wall or straight back. Remove any padded seats and cushions or heavy draperies in its path, of course, or choose another reflecting place—but stick to the job until you find the right spot. I've done this so many times, in so many lecture halls and lounges and dining rooms and gyms, that I know whereof I speak—a half-hour of testing may save you days of remorse.

You can disguise your speaker's ugly rear with a casual drape, or put a big chair or table in front of it, to hide the ugliness. Maybe a vase of flowers on top will help distract. Not a big problem, once you set your mind to it.

MUSIC FOR DANCING

If you live in an actively social community, I suspect that an inevitable extracurricular use of your hi-fi system will be for music at social gatherings with dancing—of a sort larger than your living room can accommodate. Let's put aside the permanent basement rumpus room and teen-age dance hall. If you run to that sort of thing you should have a separate (and highly rugged) machine, 100 per cent dedicated to the younger set.

However, on special occasions, you may save the day handsomely, and bring pleasure to all, via your living-room system temporarily removed to a new location, in part or in whole. I have used my own systems dozens of times for such affairs.

Thus a few days ago, as this is being written, I hauled out a speaker and amplifier to do emergency duty for a broken-down "hi-fi" phonograph—table-model type—that the kids had optimistically hoped to use for folk dancing. Their machine emitted nothing but harsh, distorted squawks, and I was called upon, but quick. To save haulage, I borrowed the record changer unit from a nearby hi-fi system to plug into my own amplifier and speaker, and we were in business in minutes. The dance was fine and everybody loved the hi-fi and its relatively tremendous volume.

What hi-fi? Well, the details are instructive. The broken-down table model, costing originally about $150, had two three-inch speakers and an amplifier of perhaps four watts. My speaker was an eight-inch model in a small box, only a foot and a half high; the amplifier was a ten-watter. A total value, new, about $80. The borrowed changer was an old Webcor, but with a GE magnetic cartridge, as good as new—maybe $50 more. Now, at best the table "hi-fi," in working order, could scarcely be heard in a large roomful of dancers, with its fixed speakers pointing straight out into people's middles. My portable outfit was enormously louder (with real bass for rhythm, too), and I could aim the speaker where I wanted, to get over people's heads and so reach all corners of the big room.

The necessities for such an affair, unless you want to do some heavy hauling, are basically the three essential phonograph units, in separate pieces, portable. The amplifier and the record player unit are the easiest to move, especially if you have a one-piece amplifier and a record player mounted in its own base. The speaker should be one of the small space-savers—which allows you a range of equipment that runs from the AR-1 system, expensive and very heavy, but small enough to fit in a Volkswagen, right down to the numerous small eight-inch enclosures and even, on occasion, a makeshift cardboard box with a speaker set in the top. I have an excellent system I occasionally use for gags, consisting of a loose eight-inch Permoflux speaker ($13) which sits neatly in the top of a pressure cooker! I stuff a batch of rags, or a small sofa cushion, inside to absorb the back wave (an infinite baffle) and enhance the quality. It sounds wonderful. Now, you may laugh. But the fact is that even that absurd speaker arrangement will outperform every table "hi-fi" system you've ever heard and it can produce a surprising wallop of noise, too, from a ten-watt amplifier. Don't disdain the simpler things in hi-fi life.

You'll find it easy to join forces with others who have equipment, just as the summer picnic outing usually combines salads and desserts from various families. Here, the wide present use of standardized hi-fi plugs is a godsend. You bring your amplifier, and speaker system; X brings his record player; they plug together on the scene.

Dancing, or other active or mobile entertainment, requires a solid location for the record player—or the needle will skip—and a good speaker position. Trouble with jumping needles comes virtually always via the floor boards. The best place then, is a shelf or side-wall extension, where the support comes from the walls rather than the floor. In one such recreation room, we built a corner shelf-table supported free of the floor and thus solved all sorts of formerly severe needle-jumping problems, no matter how lively the dancing. If you have such trouble, try first to find which floor boards are transmitting the vibration and move your record player accordingly. A pillow or two underneath it sometimes helps, though not so much as you might think since pillows transmit low-frequency vibrations very nicely. (The same with springs.)

Second—check your equipment. I had better explain quickly, right here, that needle-skipping is primarily a factor of pickup arm design and can vary enormously from arm to arm—it does *not* depend on the weight on the needle point! A major fallacy still current in most people's minds is that LP records are bad at skipping because the arm is lighter and the grooves smaller. Not at all—indeed, it is often the other way around. The fact is that, generally speaking, the lighter and more delicately made your record player arm and cartridge is, the better chance you'll have of unskipped music under duress. Groove skipping can ruin the nicest dance, and notably when the music requires exact timing in the dance figures. Skip a few grooves then, and the entire company is thrown into confusion!

If, therefore, you run into groove-skipping trouble, don't hesitate to try out the most capable arm system your social gathering can communally provide. Such arms as the Gray viscous-damped (and its Japanese equivalents), the Shure Dynetic arm and cartridge, the Weathers FM pickup and others of the sort, while not exactly of the kind to be thrown to the teen-ages without caution, will play rings around most older changers when it comes to stability under violent shaking and banging. Just see to it that a responsible person stays near the pickup to preserve order. (Recent changers are very much improved in this respect. They often compare favorably with the best professional arms.)

Do *not* place nickels, dimes or quarters on the pickup head to make it track! This is the surest way to ruin your records—and it probably won't help much anyway.

The speaker? Remember, even the smallest of the hi-fi separate speaker systems will make louder, clearer sound, with far better tonal range than the cramped and tiny facilities inside most table "hi-fis." And flexibility in placing of the speaker is an unmatchable advantage.

If you must use a floor model console or table phonograph for parties with active moving about, then try your best to set the machine *high up*, in order to get the sound out from the mid-region where it is swallowed up by moving bodies. Prop a table model up on a box or on books or on a shelf; or if it is a floor model, try tipping the front up slightly, to angle the speaker upward. Try to avoid directly blasting people in front of the speaker with too loud sound. Better to reverse the machine, facing into a corner, or against a hard wall where the sound will be reflected and dispersed, no matter how funny it looks. Results are what count.

If you have a separate space-saver speaker unit (Chapter 12), you are in the clover. Try setting it up, first of all, so that the speaker faces straight *upward*. Lay it flat on a table or on a chair (rather than down on the floor), or prop it at an angle pointing upward, toward an upper corner in the ceiling. With a roomful of people this arrangement helps achieve equal distribution. If you have a sloping ceiling, so much the better; it will angle the sound outward. An alternative is to place the speaker on a table facing directly into an unobstructed (nonpadded) corner at a distance of five or six feet. Turn the volume up to suit— you'll have plenty available.

A brief note about techniques. You won't be able to judge dancing sound very well in an empty room, ahead of time. You can be sure that with people milling about you'll need a surprisingly large volume compared to what seems right in the empty room. Also, the tone quality will doubtless need adjusting with the people present, especially in a brilliant, hard-surfaced room. That's what tone controls are for. So balance to taste *at the party itself*, adjusting both high and low tone controls. (Always start from the central "flat" position, for reference.)

Secondly, when you play your dance records, use finesse in the starting and stopping! Practice a bit with the equipment, if it is unfamiliar. Scrapes and blops due to clumsy fingerwork make horrid and amateurish sounds with the volume turned high. Slide the needle into the first groove, or onto the separation band between recorded numbers, *with the volume knob turned low*—just enough so you can hear for yourself. (Better no volume at all; do it by feel!) Then have a good idea of the proper volume setting ahead of time, so the music won't begin much too soft, or—worse—start with an ear-shattering blast.

Be sure to provide a safe place to put used records and others about to be used. If you don't have a record rack, lay a couple of pillows out on the table and put the open records on them for a moment, pending return to their proper record cases. Keep a space free around the machine, and don't serve refreshments from the same table! Same with ashtrays and the like—keep 'em away. One trick, if people *will* pile up naked records out of their cases, is to leave a stack of doilies or folded paper napkins, to slip between records as they are stacked. Their own cardboard jackets will do very well.

(P.S. Is dance music serious music—for the music lover? Well, of course. You'll find in every music appreciation book that classical music derives largely "from the dance" and I see no reason to think that minuets and sarabandes and tarantellas were the only dances likely to move into the classical area. English folk dances and American squares, similar in style, have some fascinating musical persuasions to offer, and I am far from ready to count out jazz, calypso—even rock 'n' roll. Dancing is mostly active listening, anyhow.)

HOME P.A. AND THE MICROPHONE

The ancestor of your hi-fi system was the P.A. or Public Address system. I suggest that there is likely to be a time when—if you just *happened* to have convenient equipment around—you might make very good use of a bit of portable voice amplification, for yourself or in any of dozens of community situations. Not loud, not brash, just helpful. At parties, square dances, banquets, PTA meetings (where the local equipment has, as usual, broken down), amateur shows—any one of the innumerable occasions when people are going to shout, "LOUDER!"

I should say at once that professional P.A. equipment is best for all such occasions. It's made for them. But often there isn't any available. And I have a deep-lying permanent suspicion, myself, of all local installations until proved to be in operating order. Now it happens that with a microphone attached to it your home hi-fi system becomes a ready-made (if rather cumbersome) high-quality P.A. system. It is neither as rugged nor as all-powerful, not having been specifically designed to stand up to P.A. rigorousness. I would not suggest you use it very often. But on some emergency or special occasion, you may well bless yourself fervently for having had the foresight to add a mike to your system—just in case.

Which microphone? Not just any old mike will do—and for that matter the very best mikes are usually unsuited to voice amplification. Under quiet, well-bred conditions you can use any mike at all, but as soon as there is background noise—which is almost always—a more specialized mike is needed. Mikes for music, moreover, must meet quite different needs.

Mikes come in a confusing array of types, and they resemble phono pickups in many ways. There are crystal and ceramic mikes, usually found in home tape recorders, and there are magnetic mikes (dynamic) —all requiring preamplification just like magnetic phonograph pickups (but without the equalization; mikes operate "flat"). The fanciest mikes are the condenser types, which have their own special power supplies and preamplifiers, usually in separate boxes. They are best for music, too expensive and cumbersome for voice. Mike prices range from a few dollars up to two or three hundred for professional-grade microphones; quality mikes for practical hi-fi home use run from $20 or so up. The geometric progression works, as usual, with a vengeance, but you may take advantage of it by buying a low-medium-priced mike— say $30—for very nearly top quality. Even a $5 mike will serve you well for voice use.

DIRECTIVITY. A vital distinction among microphones is their directivity. Most ceramics, and many top-quality condensers too, are *omnidirectional;* that is, they pick up sound equally well from all sides. Excellent for most music, where you are looking for liveness—reflection that comes from all directions. Not so good for voice, where you want specifically to discriminate between the voice sound and the background. *Bidirectionals* are another type, not so common in the mikes you are likely to run into; these are dead at the sides, but pick up sound equally at front and rear. Fine for across-the-table radio interviews, but poor for audience work, since the audience is invariably straight to the rear.

The very best mike type for voice and a useful one for some musical situations, is the *unidirectional* (*"directional"*) mike, often called cardioid. It is sensitive to sound in front of it, but dead, to varying degrees, both on the sides and in the rear; it picks up a highly selective "beam" of sound, ignores the rest. The really effective cardioids are expensive, but many cheaper mikes have a reasonably directional pattern, favoring the straight-ahead sound and minimizing the rest. Excellent for voice; for with such a mike you can speak at a greater distance than with the omnidirectional type, since the mike favors you over the audience at its back.

Finally, an alternative to the directional mike is the *close-talking mike*. This type can stand very high volume close-to without blasting and so you can talk—or even shout—straight into it at an inch or so distance. (Most mikes won't take such close-up treatment without distorting.) It is this type of mike that the square dance caller uses, as you have probably noticed. Not much on sound quality, but it works wonders under extreme conditions. Buy one only if you'll have to speak over very loud noises.

There are special necklace-type mikes, that hang around your neck, and also lapel mikes; but these require background silence—they pick up a lot of extraneous noise. No good at all for dance instruction or calling, as I found to my chagrin in my learning days, but fine for quiet meetings and very unobtrusive too. You can walk around with them and have both hands free.

Hooking Up. I won't try to tell you in detail how to hitch up your mike to your hi-fi system; it can be simple as pie—just plug it in, and switch the amplifier control to MIKE. (If not, your dealer can settle details.) But you'd do well to consider this, if you're interested, at the time you buy your hi-fi equipment; some home amplifiers and control units have a mike input all ready to use, others do not, though you can always find a way to connect one.

An important distinction, technical but very practical, is between the *high-impedance* mike, most home types, and the *low-impedance* type, most professional microphones. This has nothing to do with the sound and is purely electrical. High-impedance mikes and microphone input facilities are simpler and cheaper—hence their use with home equipment. But the high-impedance mike must have a *short*, well-shielded cable to the amplifier—not over three or four feet—which means that you must place it close to the associated equipment. Not always convenient. The low-impedance microphone, used by all professionals, can be put at virtually any distance from its amplifier—hence the long, snaking mike cables you have seen many a time. But it requires a special type of input, with a *microphone transformer*. Expensive. Thus you will not often find low-impedance mikes in home use. Note that some of the middle-priced dynamic microphones can be used either way, via a simple switch, and so will match any equipment. See pp. 103, 104.

Mike stand? You can just hold it in your hand or prop it up on a table or chair, but a stand looks better and is safer. A table stand must be *heavy*—light ones topple over. A floor stand that telescopes to various heights is more useful. It costs around $6. You may want a boom stand (with a long extending arm) for music, to get the mike well up in the air overhead, the best location. But booms look silly at meetings and banquets.

SETTING UP. Don't set up your loudspeaker for voice amplification the way you do for musical reproduction! First, the voice is naturally a point source and you should aim the speaker directly toward the people you want to reach, *without* reflection (as I've suggested for music). Place the speaker high up if necessary, so that the sound goes over the heads of nearby people and reaches out to those at a distance, where it is most needed.

Second, look out for *feedback*, that loud, ringing howl that builds up when amplifier volume is turned up too high and the mike picks up the loudspeaker sound and reamplifies it. It is embarrassing to have your system howl at the wrong moment.

Feedback can usually be controlled. To minimize the tendency, keep mike and speaker from facing each other. It's not necessary to separate them at a distance—just see to it that the speaker faces away from the mike, not toward it. One way to do this is to put it a few feet in front of the mike, facing out, with its back toward the mike's position. This makes for maximum sound out front and minimum feedback pickup by the mike. It also places the loudspeaker fairly near to the voice, for greater naturalness. Be sure to experiment—a small change in speaker aiming can reduce feedback gratifyingly.

You can do a lot to make your voice amplification natural-sounding. First, *keep the volume low*, as low as you possibly can and still reach your listeners. (Speaker placement will count heavily here.) Nine times out of ten, what you need is gentle sound reinforcement, not straight public address. You use both the natural sound of the voice and the reproduced sound. Sound reinforcement can be unobtrusive and pleasant if you are careful, and the lower your volume is, too, the less trouble you'll have with noise and feedback. Try to be so unobtrusive, indeed, that most people don't even know there is amplification.

Given the need for it, you can also hook up your record player (or tape machine) to provide music as well as speech; but go slowly, for there are serious complications here. You'll have to compromise in placing your loudspeaker so that the music will be served as well as the voice. Not so easy. It's always better, in this case, to speak without amplification, reserving the system for music only.

TWO SYSTEMS. As a matter of fact, music and public address don't mix at all well in one amplifying system, partly because the combination of loud voice and loud music is often more than the amplifier can handle. A highly practical trick is to have two amplifying systems on hand at such functions as square dance parties or musical shows, one system for the music and another, quite separate, for voice. This arrangement allows you to set up the music and the speech in quite different and strategic locations, and so keeps them clear and apart in your listeners' minds. Your music can be reflected, from walls and ceiling via one loud-speaker—the speech can be aimed straight at the people via the other.

Impractical? Not always. Usually there is another system on hand, anyhow—somebody's old, beat-up P.A. portable, or the built-in P.A. Use it for voice, always. Your hi-fi system can be the second one, to reproduce the music with hi-fi quality.

Let me suggest, finally, that if you must amplify living musicians, for dancing or for any species of concert, treat them gently. Reinforce their natural sound, as unobtrusively as possible, and, again, place the loudspeaker near the music, for naturalness. (No reflection needed here—your musicians are already spread out before your eyes as well as your ears, and the loudspeaker can thus be point-source for greater crispness and clarity.)

Yes, I know that a lot of this account flies more or less in the face of the usual procedures with P.A. at dances and meetings, where sound tends to blast out at deafening levels of intensity! That's the way the professionals do it, but I suggest a different approach to you for your own peace of mind. In any case, your home machine does not have the power to produce those professional roars of high-volume sound. Just as well, I'd say.

18

Home Tape

What can you do with a tape machine? So much that I quail before the task of describing it all. My suggestions, in the space of this chapter, will take off from, and will be over and above, the usual home tape activities—taping radio programs, baby's first cry, teen-age giggles, party dramatics and so on.

COPYING DISC RECORDS

First, as a preliminary idea, let me suggest that a tape machine is useful when it comes to preselecting a whole program of records by copying them onto tape in advance. You won't need the records themselves when the time comes, and your entire program, whatever it may be, will be in order and ready to play on a single tape. You can use this technique for such diverse occasions as lectures with musical illustration, background mood music for parties and—a brilliant thought—complete dance-music programs entirely free of the needle-skipping problem already discussed in the last chapter. No needle, no groove. But you will need to know how.

One of your main interests, if you are a record collector who has bought a tape machine, will be this copying of disc records. Not only of your own but also of friend's records which you may want to own and can't otherwise obtain. Given good copying (and that is vital) a taped version of a disc record is undoubtedly a useful acquisition. It isn't as convenient to play as the original disc, but it is in most respects unbreakable, and it can be played literally thousands of times without the slightest change in sound quality.

Whether it will last as many years as the disc itself is still a question; tape is relatively new on the scene, even now. Don't throw away your discs after they are copied. Keep them safely, like new, and play the tape copies. Make new tape copies when and if necessary. Tapes do break, but unless you crease or tear them, you can patch the breaks together as good as new, which is more than you can do with a broken 78 shellac.

Best of all, you can do what fifteen years ago would have seemed miraculous—you can join the old records for continuous long-play. But that requires editing. (You can, of course, simply juxtapose the sides, without bothering to make a musical connection between them, which even so is better than playing the old records on a changer or flipping platters.)

Your first concern, if you are seriously interested in taping your discs, must be an adequate recorder—that is, one which will reproduce what it receives with real faithfulness. Let me say flatly that your tape copies should sound virtually the same as the disc originals—if not better. (In rather obscure ways a tape copy often sounds better than the original disc.) If your tapes are noticeably inferior to the discs from which they come, *even by a very slight degree*, you will be sorry. For then the temptation to get "the best" will constantly drive you back to the disc itself. The tape copy will always be a halfhearted compromise, a halfway measure; each time you play it you will be distressed anew by the knowledge that the disc itself is better.

Unfortunately, many low-priced tape machines (relatively speaking—for tape is never cheap) are less than faithful in their reproduction of the sound they receive, even when new and at the higher ("high fidelity") speeds. Moreover, too many older recorders deteriorate after months or years of wear and tear. They may distort your records hideously, or worse, add wow and flutter that make your music waver as it never did on the original disc. Therefore, don't embark on a tape copying program until you are sure that the machine is in good order, *in direct comparison with the original discs* as played on your phonograph system. It's worth while to take an old recorder to a repairman for a thorough cleaning and checkup.

Next—if you want good sound from copied records, don't use the very slow tape speeds common in most home tape recorders. The economy is a false one. If you insist on the 3¾-inch speed, often called "normal" in present recorders, you will inevitably have a dull, muffled, perhaps a wavering sound in your copies. Yes, I realize that this sound at 3¾ inches is often no worse than that of most older standard phono-graphs. But your hi-fi system can do better and so can most of your disc records. Perhaps you would not have noticed the difference in the old days—but now, with a new hi-fi system in your home, the differ-ence between the sound direct from your disc records and from your slow-speed taped copies will be unpleasantly noticeable.

I recommend therefore that for all serious tape copying, whatever the purpose, you use the faster speed of 7½ inches, and put aside all dreams of super-economy. (The fifteen-inch speed, on some more ex-pensive machines, is strictly for the hi-fi perfectionist.) At 7½ you'll get a full half-hour each way on a standard 1,200-foot roll of tape, three-quarters of an hour or more on the "long-play" reels. And if you want to edit your tape (see below), and so must use only one track, you'll still find that a half-hour of hi-fi copying for one reel of edited sound is an inexpensive quality bargain. (You can buy tape in bulk and/or in professional packages, for rereeling at home, if you go in for really heavy work.) Stick to 7½ at all costs.

HOOKUPS. Let me dispose quickly of one record copying method I gather is often used—copying from your phonograph loudspeaker via the microphone. Easy, but foolish if you want quality. The proper way —and it is usually simple enough, once you get your plugs right—is to make a direct "feed" from the amplifier into the tape recorder. The manufacturers have been widely alerted to this need in recent years and virtually any amplifier you can buy will now have an output marked for tape recorder, usually independent of the out-loud volume and tone controls so that you can listen to the music as you wish while making the recording. Tape recorders, similarly, have an input plug (standard type) expressly designed for a direct feed from an amplifier. Just plug the two together. Most tape users already know all about these things, but I am to be exhaustive, when I can.

VOLUME LEVELS. Your tape machine has a recording volume indicator on it. The best are meters, but they are rare. Next best is a double indi-cator, two "magic eyes" or two little lights; one acts as a warning, the other follows when things get dangerously loud. This double warning, like the yellow caution light at traffic intersections, helps anticipate sudden volume emergencies. A single indicator will do, but you'll have to watch more carefully for overloading. A sensible copying plan, which should be followed by everyone and isn't, is to make a few trial runs first, to see how things will turn out. Always look for the loudest part of the music (or anything else) and measure it for volume level *before* you start your final copying run.

Keep your volume levels always on the conservative side. Too many amateurs waste tape blasting away at too-high levels. Better to run low and risk a bit of extra background hiss, than to run high and spoil all the louder parts with hideous blasting and distortion!

A crucial matter here is the volume level that goes out of your amplifier into the recorder—it can easily be much too high, overloading the input of the recorder so that it blasts *even when the recording volume is turned low*. Most amplifier tape outputs are fixed at a proper volume automatically, whatever you may do with your usual out-loud volume control. But some of them go up and down in volume with the main volume control and so—beware. (Easy enough to find out. Just hook things up and try the main volume knob on the amplifier as you record a sample. Any effect at the recorder?)

The best maxim in any case is to "starve" the recorder. That is, arrange things so that you must turn the tape recorder volume control fairly far around in order to get enough recording volume. Feed it a weak signal; make it work for its sound. If you overdo this, to be sure there'll be background hiss and a low-level recording, but better that than a too-strong recording and consequent distortion and blasting in all the loud parts. If you get the idea, you'll find it easy to hit the happy medium that results in good, blast-free tapes.

SPLICELESS TAPING. Once you are properly set up, according to the above, there is no great problem in copying modern records—except the little matter of starting and stopping, which can make an idiot of you in no time! You want the right music on your tape without extraneous noises and, if you don't plan to edit (as per below), you'll have to be very careful to get accurate recordings, without flubbed beginnings, squawks of unwanted sound, noisy pops and screeches and the like. You can—if you'll spend a little time learning how.

To get yourself off on the right track, try it this way. Set your machine up for copying and put the record on the turntable. Turn the recorder's volume down. Next, start the machine, in the RECORD position, *then* start the record, at the beginning (or beginning of a band); and immediately turn the recorder volume up to the right level—which you will, of course, have predetermined by experiment. This should nicely catch the beginning of the music just as you reach full volume. If you're too slow, try again. It will take a bit of practice to do it right.

If your turntable will turn while you hold the record back with a light finger, you can begin the music with high accuracy; just let go. But many turntables slow down when you hold the record. If you will use a simple Canby trick, however, you can get professional results on almost any machine. Buy some squares of green felt with sticky adhesive on the back at the five and ten. Stick a few pieces here and there on your turntable surface, covering only part of it, until friction is reduced just enough so that you can hold the record back with one finger, while the turntable keeps on running *at full speed* underneath. Then the record will start up almost instantaneously as you let go. Not all tables will do this for you, in which case you must arrange to have the music begin after the turntable has had time to reach full speed from a standing start. Allow enough silent grooves to do this.

At the end of a selection, don't just grab the needle off the record with a squawk! *Fade* the recorder volume out first—*then* stop the record and the recorder, at your leisure. Good sound tailoring requires smooth fades and transitions, not abrupt starts and stops.

If you have more material to record, reel the tape back to the point where your fade ends (not sooner!) and start again. You can time the space between numbers to suit yourself—the starting operation will usually take just about long enough, as described above, to allow a reasonable break. There will be several mild pops or clicks, but nothing else if you have done a good job.

Look out for blats and blasts of irrelevant material between numbers, left over from earlier recording. You'll learn to erase previous material before you start working with an old tape. The easiest way is this. Before each selection goes on the tape, erase ahead for eight or ten seconds. Just turn the recorder volume all the way down and turn the machine to RECORD, beginning at the end of the last piece. Then reel back again and go ahead with your recording. This will remove any material that might accidentally intervene between two selections.

That's about all that can be said, except that you will probably make a hideous fool of yourself on the first few tries, with wrong switchings, wows and squawks, accidental erasures, music that begins at the wrong place, and so on. Exasperating, to put it mildly—but don't be discouraged. You can always start again.

TONE CORRECTING. Most 78 rpm records, especially older electricals, were recorded with quite different recording curves (Chapter 5) from that now standard on LP and 45 rpm records. Your amplifier will probably have on it, in addition to the now-standard RIAA position and others for newer records, a position marked 78, or EUR 78. It is ordinarily an average one that fits a good many of the old discs, more or less pleasingly. But you should use your tone-control knobs freely to make further adjustments by ear—see below.

When it comes to copying 78s, you will do best to arrange your tonal corrections so that they are recorded onto the tape, for future playing. Then, when you play the tape copy, you can leave all tone controls at normal position, the correcting having already been done.

A slight complication here, however, which you will do well to investigate: Most amplifiers now have two outputs that you can use for tape copying. The output marked TAPE by-passes the high and low tone controls and the volume control. (Chapter 8). The other output, often labeled MAIN, goes through the volume control as well as the tone controls, so that they do affect the output sound. If you want to use your tone controls to adjust the sound of records being copied, you must then use this output, instead of the regular tape output. First, adjust your main volume control on the amplifier for the right recording level. That is vital, as already explained. Then, set your tone controls for the best sound. You will already have tried the records out, of course, adjusting the controls to suit your taste. When you play the tape back, later, reset the controls to normal position, as for any other tape, and you'll automatically have the right balance.

If you have a cut-off control (often called range control or scratch filter) and/or a noise suppressor (Chapter 8), these can be invaluable for letting through a maximum of 78 music with a minimum of scratch. Remember that your old records mostly lack the higher tones and those that are present are often distorted in the loud passages. An adjustable cut-off control can safely be set at about 5,000 cycles for most old 78 records; there's little of value above that figure. If they're good records and quiet, 8,000 cycles will do. But be sure to try the loudest passages first (for distortion) and the softest passages (for hiss and scratch) before you decide how best to proceed.

You'll find that most old 78s have strong bass—relatively stronger than on later records—and weak treble. Different recording curve. If your amplifier's 78 position doesn't take care of this, the old records will tend to sound bottom-heavy, pudgy, dull, thumpy. The thing to do, even if it goes against your hi-fi grain, is to roll-off the bass, perhaps halfway to the knob's limit or even more. Listen a while to get used to the sound, perhaps bringing up the general volume a bit, before you make up your mind. There should be an apparent increase in the highs, due to better balance, a brighter, more alive sound.

You may, of course, find that the high end of the 78 record is still weak—or that it still sounds shrill, whatever you may do to the bass. Don't be surprised. Be ready and willing to experiment by ear with tone controls for each 78 recording until you get a sound that suits your requirements—then copy.

Of course you can just hook up your recorder in the usual way and copy the 78s as they are. You can always make the adjustments ad lib via the tone controls when you play the tape on later occasions. But the above procedures, if you happen to be able to manage them, will save time and afford you more pleasure in the long run.

A brief note is in order on very old acoustical 78s, the Caruso and Galli-Curci type. Acoustical records (unlike old electrics) have virtually no bass. The middle treble is screechy and relatively distorted, the highs nonexistent. A noise filter, noise suppressor unit or range control will do wonders in reducing the very loud hiss and noise that shows up on modern hi-fi equipment.

But, before you go to a lot of trouble—look in the catalogues of reissue LPs! A large number of these old records have already been transferred to LP directly from the original vault masters, which are almost noiseless.

SPLICING TAPE

On most boxes of magnetic tape you'll see a graphic picture of tape splicing; it shows a large pair of shears and two drooping ends of tape overlapping in mid-air. Very misleading, I say. Yes, you can patch tape in this clumsy way if you must. But for speed what you need is a simple tape editing block, plus the essential white patching tape. (Do not try to use ordinary cellophane sticky tape or any other sort of tape, except for strictly temporary emergency joining.)

It is almost impossible to work with a tape machine without sooner or later breaking a tape. Most home users have been forced to try the scissors system—or reel up the loose pieces helter-skelter, ready to fly apart again next time the tape is played. Nothing is more discouragingly useless than a tape broken in the middle—yet, with a tape block for quick work, nothing is easier to repair! You can restore broken tapes to their exact original sound, without so much as a click or a pop to betray the splice, if you have all the pieces. You can, indeed, put Humpty Dumpty back on his wall.

"EDITALL." All splicing (patching) and so all tape editing, no matter how complicated, involves exactly the same series of semiautomatic movements—marking the tape, cutting it at the proper places, lining up the two ends and smoothing on the white patching tape over them for a permanent splice. If this repetitive process can only be made simple and fast, you can get into all sorts of interesting procedures.

You may, if you're gadget-minded, buy one of the numerous fancy "automatic" tape splicers, running up to fabulous prices. Or you can buy an ultra-simple splicing block, with two clamps and a place to slice the tape with a razor blade, for a dollar or less. But if you follow my advice, you'll go right out and get the device that almost every professional tape editor uses, the "Editall," at around $7—but is worth it. A junior model, somewhat less convenient, is about $4. It is a simple block of machined aluminum alloy that has a flat groove down its middle with tricky incurved sides, so that you "press" the tape in and it stays there of its own accord, held firmly in alignment without

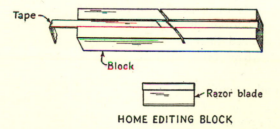

HOME EDITING BLOCK

clamps. Crosswise and diagonal slits provide for exact slicing by a razor blade. (You can get handles for razor blades at the five and ten.) Press in the tape, slice it in the guide slits, line up the ends and slap on the white patching tape; then snap the whole out of the block again by pulling at the two ends—and you're back in business in seconds, your "edit" neatly and permanently finished.

I suggest as persuasively as I can that every tape machine owner should have one of these blocks on hand, with a roll of patching tape. After a bit of practice, joining tape ends becomes so simple and quick that you'll forever be prepared for those inevitable breaks, even in the middle of a demonstration playing—no longer will you have to call off a tape performance because of an unexpected break; you'll fix it on the spot. And moreover, you'll very likely soon want to try the further tricks that are possible with editing itself.

SETTING UP FOR SPLICING. Patching tape comes in two widths. I recommend the rolls of thin tape, just a bit narrower than the recording tape itself, as much the most economical type. This kind goes on lengthwise and there is no waste. It may be used out of one of those dispensers you see in grocer's shops and offices, but you don't need to bother. I suggest the following procedure—you can use your scissors here.

Pull out enough tape to last for your immediate operations. Make a fold at the roll, so you'll be able to get hold of the free end later, and cut off this piece. Stick the far end to any handy nearby surface. Then cut off a slice at the near end with your shears, the size of a patch—an inch or slightly less. The remaining tape will stick lightly to the edge of the shear blade; transfer it to a finger on the other hand and slice again, then transfer to the finger, until you have a row of slices sticking up from one or two or three fingers, barely adhering. Finally, transfer these, delicately, to the edge of your nearby support, touching them to it only on their bottom quarter-inch or so. Later, pick them off one at a time, as you need them. I usually stick them onto the side of the recorder, or perhaps on a shelf or piece of equipment within easy reach.

If this sounds complicated—it isn't; it's just hard to describe. With this system you'll be free to think fast while you edit, without having to stop and cut a new piece of patching tape for every joint. When you are finished working, throw away any leftover pieces; they collect dust after a few hours.

You'll need a strong light that shines exactly where you can see your tape as it goes over the playing head in the recorder. This depends, of course, on the model—but have on hand a good gooseneck lamp, to adjust for best illumination. That's all. The rest depends on you and on the sound on your tapes. No matter what the problem is, soundwise, you'll go through the same motions for every splicing operation and the sooner you get the basic hang of it the better. It is astonishing to watch a professional editor, who makes hundreds of splices every day—but you do not need to approach his skill, to do a fully satisfactory job on your own tapes. And the more you learn, the wider is the range of interest this simple operation can have for your ears and your mind.

FIXING BREAKS. So far I haven't considered the sound on the tape. In fact, if you are industrious, it might be wise to practice making tape splices simply on an old roll of discarded tape, ignoring the sound entirely. Just go through the physical motions until you have the hang of it, before you entrust precious sound to the splicing operation.

First, consider ordinary simple breaks. If your tape snaps in one place, cleanly, just put the two ends in the tape block and slide them together until they touch—the irregular shapes should match up. Splice. But if the break has removed a bit of tape and they don't fit, slice off diagonally the smallest possible amount from each end that will allow them to come together without ragged holes. Nine times out of ten the removed tape will be too slight to affect the sound and your recording is as good as new.

If there are several small segments of tape from a more serious break, try to fit them together like a jigsaw puzzle and snip off only those edges that don't match up perfectly. (Always slice in the diagonal groove, not straight across.)

If your break is a multiple one and you're not sure which fragments belong where, you'll resort to listening—and so we're already into the sound aspect of editing. With your tape broken in little pieces, you've got a job ahead of you—but don't be too quickly discouraged; you can salvage a surprising amount, with care. Remember two things: (a) you can undo any splice that turns out to be wrong and (b) splices, when rightly made, do not "click" or thump but pass perfectly and smoothly through the machine as far as the ear is concerned—only an abrupt change in the sound gives them away. In many cases a slight loss of material will hardly be noticeable in the playing. A repair job with four or five unsightly patches in a row can well play, for the ear, as smoothly as a brand-new recording.

For bad breaks, assemble the bits of tape as well as you can by the jigsaw method, and if some pieces are unidentifiable, just hitch them up arbitrarily, so that the tape is in one piece and therefore playable; then listen. If the doubtful sections are upside down, they'll play backward. Undo the splice (fingernails, or the edge of a razor) and turn them around the other way. Resplice. A few tries of this sort and you'll probably find which pieces go where by audible evidence.

Note at this point that damage to tape is often in the form of folding or creasing, rather than actual breaks. Creasing is more disastrous than breaking, oddly enough, because a creased tape will not lie flat on the playing head and thus will not play. A trick that may rescue you is to lay your creased tape on a flat surface and line the entire shiny back side (not the front, the dull side) with a long strip of white patching tape. Then press flat for a while. This technique can flatten out the worst of a crease and restore much of its playing value.

EDITING

The next and easily logical procedure, and an exceedingly valuable step forward, is to "edit out" unwanted material from your tapes, first of all those clicks and squawks and pops, false beginnings, bits of older recording, that may remain between wanted items. No matter how skillful your recording technique there are bound to be a few such noises on every good tape. The professional engineer doesn't even bother to avoid them in the recording process—in big-business tape operations, he can afford to waste literally miles of tape in extraneous noises, later to be removed, rather than miss by accident a split second of important material. You can't afford that and your tapes will be relatively well filled; but the removing technique is the same, for a little or a lot.

The first necessity for all sound-editing is a means for marking your tapes. This is crucial; a misplaced splice means a wrong sound. (Some professionals are so quick they don't even bother to mark the tape, doing it all via quick fingerwork. Don't be foolish enough to try this.) The marking instrument is always a grease pencil, technically known as a china-marking pencil, the sort that will write heavily on smooth surfaces. Many editors use yellow; I prefer black since it shows up well against the rust-colored tape. Red is no good—you can't see it. Any stationery store should have one color or another.

Next—you need direct access to the playing head on your machine and this may be a problem, since most machines now use the tape-in-the-slot kind of drive, leaving no place to insert your marking pencil. On most home machines you will have to remove the outer covering below the tape slot, so that you can see the business "heads" inside.

Which ones? There are two, three, or more, heads over which the tape passes. The *last one in the direction of tape travel is always the playing head*. (In two-head models, it is also the recording head, via a switch.) The first head, in all models, is the erase head. So—do your marking on the *last* head, usually the right-hand one. (Note: If you have a single head with two "bumps," the first is erase, the second, as above, is record/playback; mark your tape on the second bump.)

When you have found the spot you wish (see below), make a *light* up-and-down mark on the tape directly in the center of the playing head. You can feel its curved surface under the tape, about a quarter-inch wide. Don't push too hard—be careful! The heads are delicate and must stay precisely aligned within thousandths of an inch. A light mark won't do the head any harm.

Now for the sound. But whoa. I've skipped past (as perhaps you have) the most obvious requirement, mentioned awhile back. You can't edit any tape with two different sound tracks on it. If you want to edit, record only one track on your tape. Doesn't matter whether it's done on a dual-track machine, standard for most home models, or on a single-track model. You can edit either type.

To remove an unwanted sound, play the tape until you hit the place you want, then stop it quickly. Move back and forth by hand, if you can, with the tape in playing position, until you locate the end of the desirable passage, where your first cut will be made. Mark. Then move on, by hand or by playing, until you come to the other end of the part you want to remove, the beginning of the new section. Mark it too. Keep the sounds of the two ends in mind and be sure that they are going to match.

Now you have two marks on the tape and you'll remove what is in between, joining the two marks together. Just how you lift out the tape for cutting depends on the machine—but I suggest immediately that you place your splicing block next to the recording slot, perhaps just in front of it or behind, and then lift out only a short section of tape, *leaving the reels in position*. Don't take off one or both reels! A waste of time. Lift the tape with both thumbs and forefingers and place it in the groove on the splicing block with the mark centered directly on the middle of the *diagonal* slot. Slice your tape across, pull out the end toward the other mark and unreel until it appears; then cut off, as above. Now you'll have your two marks neatly superimposed in the cutting block and you can go ahead and splice—then play to see what happened. Wrong place? Well, mistakes will be made. Find out what you did wrong and try again.

If you can't locate one of the marks as you pull out tape, you can often find where you are by pulling the tape lightly across the playing head by hand. Strange noises, but you can probably identify them. If this doesn't work and you're lost, then patch the tape back into its original form, temporarily, and start all over again.

Find out for yourself which is best to do, cut the first mark first, or move forward to the second mark, cut it, and then back to cut the first. One of these ways will usually turn out to be quicker, on your machine.

Never throw away a removed piece of tape until you have listened to the finished splice! (Don't, that is, until you can afford to be reckless.) Drape it in front of you, or over one leg, keeping it carefully in the right direction to avoid upside-down insertion. If your splice turns out OK, then throw it on the floor—the famed "cutting room floor" of the movies is now yours—and proceed. If your splice is wrong, patch the removed piece back in again, or take a guess at how much of it you'll need to add or snip it off, still saving the remainder. You may find yourself dealing with four or five tiny snippets a half-inch or so long, after several repairs for exactitude. You can peel up and remove one end of a piece of patching tape a couple of times, reusing it, but it's best to use a new piece if the old doesn't stick absolutely tight. To be sure of a tight seal, run the flat of your fingernail over the splice after you have removed it from the block, with the tape placed against a hard surface.

With this much information you can cover a large area of simple editing procedure. It's enough to allow you to "clean up" most of the extraneous noise from all your present tapes and those to come. It may be weeks, or years, before you are inspired to go further. But when you do, take my word for it, more complex editing is accessible to you without further preparation. When you begin tampering with Beethoven and Bach, ingeniously snipping out notes or whole sections of their music, leaving not a trace of the excision, you'll feel the full responsibility and excitement of tape editing. And the serious, useful things that you can do will be balanced by the hilarious, zany possibilities that open up, if your imagination gets to work. There's no end of entertainment in store, once you start on that kind of diabolic hobby!

Advanced editing of this sort is a matter of perceptive listening, of long memory and quick organizing. Musically, it requires a keen ear, both for the sound itself and for the subtleties of musical form—everything counts. Good tape editing is never crude.

But I must stop before I grow lyrical over a technique that can be at least as poetic as composing on a typewriter. Space won't allow further details—but I urge you to try editing for yourself just as soon as you have mastered the splicing technique. It can be a major hobby in itself, as well as a remarkably useful occupation.

19

Striking a Balance

And so at last we come to a striking of the balance, after so many chapters of detailed material. At this point I suspect you have several large questions still in your mind. First, I am sure, is, "*What hi-fi components do you recommend?*"—for though I have recommended various components, I have not presented you with a complete hi-fi shopping list. Secondly, I suspect that you are wondering how in all these pages I can stick to the basic distinction in Chapter 1 between mass-produced "hi-fi" and the named-component high fidelity. The stores and the magazines are now crammed so full of all sorts of good-looking machinery that it would seem every nook and cranny between "hi-fi" and the high fidelity system is now filled in, so that the difference simply does not any longer appear to exist.

Put aside for a few more pages this burgeoning "hi-fi" market. Component hi-fi is with us more strongly than ever, too. Granted that you intend to take advantage of its values for your home system—then what components should you buy?

I cannot give you an exact list and be fair to you or honest with myself. First, too much depends on you—upon your needs, your tastes, ear, budget. There is no universal "best" hi-fi system—in any price range. The very flexibility of component hi-fi sees to that. And in any case no single "expert" (nor any consumer's testing organization either) can hope to evaluate all of the vast quantity of hi-fi equipment now available, to choose the "best." All that any of us can do, if we are honest and straightforward, is to recommend those units of which we definitely have knowledge or can vouch for and trust that we have not been unfair by implication to other units of similar interest.

Much more important, we can do our best to give you the sort of background information that will help you choose your own hi-fi, to understand its workings and appreciate its values and its faults.

You may have noticed that in preceding chapters my various recommendations have often been in a very low-priced area, even though in the summaries of types of equipment on the market the prices mentioned are usually much higher. This is deliberate. On the one hand there is modest equipment that offers the optimum sort of listening value—for serious music listening. On the other hand there is the equipment which is most likely to be offered to you, the sort featured in hi-fi stores and catalogues. The two are not at all the same, nor should they be. Maximum economy is not always what most of us want—even when we know of it; nor is it a sales leader.

For example, I have recommended the single speaker, without tweeters, dividing networks and the rest of the complications, as the very best musical bargain, and within that area I picked out the eight-inch speaker as the most useful in a price range from about $8 to $30 or so. But most speakers and systems in the stores are more expensive, ranging in fact up to the $1,000 area for complete systems, ready to play.

This is to be expected. The geometry of values operates to favor the unusually low-priced equipment but the laws of salesmanship and business inevitably "push" the more expensive (and often better) items. Very few people actually buy the equipment that gives them the most value for the money. Most prefer something better—at more cost.

I suspect, then, that you—the hypothetical average music lover—will end up, statistically, buying equipment in the middle price ranges. Most people do. This means that if you spend your money in an average way, as the salesman persuades you, your cash will perhaps be laid down in the following fashion. (This is merely one arbitrary arrangement of components.)

AN AVERAGE HI-FI SYSTEM

Radio tuner	$100
Amplifier, complete	$70-$150
Record changer (with diamond stylus in magnetic pickup)	$75-$90
Speaker system	$100-$175

For this four or five hundred dollars you get a remarkably fine system, and make no doubt about it, if you choose your components carefully to suit your own needs and your own ear. It will outperform any ready-made "hi-fi" straight up into the $1,000 class and higher. For a complete high fidelity system, this is not actually an excessive price. A good TV set costs almost as much and covers only a single medium of entertainment; your hi-fi system is more versatile and can be expanded at any time to cover wider interests. In other areas, people buy far more expensive entertainment on slim budgets—sailboats, outboard motors, trailers, swimming pools and what have you.

Moreover, people by the thousands are treating themselves to relatively poor bargains for the same prices in the innumerable "hi-fi" machines with their skimpy innards, so glossily advertised. Even without so much as a look at my bargain-basement, rock-bottom type of equipment—see below—you can do better simply by acquiring reliable component-type equipment, even of the more expensive sorts.

I see no reason why you shouldn't go right ahead and flout the law of the geometric progression—as long as you understand how it works. We all enjoy spending money—we have the right to treasure even the smallest increment of extra value, for a large extra cash outlay—if we honestly enjoy the difference. These are the intangibles, values that cost money but bring an unmeasurable satisfaction. (I suppose, come to think of it, that even the keeping-up-with-the-Joneses approach is worth while to those who ardently want that sort of satisfaction.)

I recommend, for example, the AR-1 loudspeaker system to you because, even though it costs some $180, it is worth it in my own scale of musical values and may well be in yours. On the other hand, I suggest without the slightest hesitation that a mere $25 to $30 spent on a good eight-inch speaker and enclosure can bring an equal degree of satisfaction—and an *almost* equally good kind of musical listening. The difference is really small—it may easily be ignored, or easily treasured.

The same is true with many another component. The ubiquitous GE magnetic cartridge is an unbeatable bargain in sound. I use it most of the time, and with the greatest of pleasure. The cartridge I'm now using happens to cost some three times as much; it is slightly better, on direct comparison. An expert ear can tell them apart, though probably at the expense of the music. (If you ignore the music and concentrate on the sound itself, you can hear the difference.) Most untrained music listeners would not notice it even upon direct comparison. Paradoxically, though I can hear the better sound and value it highly, I can forget all about it after two minutes of a good piece of music via the GE cartridge. But I *still* value the difference. It is both slight and enormous.

How can I decide where your feelings, your perceptions, will lie, in such matters? How can I tell whether you should buy a GE cartridge or, perhaps, a Fairchild, Grado, Pickering, ESL, Weathers—all of them considerably more expensive? I can only state the probabilities for your evaluation: (a) at first you won't be able to tell the difference at all; and (b) you can learn to distinguish them clearly—*if* you happen to be interested. If you are a music listener you probably won't have time to bother with such subtleties. Music is well served by such cartridges as the GE, not to mention its ceramic cartridge competitors, so seldom used by hi-fi fans.

THE ROCK-BOTTOM SYSTEM

And so, with all this in mind, you'll be interested in my sampling of rock-bottom equipment, the sort that gives you optimum sound for the money. Don't underestimate it! Not only the remarkably good sound that you can buy at a low price, but also the extraordinary wearing qualities of some of the cheaper hi-fi units. They last just as long as the big components.

One of my stand-by systems, constantly on loan to friends or in use for various special occasions, is made up of: (1) A Columbia LP changer, the selfsame machine mentioned in the first edition of my first book as having then played for two years without failure; it is, as of this writing, about *eight* years old—and, with a minor cleaning up and a replaced cartridge, is running as well as new. It cost exactly $18! (2) A six-year-old ten-watt amplifier that has had one good going over, with a few minor improvements added; it is precisely as good as new—in fact, a bit better. Cost when new: about $45. (3) The EW speaker system mentioned in my earlier book, now renamed the Hartsdale, with an eight-inch speaker in a small box fifteen inches high. Cost new, unfinished about $35.

That system, averaging six years in age, costing new just under $100, is, I assure you, a thoroughly satisfactory one for good musical listening and so far ahead of most "hi-fis"—even when new—that you would have to hear it to believe me. And how many "hi-fi" machines will still operate at six years of age?

Rock-Bottom Hi-Fi System. Typical low-cost component hi-fi in the area where the geometric advantage (Chapter 10) is most favorable, sound-value for the money greatest. Systems involving this equipment can easily surpass "hi-fi" home machines costing $250 or more.

Best bargains today are (a) in "package" systems, costing less than equivalent separate components and (b) kit-form components, semiassembled, at about half the cost of the same items ready-to-use.

1. Typical low-cost package systems (others in various price ranges):

Lafayette Hi-Fi Phono System HF-188 $100. (Collaro 4-speed changer, GE cartridge dual sapphires, 12-inch coaxial speaker with cone tweeter, 12-watt LA-22 complete amplifier, "resonator" lowboy speaker cabinet.)
Allied Radio Phono System 91 PA 972 (minus speaker cabinet) $80. (Garrard RC-121 4-speed changer, GE cartridge dual sapphires, GE 8-inch 850D speaker, Grommes LJ-6 10-watt complete amplifier.)

2. Some typical kit values:

Heathkit A-9C 20-watt complete amplifier $36; A-7D 7-watt complete amplifier $18. Lafayette 5-watt phono amplifier (no preamp—use ceramic cartridge) $11. Eico 12-watt Williamson complete amplifier $35 (assembled $58). Dynakit Mark III 60-watt basic power amplifier (one of the finest amplifiers at any price) $80.

3. Record players:

Manual: Miraphon 4-speed player, less cartridge $38. Garrard T MK II 4-speed player, less cartridge $32. Bogen Economy 4-speed player, adjustable speeds, less cartridge $30. Lafayette PK-164 3-speed player with diamond-sapphire GE cartridge $38. Bases for all these, $4-5 extra.
Changer: Webcor Economy 4-speed, with GE cartridge, dual sapphire $37. V-M Tri-O-Matic (4-speed), same $42. Monarch 4-speed, with Goldring cartridge, dual sapphire $27. Bases $4-5 extra.
Cartridges: GE VR II magnetic, dual sapphire $9, diamond-sapphire about $18. Sonotone 2T-S ceramic, dual sapphire $8.50; 2T-SD diamond-sapphire $22.

4. Complete amplifiers (assembled):

Lafayette LA-22 12-watt $34. Grommes LJ-6 10-watt $34. Grommes LJ-6 10-watt $39. Allied Radio Mini-Fi 10-watt $39. Bogen Challenger 10-watt $45. Bell Pacemaker 10-watt $49.

5. **Radio tuners:**

Type One: Lafayette LT-25 FM-AM $50; LT-40 Music-Mate $65. Allied Knight Bantam FM-AM $75. Harman-Kardon Overture FM-AM $85. Lafayette LT-60 FM-only $50. Bogen FM-only $85. (*Note: Kit prices are considerably lower.*)

Type Three (with all controls, built-in amplifier): Bogen RR501C FM-AM 10-watt amplifier $135; RR50 FM-AM 25-watt amplifier $225. Pilot HF-30 FM-AM 12-watt Williamson amplifier $170. Etc.

6. **Low-cost speaker enclosures:**

Karlson 8-inch, kit (unfinished) $19, (assembled) $27. Able Wood bookshelf 8-inch (unfinished) $26, (finished) $30. Argos 12-inch modified bass reflex (finished) $25. Electro-Voice Baronet 8-inch horn enclosure, kit (unfinished) $26, (assembled) $45; Aristocrat 12-inch horn enclosure, kit $39. Knight (Allied Radio) 8-inch bass reflex bookshelf enclosure KN-1240 (finished) $25; corner horn kit KN-1320 (finished) $30. R-J 8-inch bookshelf enclosure (unfinished) $27; 12-inch $33; 12-inch lowboy (unfinished) $46, (finished) $53. Cabinart 15-inch bass reflex, kit (unfinished) $24. Norelco 8-inch FRS III (finished) $34. Able Wood 8-12-inch resonator floor enclosure with legs (unfinished) $33, (finished) $38. Etc.

7. **Low-priced speakers:**

See p. 142. (8-inch singles run from $8 to about $30; 12-inch coaxials, many with cone tweeter, run from about $14—too low—to $45-$50. Imported 10-inch models have top sound, don't fit many cabinets.)

8. **Low-cost complete speaker systems:**

Hartsdale H-3 (15" x 10½" x 12¼", unfinished) $35; (finished) $40-$45. R-J Wharfedale (8-inch, finished) $58. Permoflux Diminuette two-way (cone speakers) about $60. Kingdom-Lorenz Audette Jr. (bookshelf type, cone speakers) $50; brass legs $6. Heathkit SS-1 or Eico HFS1 bookshelf-type kit (finished) $40 (horn tweeter).

9. **Equipment cabinetry:**

Typical low-priced cabinets, for components minus speaker: Heathkit equipment enclosure (chairside, sliding drawer), kit (finished) $44. Cabinart Model 80 equipment cabinet, kit (unfinished) $30; Model 70 (same, assembled) $39. Wellcor (Allied Radio) half-door louvered cabinet (unfinished) $18; full-door $24. River Edge 100 cabinet, kit (unfinished) $40; (assembled, unfinished) $49; legs $7. (*See dealer or catalogues for details.*)

Despite all my listing of more expensive equipment, with all the sales attractions for higher-cost systems, you may find that this is the sort of system to suit your needs to perfection. And even if you choose more expensive equipment, you may use my similar recommendations, herewith, as a basis for sharp thinking and careful comparison, an anchor to windward against the joyful breezes of hi-fi publicity. (See pp. 268-269.)

WHAT ABOUT THE NEW HI-FIS?

For the first time since the first chapter I have used that term, hi-fi, with the quotation marks deliberately removed. That is because I suspect—and I must say in concluding this volume—that in the next years to come, the still-sharp distinction between named-component high fidelity and the mass-produced "hi-fi" will blur in actuality—not in claims—and will eventually disappear.

That is not to say, I must quickly point out, that the cheap, unworthy "hi-fi" will suddenly cease to exist, or take on universal new values that will raise it to component hi-fi status in terms of sound for the money. Nor is this to suggest that the basic usefulness of separately designed components, produced by specialized companies, will vanish.

I am not saying, either, that present intermediate "hi-fi" types, those with hi-fi "components" of studiously vague description, designed to seem like separate-unit packages, are the ultimate values that will overthrow the component system. We are still a long way from reliability in this in-between area. There are already some machines that do offer good values in semicomponent package form. There are many others, outwardly just as attractive, that merely claim these virtues. It is very difficult at this point to tell the sheep from the goats, except by painful experience—and then it is too late. I assure you that there are goats galore. I have heard and been shocked by some "hi-fi" machines, marked with those eternal words "high fidelity," that were so outrageously bad, at such outrageous prices, that I cannot imagine why they are sold—except that industry-enforced hi-fi standards do not yet exist.

But make no mistake, the trend is inexorably toward the combination high fidelity machine, a ready-made complete "package" that offers many of the best and most useful features of component high fidelity. In these coming years, if all goes well, the sleazy equipment, with its blown-up claims and vague specifications, will slowly depart, or will be revalued at a proper and legitimate price. There is already a great deal of indignation in the component high fidelity industry at the unprincipled stealing of terminology that has been going on; the component people are seeking to establish standards—but again, they are at a loss for sheer words. The relevant terms have been stolen, are stolen again and again as soon as they are put forth in any legitimate way. The Institute of High Fidelity Manufacturers, for example, can be counted upon eventually to exert its weight on the side of reasonably competitive standards for hi-fi terminology. Sooner or later, the mass-production companies themselves will be forced to take steps, to protect their own interests; for if "high fidelity"—and all the other related terminology—can be applied without discrimination to good and bad, then even the "hi-fi" makers will suffer.

Thus you will find more and more solid values in the "packaged hi-fi" area, month by month, and there will be increasing reason for you to consider the one-piece (or to two-piece, with separate speaker) ready-made system as an alternative to separate components. A good many of them will come from the component manufacturers themselves, or from various larger hi-fi dealers, who will do the assembling, perhaps order special components for their own use. Stereo will be a tremendous spur to these new developments.

But how can you tell what is good hi-fi and what is merely "hi-fi," the same old exaggerated claims in handsome, fall-apart packages?

Three factors will count. First, on a factual scale, you will need to find out what components are actually offered—which means, of course, that you will want specifications that mean what they say (specifications that are at least as definite as those common in component hi-fi). You will want to know what the elements inside the machine are, how good they are, how they compare with others that you may acquire. If these elements are actual named models—a well-known changer, for instance—so much the better.

Secondly, as you can quickly guess, you will want to know what all this costs, in relation to other possible kinds of hi-fi, for mental or actual comparison. The more definite the description, the easier will be your task—and you will find every variety of account from nothing specific at all to descriptions that are quite surprisingly detailed. You will add up the known prices of the components, if any. Add a bit for the fact of ready-to-play operation, perhaps 10 to 15 per cent. Then see how much the hi-fi ready-made convenience is going to cost you in comparison with its approximate equivalent in component hi-fi.

Yes—I know; this is a pesty nuisance, this fussy figuring of relative values, and you will run into salesroom opposition if you try it. The salesman doesn't expect such questioning and won't like it. But, I can warn you, the values currently offered in ready-made equipment range so violently from terrible to excellent, that you must do something about it. The terrible stuff is everywhere; the so-so stuff is widely offered in respectable "hi-fi" lines that will satisfy well enough if you don't know what is better; and the good material, really solid value in "packaged" hi-fi, is just beginning to filter into the shops.

My third category of inquiry is simply the listening test. If you are unable to get specifications that are definite enough to allow you to form a judgment on paper, so to speak, you'll have to fall back on your own good ear. And that requires a mental comparison, if not an actual one. You must have some kind of standard, and it should surely be the best—the component type of sound that demonstrably gives the best sound values, if at more inconvenience and confusion compared to "hi-fi."

You may arrive at some sense of values by listening to component equipment in one store—and perhaps to "hi-fi" equipment in a different store nearby. A better way is to visit a friend who owns a good system that you admire—or even a modest one—and get an idea as to the sort of sound to expect from this kind of equipment. (Choose a musical friend—not a hi-fi addict.) Preferably listen to a recording that is already familiar to you. Then, go to the store you have in mind and listen, compare, weigh costs. Play the same recording, if you can. Try the same sort of music.

You will not forget, of course, that the acoustical effect of the listening place must be taken into account and you will allow for it in the showrooms where you listen. Most stores are abominable places to hear music—and the better the music, the worse it sounds. Not all stores. Judge the sound of the machines you hear in the light of the rooms in which they play, for better or worse (Chapter 15).

To put all this in a more precise framework, I would like to cite one particular line of intermediate ready-made equipment that I have not even heard. It is not the equipment itself so much as the intention that is of interest—for this was a pioneer line in a new effort to bridge the gap between conventional "hi-fi" and component high fidelity. It was launched on this basis by a company that has produced excellent component equipment, notably in the radio tuner field, but has always had a certain enterprising eye cocked in the direction of other fields perhaps as green or greener. This is my own private evaluation of the Pilot Radio Company, of course, but it indicates a favorable environment for an experiment in the new in-between area.

Let me put before you merely the outward publicity in some of these early Pilot offerings. They were deliberately sold through regular music stores and radio outlets—not hi-fi dealers. The entire line is calculatedly slanted in detail to hit between the component and the usual "hi-fi" approaches—even the prices were angled to this purpose, being generally higher than component prices to compete directly with the retail "hi-fi" equipment, but offering component-type values in the machines that modified the relationship in Pilot's favor, I should say. The degree of "component thinking," too, varied from model to model, and was so indicated in the advertised descriptions.

Here are some details, along with my comments as to the kind of paperwork reasoning you can apply to this sort of model description. More precise details, of course, could be followed up with the dealer—if he knew them. Pilot's advertising asked, in large heads, "How Will You Have Your High Fidelity—a High Fidelity Component Console or a High Fidelity Component System?" and both types were displayed, the emphasis on the one-piece "ensemble":

1. *A Phonograph Ensemble* (#1028), $280. Contemporary cabinet, hinged at top; Pilot AA-900 10-watt amplifier; Garrard 4-speed changer (model and cartridge not specified) with diamond needle; a "Pilot 3-Speaker System," details unspecified.

The cheapest of the three then-current Garrard changers sold at about $60 audiophile net, with GE cartridge and diamond LP point. The 10-watt amplifier would compete with other amplifiers perhaps in the $45-$50 range. A cabinet of the sort described might cost separately about $75 (but could not be recommended for best sound; speakers are not separate). Add, at a guess, $30 for the speakers. Rough hypothetical component equivalent, around $210-$230, not including assembly of the parts.

2. *A Portable Table-Type Phonograph, Pinseal Finish* (#1015), $170. Pilot 8-watt amplifier; 2-speaker system (in usual small front space ahead of the changer); Garrard 3-speed changer with dual sapphire styli. (No mention of cartridge.)

A conventional "hi-fi," this one, but with unusual features. Eight watts is more power than in most table models of this sort. The amplifier probably approaches component-type performance, might equal a $30 value in components; the changer, with sapphires and probable GE cartridge, would have sold for about $50; the box and speakers have no component equivalent; in such a confined space the sound would certainly be boomy and subject to distortion. The same $170 could buy a complete separate system with better sound quality, though larger and clumsier.

3. *Pilot 5-Speaker System*, $200. "Precisely matched speaker system in acoustical enclosure"—a fairly large and imposing box, but the speakers and type of enclosure are not specified. A poor risk, unless more details could be learned from the salesman. Is the tweeter a horn or a cone? Mid-range cone speaker? Two woofers, perhaps 12-inch? A bass reflex box? Investigation decidedly necessary.

4. *5-Speaker FM-AM Radio Phonograph* (#1041), $575. Built-in 5-speaker system (as above); louvered large cabinet, top opening for changer, side opening for tuner amplifier. Pilot HF-42 Tuner-Amplifier (Type Three —see page 114); Garrard De Luxe Changer, diamond needle.

This large machine included the 5-speaker system as one-half of its cabinet. The HF-42 Tuner-Amplifier, 20-watt, less than 1 per cent distortion at full output, sold as a component for $210. "De Luxe Changer" implies either the Garrard RC-98 at $84 or the RC-88 at $72 with GE cartridge and diamond LP stylus; those were the two "de luxe" models. The cabinet is clearly a major item of cost and might be bought as a component, in theory, for $150 or more. Aside from the speaker, this machine can be pinned down to fairly realistic comparative values—but the 5-speaker system would have to be investigated carefully.

There are now many other lines of similar half-and-half merchandise; but you will still find plenty of machines, much like these in outward aspect, that give no true specifications of any usefulness—they may or may not be good values. Even without complete details, as you see from the above analysis, you can gather a rough idea of the values you are about to receive—if you buy. And your ear, again, can help you immensely in a comparative sense, *provided* you have listened to known worth-while equipment.

Cast a speculative but wary eye, then, upon the myriads of attractive magazine ads for "component high fidelity" console machines. Go and look at or listen to them in the hundreds of showrooms where they are so decoratively placed. And when you have come to the end of your quest for a really reliably described and good sounding one-piece "hi-fi," then return to the component idea with me and settle all your doubts—or most of them—in favor of a named-component high fidelity system. That, with all the lengthy terminology I have had to use for it, is still the best chance for good listening at modest cost, for long-time satisfaction and flexibility.

If I didn't still think so, I would not have bothered to write this volume.

20

Breakdowns

Undoubtedly one of the chief unanswered questions in your mind as you have read through this book is put bluntly in the title of this chapter, "What shall I do about breakdowns?"

It would be much nicer if we could refrain from any such questioning. The advertising men are silent on this subject—you will find relatively little about such unspeakable matters in the catalogues. But that is to be expected. It is our good, positive, "constructive" American way to ignore failure, to hail success.

It Won't Break Down Soon. In fact it is good to be able to assure you that trouble with your separate-unit system—real, basic, serious trouble—is remarkably unlikely. The high fidelity system, even the low-priced variety, is usually very much more reliable than most "hi-fi" phonographs or radios. Standards are higher, where standards count—not on the outside but inside, in the wiring, the switches, resistors and capacitors. I have experimented with enough cheap amplifiers, cheap speakers and record changers, to know by personal experience that they go right on working, without trouble, under remarkably tough conditions.

I find myself having to deny the implication that there is a "conspiracy" among standard "hi-fi" makers and repairmen. No such thing, at least in any conscious, planned way. But standards have long since been set low enough in the mass radio-phonograph industry so that the repairman's shop is normally busy and the replacement market is very much alive. This is no more than another aspect of the basic situation in any consumer industry. Even our automobiles are made to fall apart (at least in the nonessentials) before long.

VALUES AGAIN. We must look out once more for the old bogey of relative values. The gap between professional engineering standards and mass-production home radio is as huge as ever. The hi-fi system, midway between the two, runs into the old contradictions as to what is "well built" and what is not. Ask an engineer or advanced hi-fi amateur whether the cheap amplifier is well constructed; he will probably tell you that it is not—in comparison with professional equipment. But again, that isn't the point! The important fact is that component hi-fi equipment can be counted on to give far longer service than the "hi-fi" radios and phonographs it replaces in your home.

All of this I say as a preface to discussion of actual trouble—when and if. Not even the hi-fi system is perfect and trouble may occur sooner or later. What can you do when it does occur?

Let me break that down, considerably. First, guarantees and replacements. Second, the practical means of diagnosis in case of actual failure. And third, is it bad? Nine-tenths of the trouble in home high fidelity systems turns out to be minor, a wrongly made connection or a slight loosening of wires, or the like. You'll save yourself endless distress if you can manage to recognize petty trouble and perhaps fix it yourself in a few seconds, instead of boxing up your machine and sending it away, for weeks of anxious waiting.

GUARANTEES. Most component hi-fi equipment is sold under a standard manufacturer's guarantee, that of the Radio-Television Manufacturers Association, the R.T.M.A. guarantee. In practice, the details are rarely important; the good will of your dealer and, more practically, his own capacity for rendering service are what count. Guarantees apply to the individual sections, each manufacturer in the last analysis being separately responsible for his part of your system and not the others. But this seemingly undesirable state of affairs actually is not as bad as it sounds, for the dealer who sells you a system will take responsibility for the guarantee and do the negotiating with the original maker himself. Guarantees in hi-fi are as good as they are anywhere else.

To my mind, guarantees are not nearly so important as basic quality itself. Given a good machine, the guarantee is superfluous. A poorly made product is merely replaced by another of no better quality—

which is hardly "protection." I would suggest that you trust the basically good quality of hi-fi equipment as your best unwritten assurance of satisfaction.

REPAIRS—AND THE HI-FI HYPOCHONDRIAC. The repair picture for hi-fi equipment looks very bad, on the surface. If you investigate, you will find that, officially speaking, it scarcely exists. Many high fidelity mail-order dealers side-step the whole question of repair and offer no service at all to their mail-order customers beyond that of the guarantee. Not because of dishonesty. Instead it is because repairs by mail simply cannot be made to pay—or to satisfy the unknowing, all-blaming customer. Even the local hi-fi dealer who can contact you personally and help you straighten things out under the best possible circumstances is loath to undertake formal repairs—people treat him too badly. By mail, the situation is hopelessly difficult. It is our own ignorance that is at fault.

Perhaps you can put yourself for a moment in the dealer's place. An agonizing number of customers mail their entire systems in to him, at great expense of time, cash and nervous energy, for defects that are trivial. Others, not knowing of their own listening situation (Chapter 15), blame the machine, the dealer or the manufacturer, for faults that the serviceman can't for the life of him trace—because they do not exist.

I'm no serviceman myself, but I'm the recipient of enough of these complaints, sent on to me after allegedly futile negotiations with recalcitrant dealers, to know the situation from their point of view. I have tried my best to answer such mail intelligibly and constructively —and, as a nondealer, as an "objective outsider," I have an advantage in that my opinion is supposed to be sacrosanct, not for profit.

Enough said. If you run into delays or inconsistent, hasty answers to your letters seeking advice, remember all this. The chances are good that the trouble is acute repair-shop indigestion. Don't ship your system back, or any part of it, until you have explored other possibilities. Do write first—most dealers will try to answer you intelligently and with care, if you give them the sort of information that makes sense to them at a distance. Be sure to give specific details as to what equipment you use, what the symptoms of trouble are. And allow time. After a few weeks—it may well be that long—write again or send a carbon. Don't send a postcard; it invites inattention and is easily mislaid.

The local hi-fi outlet is a better place for you to go for your repairs;

you can face your man personally there and talk them out with him in minutes instead of weeks. If it is at all possible, take yourself to one of these shops in the nearest town or city. And don't take your machine with you, unless you know exactly where the trouble is.

If not the mail-order house or the local hi-fi dealer, where can one turn for repairs?

To put it negatively, you will not lose much by avoiding your local radio repairman. At present he is still a poor bet. Lack of knowledge of hi-fi equipment; unfavorable attitude thanks to the fine institution of the net price, which by-passes him; technical training that leaves him without imagination, unable to cope with problems that are not standardized and blueprinted ahead of time. Unless you have no other recourse, or unless you are sure what is wrong, keep the local repairman off your hi-fi set.

If you are to take your repair troubles outside, a very likely man for the job in general is the hi-fi custom builder—if there is one available. Even by mail. The reason is simple. The nature of his business is personal; he specializes in individual jobs; he spends most of his time in consultation both by mail and in person. Try him—if he'll take your work.

Some hi-fi firms at last are beginning to emphasize good repairing. Note the Audio Exchange, for one. But the real trouble, of course, is American Business—based on quick "turnover," brilliant performance, short life, easy replacement. Repairs run "against" the system and there is no room in the business mind to think seriously about them.

REPAIRS IN THE FAMILY CIRCLE. So before you send out anywhere, and short of doing your own diagnosing and repairs—that should come first, but I'm getting to it last—look around you for help on a nonpaying basis. Your best possible local source of aid and comfort is a friend who knows more than you do about hi-fi's ills. There are plenty of them, in every city and town nowadays. There's no accounting for skills. A surprising number of people whose official specialties are far removed turn out to be natural-born wizards with the elements of hi-fi, mechanical and electrical. What to you is a nightmare may to them be no problem at all. They'll be pleased to help. And don't forget the kids. The younger generation, down to age twelve or so, produces electrical geniuses right and left.

These people can often spot the trivialities before you get yourself worked up over them and save you time and money.

SELF-HELP. Before you try any of these alternatives—do your own diagnosing. The best possible way to satisfy yourself is to manage your own business without obligation to anyone else, for cash or for friendship. I repeat, most troubles with hi-fi systems turn out to be very minor, more often than not a wrongly made connection or a connection come loose. The equipment is fundamentally well built.

You do not need technical knowledge for this so much as plain common sense and the power of reason and deduction, the ability to put two and two together cannily, eliminate irrelevancies, avoid too-easy traps of false logic. You need not feel inadequate here! I cannot feel that you are seriously outclassed in rational logic by the professional.

Above all, you must spot that old bogey, plurality. More than one thing at a time. Plural troubles are the rule; things seldom come singly, for your convenience in analyzing them. There isn't a one of these compound difficulties, though, that can't be resolved into its elements by plain careful observation, process of elimination; nor is there any single difficulty that you can't at least partially isolate and pin down, even though you may not be able yourself to repair it.

PROCESS OF ELIMINATION. Suppose, for example, you notice that a recording sounds fuzzy and distorted at normal volume. Common sense will tell you that a number of things might cause such a sound—but which?

Is it in the record? It might not be in your system at all. Try another record. If the fuzziness persists unchanged through several, you can deduce that the trouble is definitely in your system.

Bad needle? Try a new one and see what happens. This may fix the trouble at once—but be sure to try the same record as before, just to be absolutely clear. Suppose with a new needle the fuzziness still is there; then it is not the needle after all. Is it perhaps in the amplifier? If you have a radio tuner, turn that on and see how it sounds. If its sound is clear, you know that the trouble must be somewhere *after* the needle but *before* the amplifier, i.e., in the phonograph system. The amplifier serves for both radio and phono and could hardly be fuzzy for one and clear for the other.

That is the kind of sensible diagnosis that, with a small basic knowledge of your system's operation, can save you a very large amount of anguish. Such logic is not the serviceman's forte, nor always the engineer's. The best of them are only human—like most of us they dodge inescapable conclusions, confuse one symptom with another, point emphatically at the wrong source for trouble.

I could give you many exhilarating examples of the ease with which a disturbing factor may be isolated and uncovered, if not repaired, with this sort of common sense. I've seen needless agony wasted over hum that turned out not to be in the machine at all but recorded along with the music on a commercial record! How can one be sure? Incredibly simple. Play the record too fast or too slow; if the hum is on the record its pitch will change; if it is in your hi-fi system it will stay put, whatever the record speed.

One lives and learns in this field as in another. Signs of trouble to come are not hard to spot. You usually have good warning, if your ears are open. It is very rare that a system goes completely dead or begins to burn up without some previous indication. After a period of acquaintance, you will find that your ear is tuned to good performance, like a watchdog; unusual noises or effects quickly intrude themselves on your consciousness. It is at these moments of warning that you begin to observe and deduce for all you are worth.

LISTENER'S SYMPTOMOLOGY

For your assistance—and to implement as well as I may these somewhat vague words of encouragement—here is a listener's guide. With it you may perhaps make the most important distinction of all—is your trouble serious or trivial?

A. SIXTY-CYCLE HUM. Hum trouble occurs almost exclusively before the main amplifier—usually in the connections between phono or radio (or other input) and the amplifier. It may also originate in the preamplifier, if you use magnetic phono cartridges.

  1. **Steady Hum, Faint to Medium, While Music Plays.** Probably due either to hum from the preamplifier (common, though inexcusable) or more likely to insufficient shielding on the (high-impedance) input connections from phonograph or radio tuner to the amplifier.
     a. If the latter, pulling out the phono or radio connector plug from the amplifier should stop it or reduce it noticeably. The shielding is the metal braid that acts as one connector in the pickup-to-amplifier or radio-to-amplifier cable; it surrounds the "live" signal wire and

must be firmly connected both at the pickup or radio end and to the outside collar of the plug that goes into the amplifier. It must physically cover or shield the signal wire from one end to the other. If you find a stretch unshielded, try twisting one end of a length of thinnish wire through the braiding to make a connection; than wrap it spirally around the uncovered part of the signal wire in close turns. Be sure the signal wire is insulated from the shield. It's best to solder the connection to the braiding if you can. If possible, connect both ends to the ground (the braiding or the frame of the pickup or amplifier, as convenient)—but one end will do if the connection is firm. This extends the shielding and should reduce the hum. Or substitute a whole new length of shielded cable (with braiding), if you can get it, in place of the unshielded lead. Ask for "low capacity" shielded cable with a black covering. It's best.

b. There may be hum in the preamplifier. You can check this by elimination. First, try the radio (a high-level input) as compared to the phono. If the hum seems always to be present whenever the preamplifier is used, you can suspect it. Then try shorting out the preamplifier input; put the volume up, stick a bare wire into the phono (magnetic) input socket (no danger!) and touch the other end to the frame or side of the amplifier. Loud hum will indicate when you've hit the inside connection in the socket; when the other end of the wire is touched to the amplifier frame the hum should disappear completely. If hum remains, at a lower volume, the preamp has hum in it. Bad.

A preamplifier with hum is unacceptable. If it is in a new amplifier, return the amplifier to your dealer before the guarantee is out. A good repairman can sometimes reduce hum.

Most amplifiers and preamplifiers have one or more hum-adjusting screws. If you hear objectionable hum, try turning these with a screwdriver, to find the point at which hum is lowest. Usually less than one turn will take you from the highest to the lowest hum; often there seems to be no difference, in which case ignore. See amplifier instruction book for details.

2. **Very Loud Blasting Hum, but Music Still Can Be Heard.** (Phono, radio or other input to amplifier.) The ground (or shield) connection to the amplifier is broken. A common spot for this trouble is at the neck of the plug that goes into the amplifier, where the braiding is soldered to its outside collar. If this connection breaks, loud hum results—sometimes sputtering or intermittent if the connection is partly made. Wiggle the plug while music is playing—pull it out and examine closely. You may make a temporary ground connection as above, by winding a bare wire around the braiding and then around the collar of the plug, or even to the nearest metal part of the amplifier, to reestablish the ground connection. In the end, the plug should be resoldered.

You may double-check this type of hum by touching the braiding
and the amplifier's metal simultaneously with your fingers to make a
human connection—the hum should decrease somewhat, increase when
you let go of the amplifier. No danger!

3. **Loudish Hum, No Music Heard.** (Phono or radio or other input.) This
characteristically "empty" sound indicates that there is an open circuit—no connection for the signal to enter the amplifier. Trace the
connections from the radio or phonograph to the amplifier—something
is missing. Repair should be simple. Have you left a switch in the
wrong position?

4. **Sputtery Music with or without Hum.** Loose connection again. Sometimes the inside signal wire gets partly shorted, touching the braiding
at some point. (Sharply pointed metal strands of it often pierce the
insulation where the braiding is frayed or where it has been soldered.)
Look over the wiring carefully—bend or twist it while the music plays
to find where the trouble spot is.

5. **Polarized AC Lines.** Some house-current lines are polarized—which
means as far as you are concerned that there is a difference between
the two ways you can insert a plug into the house-current socket.
Extra hum may be caused if the amplifier plug is in the wrong relationship to the radio tuner or phonograph motor plug. Try reversing
the amplifier plug—if that does not reduce the hum, reverse the radio
and/or phonograph wall plugs just to be sure. If there is no difference,
then this factor doesn't count in your situation.

6. **Hum When Pickup Arm Is Touched.** When this happens, you have
reversed connections in a ceramic pickup cartridge. (Or the arm itself
is not grounded—connected—to the shielded braiding on the cable
to the amplifier. The arm should be grounded to act as extra shielding
and usually is automatically when the cartridge is screwed in; but some
cartridges may be insulated at their screw mountings.)

Look at the cartridge itself; the "hot" or signal connection is an
insulated prong, the ground or shield connection in many cartridges
has a metal band running to the cartridge frame. As you look down
on it, the ground prong, which should be connected to the braided
shielding, is usually on the right. In any case, reversed connections can
make the pickup arm part of the signal circuit itself, unshielded, right
out in the open. Music will play, but hum varies according to how
close you or your hand come to it. With right-side-around connections
touching, the arm should make no difference in the sound. Along with
your body, it is then part of the shielding.

If you think along these lines in a common-sense way, using process-
of-elimination to your utmost, you can usually decide for yourself
where hum trouble originates even though you may not want to do
anything about it by yourself without help.

Remember that a broken ground connection causes violently loud hum; lack of enough shielding (though the connection is complete) causes only moderate to faint hum. The loud squawk that you may have heard when plugging your radio or phonograph into the amplifier input occurs because the inside signal contact is made first by the prong; the ground connection comes only when the outside collar fits over its ring on the socket. For a brief instant there is no ground connection— and the squawk results, as always when the ground connection is broken.

As always, look out for plurality. There may be more than one cause for hum.

B. FUZZINESS OR DISTORTION IN MUSIC. As described above, there are numerous possibilities here. Careful comparison and elimination should narrow them down rapidly.

1. **Is the distortion in the record**—or in the radio broadcast—and not in your system at all? Try other records; try other stations; compare radio and records.
2. **Wrong needle**—microgroove point on a 78 rpm record or vice versa? If so, change quickly. An LP sapphire or metal point (the latter not recommended) is quickly ruined by a 78 rpm record.
3. **Bad needle?** Replace to see; or take to your record store.
4. **Dust or grit caught in the stylus** of a magnetic pickup can cause acute fuzziness, sometimes stopping the music altogether. Remove with fingers, or (best) with small, soft brush. This is a very frequent complaint and the easiest of all to remedy. Common in GE, Audak, ESL, other cartridges with side pieces at the stylus.
5. **Crystal pickups** fail sometimes—the crystal warps or cracks. Music is then distorted and fuzzy on all records, if it plays at all. A new needle won't help this, naturally. Same with ceramics.
6. **Stereo record?** Standard cartridges may produce varyingly fuzzy sound from stereo discs—and can ruin the stereo groove.
7. **Is it in your radio tuner?** FM tuners must be realigned every so often (more often than most people realize) for correct performance. If you get stations at several "humps" on the dial, if the sound is distorted or fuzzy, especially on weak stations, have it checked.
8. **Failing tubes** can gradually introduce distortion into your system, or into parts of it, according to their position. If in doubt, take them out and have them tested at a radio store. (A small suitcase with a sofa pillow inside is a good way to carry them safely.)
9. **Speaker voice coil trouble.** If you hear blasting distortion in some loud passages, but other softer passages seem all right; or if there is a persistent scratchy sound to most music, your speaker voice coil may be out of true and occasionally scraping the sides of its narrow slot,

or—more common—there may be a bit of grit lodged in the slot. To check, push center of speaker cone in and out firmly (but carefully) with fingers. If you hear any scratching sound, you have trouble. Usually, only an expert can make repairs, though you may try to dislodge possible sand or grit by blowing, or by flexing the cone.

C. Intermittent or Background Noises. A good many things can cause extraneous noise in your system or interfere erratically with the music itself. Here are some of the more usual troubles and their probable causes.

1. **Background "steaming" and sputter when records are being played.** Persistent noise of this type is usually from the preamplifier—possibly a bad tube. Tap the tubes to see if you can locate it; sometimes this will stop the noise, or increase it. Try a new tube in place of the one that seems most sensitive. Very often a tube that is perfectly good otherwise will create abnormally loud tube noise of this sort. Transistorized preamplifiers sometimes "steam." Tap the amplifier *gently*—sometimes helps.

2. **An occasional erratic high-pressure "bzzzt, bzzzt,"** like leaking steam or an intermittent buzzer, may indicate that an electrolytic condenser is beginning to go bad. Tap the aluminum cans in the amplifier; this may joggle things back to normal and stop the noise. Not serious unless it becomes very persistent, or there are sudden louder squawks at random, indicating larger current leakages past the condenser.

3. **Sputtering or intermittent breaking up of the music** invariably indicates a simple loose connection in the signal current wires. Look first at the inputs; check as above, wiggling wires to see whether you can spot where the looseness is. (No danger.) If no change, try the speaker leads; loose connections or partial short circuits here are very common. If the amplifier has the screw-down type of speaker connections, a loose strand of the twisted wire may accidentally be touching the amplifier frame, partially grounding the signal current; or the two wires may be lightly touching somewhere. Give the speaker wires a gentle tug and wiggle at both ends. Any change? (No danger—you may occasionally get a small spark while making a speaker connection at loud volume but short circuits here will not overheat the wires; the music simply sputters or stops.)

   Check your volume control. Dirt or carbon inside it can cause a partial broken connection and sputtery or thin music, sometimes a complete break. (Common in household radios.) Usually a vigorous on-off twisting of the knob for a minute or so will scrape the contacts and reduce the trouble. A new volume control is the answer, sooner or later.

4. **In FM radio, loud "zooming" noises, strong hum.** FM radio is supposed to be static-free but a few kinds of man-made static get through

—this sort may originate in a nearby hospital or doctor's office from such equipment as short-wave diathermy machines. Not much you can do about it except try another time of day.

5. **In FM radio, a steady hiss or swishing back of the music** usually indicates a weak signal—the cause may simply be a too-distant station or one that is behind hills or tall buildings. In many cases, however, it means that your antenna has accidentally been disconnected, or that it is insufficiently good.

6. **On LP records, an "echo" of the music,** sometimes after, sometimes before a loud passage. This is in the recording, not your machine; a heavily recorded groove with very wide wiggles may force its pattern right through the groove walls into the next groove. If it happens to be a silent groove you will hear this trace of pattern as a faint musical echo. Nothing can be done, aside from the recutting of the record by the manufacturing company.

   Tape print-through, a similar "echo," is sometimes heard from a tape recording, caused by a magnetic printing of a strong recorded signal through to adjacent layers of tape in the roll. Thin "long-play" tape is more likely to cause trouble than the standard thickness, but generally speaking, print-through is not often a problem, in home tape. Special low-print-through tape is available at extra cost, for high-quality work. There is no remedy for print-through that has already occurred.

7. **Slow fading-out of the music, or fading up and down.** This is almost sure to be due to a loose connection in the filament circuit that heats up the amplifier tubes, either in the amplifier wiring or inside a tube. If this circuit breaks intermittently, the cooling off and heating up produce a slow fade in and out of the music. (While it is broken, the tubes, or a single tube, won't light up and/or get warm. You can spot them this way.) This calls for a new tube or a technical repair job by a relative expert—but if you know what the trouble is yourself, you are less likely to be gypped.

8. **Sudden, rapid machine-gun-like pops or buzz; or a single loud report.** Turn set off immediately—this may be a serious short circuit. After checking for burnt smell, overhot parts, turn on cautiously and await events. If nothing happens, keep your mind ready, for a good while, to jump for the switch if any further symptoms occur. Sometimes these things are temporary—a big condenser may have shorted and jarred itself so heavily that the short is repaired for a long period of further operation.

D. TONAL BALANCE—HIGH AND LOW TROUBLE. Most troubles with tonal balance, given a good recording or broadcast or tape, are due to three general overlapping causes: (a) wrong connections, (b) faulty equalization, (c) adjusting tonal balance for the listening room. For this last, see Chapter 15.

1. **Music Heavy, with Muffled Highs and/or Heavy Bass**
   (a) *Ceramic cartridge plugged into magnetic phono pickup input—* this will double the bass as well as overload the preamplifier; music may or may not sound distorted, according to the amount of overloading. (But see p. 53.)
   (b) *Radio tuner plugged into magnetic phono input.* Similar effect.
   (c) *Tweeter unit in two-way speaker is disconnected or turned off accidentally.* If speaker system has its own control for the highs, check for dirty or worn-out volume control. Put your ear to the small tweeter. Is it working?
   (d) *Two or more inputs connected at the same time—*radio and phonograph, or perhaps two phono cartridges. This is allowable only when the inputs are electrically isolated.
   (e) *Loudness control not set right,* adding too much compensation (bass). Adjust input level lower, main control higher. (In "loudness contour" step-type controls, lessen compensation.)

2. **Music Thin, with Weak Bass and/or Screeching Highs**
   (a) *Magnetic phono pickup plugged into radio or ceramic phono input on amplifier.* Change it to the correct input socket. The magnetic cartridge, being "flat" in response, plays records exactly as they are, with reduced bass and extra-strong highs. Equalization in the preamplifier is designed to take care of this for average recordings. (But see (b) below.) Music will also be weak in volume, because of lack of preamplification for the magnetic pickup's very low output. The preamplifier will take care of this too, when you have corrected the mistake.
   (b) *A partial short in the connections from radio or phonograph,* acting as a condenser to remove bass. Look for stray loose strands of braided shielding or of the signal wire itself; joggle the connections at the radio tuner, check the slip-on connections at the back of the pickup cartridge (underneath the arm); this may uncover the trouble.
   (c) *Selection switch in wrong position;* some music may leak across the switch, playing weakly and without bass.

3. **Rumbling, Thumping Noise in Low Bass**
   Likely with larger speaker systems, especially those with extended bass response.
   (a) *Turntable rumble.* Cheaper changer motors are not smooth enough for big speaker systems. You may have to replace your changer if this is a constant trouble, with normal playing. (Any of the above causes for extra bass may exaggerate turntable rumble.) Note that the rumble can originate (1) in your own turntable, (2) in that of a radio station, via your radio tuner, and (3) in a recording— a not uncommon fault.
   (b) *Badly mounted changer, transmitting vibration to pickup.* Changers come with springy mounts, but sometimes these are screwed

down tight for shipping or by an unknowing home listener. Be sure that your changer sits free on its spring or rubber mounts. Outside vibrations of various sorts may turn up at the speaker, via the pickup, as unpleasant thumps and rumbles. To test, put pickup on a record while it is not turning, open the volume up, stamp on floor or knock the cabinet.

(c) A *standing wave resonance* in a room can sometimes hit the very low pitches where rumble or thumps occur, and exaggerate them. Try moving speaker a bit. (See Chapter 15.)

E. PITCH TROUBLES. Music that wavers up and down or plays at the wrong pitch is a widespread complaint. Here are some reasons. In most cases the causes are plural, complicating the issue.

1. "Wow"

Regular rising and falling pitch, as the turntable (yours or radio station's) revolves. "Wow" can come from a variety of sources; you'll need to use careful deduction to pin it down. It occurs at 16, 33, 45 or 78 times a minute, according to turntable speed.

(a) *Bent turntable shaft, and/or bent table.* Almost impossible to fix. If this is definitely your trouble by trial, replace the turntable or, if you must, the entire motor unit. (Most recent changers do not have a central shaft to bend.) But check the following first.

(b) *Off-center and/or enlarged hole in record*—will show up variably with different records. Pickup sways *back and forth* sidewise. You can remedy by (1) returning the record for another—the trouble may not be in all copies; (2) tap record on edge as it turns, to move it toward better centering—the hole usually has some play in it; (3) enlarge hole a bit (very little), try to find best position, where pickup moves the least. Mark on record which direction to push it for best centering. No use if you are playing automatically on a changer.

(c) *Warped record*—pickup moves *up and down*. You can flatten most records by putting them under flat pressure—a pile of records will do—for a long time, weeks or months. Not as serious in effect as off-center hole.

(d) *Record grooves stretched or warped.* An occasional fault with LP records, due to trouble in manufacturing. Pickup moves erratically back and forth sidewise. Usually combined with plain off-center "wow"; if you can eliminate the off-center complement the irregular waver will be less noticeable—the two together can be dreadful.

(e) *78 rpm "wow" copied onto LP edition.* A common trouble in the numerous LP reissues of older 78 rpm recordings. Not a thing you can do about it.

2. Pitch Is Uniformly Too High on All Records

If you have regular power-line AC current, in the U.S. or Canada, this trouble is in your player mechanism. Some changers are made to run fast, partly to allow for wear, partly to allow for playing with heavy load of eight or ten records on table at once, which tends to slow it down.

In some turntable systems wear on the rubber drive wheel will change the speed; others are not affected. You can figure this out by studying the drive—just lift the turntable off. Virtually all phonograph motors are now of the fixed-speed type. Adjustment must be made in the drive system, not in the motor.

3. Pitch Sags, Irregularly, as Record Plays

Usually due to mechanical slipping, though a defective motor or loose motor connection occasionally will have this effect.

(a) *Record slips* (on turntable; or on the records below in changer operation). Very common trouble with 45 rpm records—sometimes the records stop turning entirely. Occasionally happens with other types. Remedy: stick a small piece of adhesive plaster or Mystic cloth tape on each record label, to cause friction. Or, for the time being, remove lower records from changer so that the record which is playing is next to the turntable.

(b) *Oil* or grease on inside rim of turntable or on rubber drive wheel or belts. Remedy: clean with carbon tetrachloride, or soap or detergent plus water, if nothing better. (Don't use gasoline or inflammable cleaning fluid; natural rubber parts will deteriorate.) Sometimes a hard wipe with a soft cloth will be enough.

(c) *Something is dragging on the turntable.* Often merely a tool, pencil, etc., inadvertently left where it touches the table; sometimes the drag is underneath—lift off the turntable, look for wires, pencils, etc., that may be scraping.

4. Pitch "Flutters," Like a Musical Tremolo

A fairly common occurrence due to two main causes: (1) trouble in phono turntable drive and (2) recorded flutter (in the record), usually from tape recorders. Note that flutter is far more noticeable in some types of music than others—piano music shows it up relentlessly; violin music, with its own proper vibrato, masks flutter. Don't be fooled by this into thinking your machine is temperamental and changes from record to record!

If you can find just one piano record that plays with a satisfactory lack of flutter, you can assume that the flutter in other piano records must be in the recordings themselves, not in your machine.

There is nothing you can do about recorded flutter. Flutter in your own phono player may be caused by:

(a) *A rubber drive wheel worn out of round*, or with a "flat" on it from long stationary contact with drive shaft when machine was out of use.

(b) On some changers, *trouble with rubber belts* that drive the various speeds. Clean them and check for signs of wear or stretch.

(c) *Too tight pressure on drive wheel.* On some players this may cause fluttering of pitch. Remedy: adjust tension, if possible, so that wheel presses less heavily. Older Rek-O-Kut tables (and present Jr. series) can develop this trouble.

(d) *General dirtiness* and lack of lubrication often cause wavering pitch. Clean your player, or have it cleaned and oiled (not on rubber parts!).

(e) *Your own tape recorder*—it may have flutter trouble. Best test is to record piano notes, play them back.

5. **Pitch Is Considerably Too High**
Music sound tinny and childish. A trap for many an unwary listener, this—an LP recording played accidentally at 45 rpm instead of 33! It is surprisingly easy to make this mistake and miss it for minutes at a time.

F. No Music at All. The discovery that your machine is entirely dead is usually a disheartening one; most listeners promptly lose their heads and jump to all sorts of dire conclusions. Nine times out of ten the trouble is absurdly simple. Try the following kind of rational procedure:

1. **Look for the obvious.** Is the power plug pulled out of its wall socket? Is the switch on? Do all the amplifier tubes light up or warm up? If not, check house current, the fuse, if any, on the amplifier. If tubes light, then . . .

2. **Put your ear to the speaker**—is there the faint hiss or hum that says it is alive? If so, at least all is OK from the body of the amplifier on. If not, check the speaker connections—they may have been pulled loose. A speakerless amplifier is completely silent.

3. **Try both radio and phono,** if you have them. Does one work and not the other? If both are dead, trouble is probably beyond where they join the amplifier. Look again—do all the tubes light up? Or warm up? Sometimes the filament of one tube goes out, putting it out of action and breaking the sound circuit.

4. **Turn the volume control up high.** Test each input by lightly inserting one (any one) of the plugs just far enough to make contact, without the ground connection via the metal collar. A "live" input will emit a loud blat through the speaker, indicating that all is well from there on. If your phono is dead, but the phono input itself is alive, you know that trouble must be previous to the input, in the phonograph pickup circuit. Might even be in the input plug itself—a short. If you can get one good blat from any input, you know that the main amplifier is all right and trouble is definitely elsewhere. The first thing to do is to try to make the speaker "speak."

5. **If the speaker emits a satisfactory blat,** you have only to figure out where there is trouble previous to the main amplifier. Use the process of elimination. If the speaker is definitely alive but cannot be made to emit any larger sound at all, your amplifier is suffering, probably from a relatively mild disease, and must be checked internally in detail. Probably only a loose connection or a weak tube. If it lights up normally and the speaker hisses away contentedly there cannot be much that is seriously wrong.

G. SMOKE, HEAT, MELTED PARTS. It is extremely rare that a home hi-fi amplifier develops a really bad short in its heavier current circuits—the high-voltage "B" circuit or the house-current lines. Almost all such major catastrophes are due to listener negligence or ignorance—preventable mistakes. Some of the more probable of these are:

1. **An AC system plugged accidentally into DC (direct current) lines.** The older large cities still have DC areas. Either the amplifier fuse blows or if there is none, the transformer burns out within seconds. (Check on your amplifier for a fuse—it will pay you, at a convenient time, to have one installed if cost-cutting has left it out.)
2. **A wrong plug connection** may throw heavy current and/or high voltage into one of the low-voltage circuits, burning out parts.
   (Note: Plugs should be of differing types so that it is impossible to make such mistakes; but many an installation is done without common-sense awareness of this potential danger. Look your set over carefully for such possibilities when you first receive it.) Here are usual voltages in the hi-fi amplifier:

Pickup-signal circuit:	.01 to 4 volts
Radio-tuner output:	Up to 8 volts, or so
Speaker circuit:	Momentarily to 30 volts or so—but never 117 volts
"B" or plate circuit:	150 to 450 volts, DC
House-current circuit:	117 volts, AC
Tube-filament circuit:	Usually 6 or 12 volts

Typical deadly sins in plug connection: (a) Standard house-current plug used for connecting speaker wires to amplifier—speaker can be accidentally plugged into 117-volt current, burning out voice coil instantly. (b) Input and output amplifier connections same type; pickup cartridge accidentally plugged into amplifier output instead of input, damaged by high output voltage.
3. **Internal short circuit in the power transformer.** This transformer takes AC house current, delivers low-voltage filament and high-voltage "B" currents to amplifier. Once in a long while the internal insulation breaks down—probably because of some momentary overload due to mishandling, and the transformer suddenly burns out. If when you

turn on your set someday the house lights dim a lot more than usual—
a heavy load—or if, failing this, you hear an ominous crackling sound
from the amplifier and smoke appears—grab all the plugs and pull
them out of the wall socket as fast as you can. With luck, you may
get a new transformer and no further damage done; but usually other
parts burn out too. Speed is of the essence!

4. **Lesser internal short circuits.** Shorts can occur in all sorts of places in
an amplifier, but the results are in one way roughly similar: a heavy
current is drained in the circuit involved and heat is generated. Such
heat-generating shorts divide into (1) those in the 117-volt house
current, to the transformer, extra power outlets, and (2) those beyond
the transformer and isolated by it from the house current—the transformer burns up before the house fuse blows. (Shorts in the signal-
current wires are too tiny to generate dangerous heat.)

In the first case a short will blow the amplifier fuse or the house
fuse, probably harmlessly. In the second case, the drain is directly on
the power transformer and the power-rectifier tube that follows it
(which changes AC to DC). The power tube (usually long, with
chimney-like structures inside; or if of metal, thin and long) makes a
good danger signal; when a short occurs beyond it, the tube's insides
become brilliantly red or even red-white-hot, like an electric stove,
even the glass turning red in extremes; if a metal tube, the outside
becomes smoking hot, possibly turning red. This kind of short often
does no serious harm if you catch it in time. Any unnatural heat in
either a tube or transformer should put you on emergency guard immediately. Sometimes this can occur even though the music continues
to play normally. Allow of course for normal heat, which is pretty hot
in many amplifiers.

Appendix

MAIL ORDER HI-FI. Here are some of the leading firms selling high fidelity component equipment at audiophile net prices by mail. They offer standard lines, plus (a) their own brand-name equipment, usually special value at low prices; and (b) assorted special sale items, often imported goods. Yearly catalogues, plus frequent "flyers," on request. (Over-the-counter sales in the main stores and at various branches.)

Allied Radio Corp.
100 North Western Ave.
Chicago 80, Ill.

Hudson Radio & Television Corp.
48 West 48th St.
New York 36, N.Y.

Lafayette Radio, Inc.
100 Sixth Ave.
New York 13, N.Y.

Newark Electric Co.
223 West Madison St.
Chicago 6, Ill.
also
4736 West Century Blvd.
Inglewood, Calif.

Radio Shack Corp.
167 Washington St.
Boston 8, Mass.

Sun Radio and Electronics, Inc.
650 Sixth Ave.
New York 11, N.Y.

OTHER HI-FI OUTLETS. Additional large and medium-sized high fidelity outlets are located in dozens of larger cities. A sampling of these follows. Some feature custom design and installation services, repair services; some will accept trade-ins. Many issue catalogues, sell by mail as well as over the counter.

Arrow Electronics, Inc.
65 Cortlandt St.
New York 7, N.Y.

Asco Sound Corp.
115 West 45th St.
New York 36, N.Y.

Audio Exchange
159-19 Hillside Ave.
Jamaica 32, N.Y.

Classic Electrical Co., Ltd.
352-364 Lower Addiscombe Rd.
Croydon, Surrey, England
(British exporters)

293

Customcrafters, Inc.
2259 Gilbert Ave.
Cincinnati 6, Ohio

Santa Monica Sound
12436 Santa Monica Blvd.
West Los Angeles 25, Calif.

Friend's
614 Arch St.
Philadelphia 6, Pa.

Terminal Radio Corp.
85 Cortlandt St.
New York 7, N.Y.

Harvey Radio Co.
103 West 43rd St.
New York 36, N.Y.

Trevor Peck Co., Ltd.
1498 Sherbrooke St.
Montreal, P.Q., Canada

High Fidelity House
536 South Fair Oaks
Pasadena 1, Calif.

World Radio House of Hi-Fi
34th & Broadway
Council Bluffs, Iowa
also:

Hollywood Electronics
7460 Melrose Ave.
Los Angeles 46, Calif.

World Radio House of Hi-Fi
4628 Dodge St.
Omaha, Nebr.

Kierulff Sound Corp.
820 West Olympic Blvd.
Los Angeles 46, Calif.

Zack Radio Supply Co.
1424 Market St.
San Francisco, Calif.

TRADE-INS. The following offer trade-in values as a special feature:

Arrow Electronics, Inc.
65 Cortlandt St.
New York 7, N.Y.

Audio Exchange
159-19 Hillside Ave.
Jamaica 32, N.Y.

World Radio House of Hi-Fi
34th & Broadway
Council Bluffs, Iowa

(See also the equipment exchange columns in various magazines.)

MAGAZINES. The following specialize in high fidelity, audio and related musical subjects. (See also hi-fi sections, features in other magazines, newspapers; also various hi-fi annuals.)

Audio
Box 629
Mineola, N.Y.

Hi-Fi and Music Review
1 Park Ave.
New York 16, N.Y.

Audiocraft
Great Barrington, Mass.

Hi-Fi Music at Home
105 East 35th St.
New York 16, N.Y.

High Fidelity
The Publishing House
Great Barrington, Mass.

INDEX

Set in Linotype Electra
Format by Steven King
Manufactured by American Book–Stratford Press, Inc.
Published by Harper & Brothers, New York